STUTTERING: A SYMPOSIUM

Contributors:

Oliver Bloodstein
I. Peter Glauber
Joseph Sheehan
Robert West
Jon Eisenson
Charles Van Riper

STUTTERING

A Symposium

JON EISENSON, Editor
Queens College

With an Introduction by

WENDELL JOHNSON

Harper & Brothers Publishers New York

Stuttering: A Symposium

Printed in the United States of America

L–H

Library of Congress catalog card number: 58-11589

CONTENTS

Foreword

THE PUBLICATION of a *Symposium on Stuttering* is a recognition of the fact that to find some answers to the disorder or disorders of speech referred to as stuttering, many different points of view need to be presented. On this basic assumption the editor invited a number of authorities whose interests and experiences have identified them with the problem of stuttering as well as with the problems of stutterers to commit their points of view to writing.

Each authority has written considerably on the subject of stuttering. This time, however, the contributors were invited to write without concern for page limitation. Each contributor was assured that he could be as expansive, or as concise, as he thought necessary for the presentation of his point of view. Furthermore, he was not to be confined by an editorially imposed format, or by any special consideration of style. The only limitation imposed at the outset was that three questions were to be answered, directly or indirectly, in the individual essays:

1. What is stuttering?
2. What is the cause or what are the causes of stuttering?
3. In the light of your concept of stuttering, what are your suggestions for the treatment of stutterers?

Each of our contributors chose to answer the questions in a manner consistent with his specialized interests and experiences as they related to the problems of stutterers and their difficulties in speaking. In each instance, of course, a professional lifetime of reactions, evaluations, and reëvaluations is reflected in the manner as well as the matter of the answers. So, it was to be expected that Dr. I. Peter Glauber, one of our leading psychoanalysts, should want to discuss stuttering from the point of view of a psychoanalyst. But Dr. Glauber happens also to be someone who for at least two decades has engaged in research with stutterers, written on his observations, and presented his theoretical position for critical reaction before professional societies and in professional periodicals. Moreover, he made a study of everything he could obtain written or spoken by Freud on the subject of stuttering.

Dr. Charles Van Riper chose to tell us his position on stuttering by reviewing his experimental procedures in stuttering therapy over a period of more than twenty years.

Dr. Robert West, believing that we are just on the way to getting some answers to the problem of stuttering, calls his contribution "An Agnostic's Speculations About Stuttering." There is little question that we need more agnostics like Robert West in our midst if we are to get some answers to the enigma of stuttering.

Dr. Oliver Bloodstein and Dr. Joseph Sheehan are youthful, spirited scientists. Both, despite if not because of their youth, possess the objectivity which permits them to scrutinize their own writings, their own thinking, and their therapeutic procedures as they would those of others, and as they expect others to examine their efforts.

The editor, in his role as a contributor, reflecting upon his research and experience, presents a point of view that attempts to find a common immediate causal factor among the various theoretic positions presented in this *Symposium* and elsewhere in the vast literature on stuttering.

We anticipated considerable diversity among our contributors and, of course, we found it. On the other hand, we were pleased and not overly surprised to find a core of unity amidst the diversity. There seems to be an underlying agreement as to the characteristics of stuttering and possibly as to the essence of stuttering. This is so despite the fact that the represented theoretical positions as to the etiology of stuttering range from one which views stuttering as a disorder having an essentially organic basis to one which looks upon stuttering as a neurotic manifestation of a type of neurotic individual called a stutterer.

The editor was aware in his undertaking that if he were to invite these authorities to write without the imposition of page limitation, he had to accept another limitation in the form of the number of contributors. This, of course, was a difficult responsibility. The selection of six contributors meant the exclusion of many times six authorities whose points of view were significant and deserving of representation. The task of selection was made somewhat easier by the appearance of the second edition of Eugene Hahn's *Stuttering: Significant Theories and Therapies,* prepared by Elise S. Hahn (Stanford University Press, 1956). A great many points of view, including those of some of our own contributors, are concisely presented in the Hahn book. We had, therefore, no need to reproduce the scope of an earlier effort by another editor. We did wish to provide opportunity for a few newer voices as well as some "older" voices to explain their points of view in breadth. Accordingly, a balance of "new" and "old" became one of the criteria for the selection of our contributors. The editor had the distinct privilege of conferring personally several times with each of the contributors.

For each contributor, the present writing was mostly a labor of love and of professional obligation. For the editor, there were additional compensations. He was afforded an opportunity not only to have his own say on the subject of stuttering, but he had an opportunity to work with pleasure with a group of his colleagues. His only regret is that a larger number of colleagues could not have been invited to make their contributions.

The editor and the contributors are grateful to Dr. Wendell Johnson for his Introduction to our *Symposium*. The Introduction, we feel, makes a distinct contribution to our book in particular as well as to any field of investigation in which there are respected differences of opinion.

JON EISENSON

July, 1958

that privilege of conferring personally several times with each of the contributors.

For each contributor, the present writing was mostly a labor of love and of professional obligation. For the editor, there were additional compensations. He was afforded an opportunity not only to have his own say on the subject of stuttering, but he had an opportunity to work with pleasure with a group of his colleagues. His only regret is that a larger number of colleagues could not have been invited to make their contributions.

The editor and the contributors are grateful to Dr. Wendell Johnson for his Introduction to our *Symposium*. The Introduction, we feel, makes a distinct contribution to our book in particular as well as to any field of investigation in which there are respected differences of opinion.

JON EISENSON

[illegible]

Introduction: The Six Men and the Stuttering

WENDELL JOHNSON, Ph.D.

THE SIX distinguished contributors to this *Symposium on Stuttering* represent, strictly speaking, six different points of view. Taking considerable liberties and risking undue simplification, one may, however, reduce these six to three, by grouping them according to the system of classification proposed by one of the authors (Bloodstein) in this manner:

a. The "repressed-need" point of view: "The stutterer blocks because he unconsciously wishes to block . . ." This position appears to be represented, in one of its possible forms of elaboration, by Glauber.

b. The "breakdown" point of view: According to this notion, "stuttering" signifies "a temporary failure in the smooth, integrated performance of a complex neuromuscular activity in certain individuals who are emotionally or constitutionally predisposed to such breakdown under conditions of stress." West and Eisenson seem to speak for the most part, each in his own way, within this general frame of reference.

c. The "anticipatory-struggle" point of view: "Stuttering is an avoidance reaction performed in the fearful anticipation of speech interruption, or essentially . . . it is the effort not to stutter." The hypothesis has been variously developed with or without the assumption that a predisposition of some sort is essential to the learning of the anticipatory-avoidance behavior. This notion, formulated in three distinctive ways and with varying patterns of overlapping with the other two points of view, appears to be presented by Bloodstein, Sheehan, and Van Riper.

Why Do Investigators Disagree?

Aside from the question of other conceivable theories, there would seem to be a need, and the possibility, of one additional hypothesis of a different sort—one designed to account for these differences in point of view. Why do investigators concerned with a common problem arrive at varied conclusions about it?

Doubtless the overriding common-sense assumption is that it is knowledge that determines hypothesis, or point of view, or belief, and that, therefore, when men express divergent beliefs they do so chiefly because they speak from differing funds of information or data. Indeed, this general view of the matter is enshrined in one of our most widely esteemed parables, the one about the six blind men who investigated the elephant, only to arrive at six different conclusions about what it was they had investigated.

Due reflection must surely leave one with the conviction, however, that there is a gravely misleading detail in this story—and a corresponding flaw in the theory of human disagreement which the story represents. The misleading detail is that the six investigators are described as blind.

As a consequence, millions of children have been insidiously affected by the implication that if only these six legendary companions in research had been able to see reasonably well they would have agreed perfectly.

No redder herring, surely, has ever been dragged across the faint, faint trail of truth.

The parent who finds these comments congenial will, upon discovering that his child has been told the story of the six blind men and the elephant, hasten to counteract its disorienting effect by acquainting his mistutored fledgling with that classic of folk realism known as "The Emperor's New Clothes." This yarn about the practical tailors who applied elementary semantics to produce a gorgeous invisible garment which the Emperor wore with innocent pride to the huzzahs of all his Platonic and romantic subjects—all except one small child who did not possess the vision to see what was not there—this yarn is conducive to an insight without which one assails the hazards of responsible adulthood at enormous peril. Equipped, however, with the lesson that can be learned from this peculiarly liberating tale, a boy may venture to become a man with fair likelihood of acquiring in the bargain a protective down of sensitivity to the fateful interaction between what is symbolized and what is symbol.

Nouns, Verbs, and Animisms

Among those known to have learned and cherished this lesson was the late Benjamin Lee Whorf, who lived all too briefly from 1897 to 1941. Probably the most influential teacher of Whorf was Edward Sapir, among whose reasons for being remembered thoughtfully is the fact that he once wrote these words: "Language is a guide to 'social reality.' . . . Human beings do not live in the objective world alone, nor alone in the world of social activity as ordinarily understood, but are very much at the mercy of the particular language which has become the medium of expression for their society. It is quite an illusion to imagine that one adjusts to reality essentially without the use of language and that language is merely an incidental means of solving specific problems of communication or reflection. The fact of the matter is that the 'real world' is to a large extent unconsciously built up on the language habits of the group. . . . Even comparatively simple acts of perception are very much more at the mercy of the social patterns called words than we might suppose. . . . We see and hear and otherwise experience very largely as we do because the language habits of our community predispose certain choices of interpretation." [1]

Now, what we have seen and heard and otherwise experienced about that which we have symbolized as "stuttering" we have done, to speak from Sapir's view, largely because our perceptions and judgments have been influenced by the patterns of selection and organization characteristic of our respective languages. And, while with the particular words quoted above Sapir seemed to imply that all members of a community or a group are affected alike by a common language, we must appreciate, of course, that the matter is not this simple. There are thousands of languages spoken by those of us who use the English code, and each one of us, moreover, speaks a considerable variety of English languages, each one of which affects us at least a little differently from any one of the others. Through any utterance the structure of our language shows. Whether we refer to what we speak about as "stuttering" or "electricity" or "education" or whatnot, the statements we make contain or imply information about the systems of symbolization by means of which the statements themselves are formed,

[1] Sapir, Edward, "The Status of Linguistics as a Science," *Language,* 5, 1929, 207–214. Reprinted in *Culture, Language, and Personality,* selected essays of Edward Sapir, edited by David G. Mandelbaum, Berkeley and Los Angeles, University of California Press, 1956, pp. 65–77. The quotation, from pp. 68–69 of *Culture, Language, and Personality,* is reproduced by permission of the publisher.

as well as about the experiences or observations they may be intended to symbolize.

This basic notion was put lucidly by Whorf in these sentences: "We cut up and organize the spread and flow of events as we do, largely because, through our mother tongue, we are parties to an agreement to do so, not because nature itself is segmented in exactly that way for all to see. . . . Thus English and similar tongues lead us to think of the universe as a collection of rather distinct objects and events corresponding to words." [2]

Among all that Whorf had to say in this connection, his statements concerning the subject-predicate form would seem to be most significantly relevant to a consideration of our traditional ways of formulating and discussing the problem we call "stuttering." He said: "The Indo-European languages and many others give great prominence to a type of sentence having two parts, each part built around a class of word—substantives and verbs—which those languages treat differently in grammar . . . the contrast has been stated in logic in many different ways: subject and predicate, actor and action, things and relations between things, objects and their attributes, quantities and operations. And, pursuant again to grammar, the notion became ingrained that one of these classes of entities can exist in its own right but that the verb class cannot exist without an entity of the other class, the 'thing' class, as a peg to hang on." [3]

In consequence, according to Whorf, "The English technique of talking depends on the contrast of two artificial classes, substantives and verbs, and on the bipartitioned ideology of nature, already discussed. Our normal sentence, unless imperative, must have some substantive before its verb, a requirement that corresponds to the philosophical and also naive notion of an actor who produces an action." [4]

The most crucial effect of this, so far as our discussion of the stuttering problem is concerned, is that we usually talk as if such words as "stuttering" and "speech" were considerably more nounlike than verblike. We tend strongly, therefore, to do something that Whorf expresses in these words: "We are constantly reading into nature fictional acting entities, simply because our verbs must have substantives in front of them. We have to say 'It flashed' or 'A light flashed,' setting up an actor, 'it' or 'light,' to perform

[2] Whorf, Benjamin Lee, "Languages and Logic," *Technol. Rev.*, 43:250–252, 266, 268, 272 (April 1941), reprinted in *Language, Thought, and Reality, Selected Writings of Benjamin Lee Whorf*, edited and with an introduction by John B. Carroll, Technology Press of Massachusetts Institute of Technology and John Wiley & Sons, Inc., New York, and Chapman and Hall, Limited, London, 1956, p. 240. This and other quotations from the writings of Whorf used in this essay are reprinted from this source with the permission of the publishers.

[3] *Ibid.*, p. 241.

[4] *Ibid.*, p. 242.

what we call an action, 'to flash.' Yet the flashing and the light are one and the same! The Hopi language reports the flash with a simple verb, *rehpi:* 'flash (occurred).' There is no division into subject and predicate, not even a suffix like *-t* of Latin *tona-t* 'it thunders.' Hopi can and does have verbs without subjects, a fact which may give that tongue potentialities, probably never to be developed, as a logical system for understanding some aspects of the universe. Undoubtedly modern science, strongly reflecting western Indo-European tongues, often does as we all do, sees actions and forces where it sometimes might be better to see states. On the other hand, 'state' is a noun, and as such it enjoys the superior prestige traditionally attaching to the subject or thing class; therefore science is exceedingly ready to speak of states if permitted to manipulate the concept like a noun. Perhaps, in place of the 'states' of an atom or a dividing cell, it would be better if we could manipulate as readily a more verblike concept but without the concealed premises of actor and action." [5]

The relevance of these remarks to the matter at hand may be pointedly suggested by these modifications of the first three sentences in the passage just cited: "We are constantly reading into our speech behavior fictional acting entities, simply because our verbs must have substantives in front of them. We have to say 'It blocked' or 'My speech blocked,' setting up an actor, 'it' or 'speech,' to perform what we call an action, 'to block.' Yet the blocking and the speech are one and the same!"

The blocking and the speech are one and the same, that is, in the sense that "they" are what I do when, as we say, I am speaking. (For the present limited purposes, I shall pass by the question of whether the pronoun "I" in this sentence also serves to conjure up a fictional agent.) We approach the Hopi mode of symbolization if we say, more elaborately perhaps than would a Hopi speaker, "When I speak I sometimes contract my muscles so that instead of saying words I press my lips together tightly for a time, stop exhaling momentarily, and the like." Such language seems not to intimate that an agent in the form of "my speech" or perhaps "my stuttering" or "the block" or "my predisposition to stutter" is doing these things, or that "it" is somehow asserting "itself" to make me stutter, or to keep me from talking, by producing these effects or "symptoms of it." This is to say that in English it is possible to make statements about what a person, oneself or another person, does when speaking, without implying that fictional agents referred to by such names as "speech," "stuttering," "the block," or "it" are responsible for what the person does, provided one simply describes the actings or performings "of the person."

There is a marked difference between describing what a speaker is *doing,*

[5] *Ibid.*, pp. 243–244.

on the one hand, and on the other stating what he *is* and what he *has*—or, that is to say, what there *is* within him. To say that a person *is* a stutterer or that he *has* a stutter or a speech impediment, is apparently to refer to something distinctively different from whatever is referred to in saying that when he speaks he sometimes *does* such things as tensing the muscles involved more than most speakers do, or more than he himself does at other times. And to say that he tenses his muscles as he does "because he is a stutterer" or "because he has a stutter" is to make a statement that is redundant, if intended as descriptive, or else it asserts that he is possessed of something or other that will have to be dislodged and removed from within him before he may be expected to talk "without stuttering."

Description and Projection

The six men who went to see the stuttering and reported in this book what they found differ necessarily in what they say so far as the languages they use are different. Their respective languages do appear to differ in one particularly important respect in that some are in general, or in fundamental emphasis, or "on the average" more descriptive of what speakers *do* when they are said to be stuttering, and others are more assertive of what speakers *are* and of what they *have* presumably because of what they *are*. An essential guide to the reading of the six reports with an eye to the differences among them with respect to language, as here considered, is provided by the following list of general kinds of statements that are to be found, with more or less distinctive relative frequencies, in the several reports:

a. Statements descriptive of what speakers do when they are assumed to be stuttering.

b. Statements descriptive of what speakers, classified as stutterers, do other than what is called "stuttering" that allegedly distinguishes them from what is done by speakers who are not classified as stutterers.

c. Statements about "characteristics" or "tendencies" or "predispositions" of, or "entities," "agents," or "forces" within or acting upon, speakers classified as stutterers that allegedly distinguish them from speakers not so classified. The word "stuttering" itself may be used to name such an entity or agent, as in assertions to the effect that stuttering produces tension or that the speaker holds his breath "because he is a stutterer" or "because he stutters" (i.e., "because he has stuttering within him and it causes him to hold his breath"). These entities or forces may be discussed in direct relation to stuttering—that is, to the disturbances in speech which they presumably cause—or in relation to something that is explicitly or implicitly asserted to be the basic character or structure or dynamic patterning of forces which distinguishes a speaker classified as a stutterer from one not so classified.

The term "symptom" is of peculiar interest in this connection. It appears to be used in three different types of sentence: (a) in those which assert or imply that stuttering is a symptom of (i.e., is caused by or is a manifestation of) something else, some force or entity or pattern of stress among forces; (b) those which assert or imply that something or some action, such as unusual muscular tension or the repeating of a syllable, is a symptom of (i.e., is caused by or is a manifestation of) stuttering conceived presumably as a force or entity; and (c) those in which reference is made ambiguously to "the symptoms" or "the symptom," apparently without acknowledgment of the linguistic convention of employing the word "symptom" in constructions in which it is followed by "of" and in which the "of" is followed by other terms designative of some condition or agent that is alleged to stand in causal relation to whatever is said to be the "symptom." Sentences in which reference is made to "the stuttering symptoms" without relating these words by means of "of" to other terms are ambiguous—in the special sense that usually it is not clear how they are to be classified among the three types of statement indicated immediately above. In general, however, it would seem that any use of the term "symptom" in statements intended to be descriptive or explanatory of whatever is meant by "stuttering" is indicative of a frame of reference, or basic language structure, in which certain kinds of substantive nouns stand in relation to verbs in the manner described by Whorf in the passages previously cited.

Now that we have returned to Whorf's substantives and verbs, it is essential that we take pains to make a clarifying distinction between some subject-predicate sentences—especially those indicted by Whorf—and others. So far as this distinction was not developed by Whorf, the explanation may well lie in the fact that, in contrast to certain other investigators of semantic problems whose range of interest has been more general, he did not appear to be comprehensively or systematically concerned with the process of abstracting. The distinction in question is not one to be drawn between the subject-predicate form of sentence, as such, and other forms that do not involve verbs preceded by substantives. It is one, rather, between statements that are more and those that are less descriptive of observed events, phenomena, or doings. Stated with more relevance to the present matter, the distinction is one between statements about what we observe (objects and events) and those about what we construct or imagine or suppose (constructs and, in general, abstractions of an inferential order). And we are most pointedly concerned with the distinction between, on the one hand, statements descriptive of what we can see or hear or feel ourselves doing when we speak, or what we can observe (with or without the aid of special apparatus) that others do when they speak, and, on the other, statements about constructs treated essentially as animistic entities called by such names as "speech," "stuttering" (as used on page 193, footnote 15, to denote "a real entity"), "the block," "predisposition to stutter," "the ego," "the id," "perseveration," "emotional instability," "conflict," "habit," "ictogenic factors" and "the ictostat" and "phemolepsey" (see chapter by West), "the word" (that "won't come out"), "tension" (that "comes and goes"), and the like.[6]

Both kinds of statement involve substantives and verbs, and while it is true that animistic constructs could not readily be represented except by substantive nouns—and the substantive pronoun "it"—it is also true apparently that the Indo-European languages, as represented by conventional English, provide for the description of behavior, including the doings of speakers, almost exclusively in sentences in which verbs are preceded by substantives. What is crucial is the degree to which the sentences are animistic in asserting that what is named by the substantive nouns are agents with wills and whims of their own, and that it is they who perform the actions referred to by means of the verbs. One of the rewarding pleasures to be experienced in reading this book is to be gained by searching through certain passages of it for the animistic substantives, a pastime pleasantly, if also soberingly, remindful of childhood evenings spent trying to detect faces hidden in the trees of picture puzzles in children's magazines.

The Languages of Disagreement

Now, an approach to the question of why returning travelers disagree in their reports of where they have been and what they have seen may be made with reference to the sorts of statement concerning which they disagree more and less. In general, in the present instance, there would seem to be greater, probably maximal, possibility of agreement with respect to statements descriptive of what speakers do when they are said to be stuttering. In weighing this, however, it is not to be missed, particularly in comparing the chapters of Glauber, West, and Eisenson with the chapters by

[6] A peculiarly provocative discussion of linguistic animism as observed in clinical work with the stuttering problem is to be found in Williams, Dean, "A Point of View about 'Stuttering,'" *Journal of Speech and Hearing Disorders,* 1957, 22, 390–397.

Bloodstein, Sheehan, and Van Riper, that statements that are presumably of this kind may differ to a degree that is indeed confirmatory of the assumption that the six men who went to see the elephant were necessarily visually distinctive. Even so, differences between statements of this type are to be more or less readily resolved, for the good reason that reports of one person's observations can be checked by independent observers.

There are two obvious obstacles, however, to the achievement of full agreement even on the level of first-hand observation of "facts." One is implied by the quotation marks around the word "facts" in that sentence. Two different observers may see with dissimilar perceptual sets, and as a result they may innocently—though not necessarily unmischievously—make divergent reports of what seem to be observations of presumably identical things or events. To recall Sapir's words, "Even comparatively simple acts of perception are very much more at the mercy of the social patterns called words than we might suppose. . . . We see and hear and otherwise experience very largely as we do because [our] language habits . . . predispose certain choices of interpretation."

The ever-present risk involved in discussing this, or any other relatively complex matter, is that of the oversimplification we tend to effect by focusing verbally on some nameable aspect of the flowing field or "ever-dissolving pattern" of experience. In this case the risk is that of obscuring the intricate complexity of interactions among the facets of the total experience under consideration by virtue of distinguishing them, more or less arbitrarily, by such apparently distinctive names as "sensory stimulation," "perception," "description," "interpretation," and "logical inference." The education, especially the early and continuing informal indoctrination, of most of us has been such that we are not unerringly sensitive to the relative level or degree of abstraction on which any given statement is made, whether by others or by us. We seem particularly prone to make little or no distinction between relatively gross or crude "descriptive" statements and highly detailed descriptive reports of relatively very low order of abstraction. In consequence, for example, we tend to treat such a remark as "Alexander has started to repeat sounds and words" as though it were the equivalent of, and might be substituted for, "Alexander has started to stutter." Or, to cite a more common example, we are inclined to say that "Reginald is a nervous child" and feel no need to specify any details, as though "nervous" were being used as a term descriptive of Reginald rather than as a name for our evaluative reaction to him. It is especially important that we tend to talk and write as though we were not aware of using "stuttering" as the name for a personal judgment, while implying by the contexts we give it that the term is descriptive of whatever we are judging.

We apparently use the word "stutterer" quite commonly as though it were descriptive of a particular person rather than designative of a class or categorical abstraction; moreover, we seem generally to disregard the fact that since it designates a class it necessarily implies or "stands for" an interaction involving two individuals, both of whom are essential to the transaction in which one classifies the other.

In general, the behavior involved in what we refer to variously as perceiving, reporting, and interpreting is pervasively influenced not only by what Sapir called "the social patterns called words" but also, and with peculiarly complicating effects, by the degree of awareness, especially the relative lack of awareness, that this is so. Investigators disagree not only in their interpretations and theories, but also in what they call their data or observations, in part because they make their observations through the perceptual filters provided by their theories—and the less aware they are of this reason for disagreeing the more they disagree. (Moreover, incidentally, the less understanding they are of all this, the more disagreeable they can, but need not, become in disagreeing with one another.)

The other obstacle to agreement on the level of first-hand observation is the more familiar one of differences among observers in equipment, circumstances under which they make their observations, specific purposes for which they make them, modes of recording the observations made, controls or lack of controls employed, and methods of analysis of measures regarded as relevant to the problem or purposes involved. The importance of this class of factors in relation to disagreement need not be labored, but the significance of disregarding it in evaluating particular instances of disagreement can scarcely be overstated. Because of the operation of these factors it is to be commonly noted that two different investigators may be essentially "talking past each other," discussing two quite different sets of data, or what are accepted as data. And what a person accepts as data he would, in the spirit of scientific integrity, discard, far more frequently than might generally be supposed, if only he were aware of the more recent or more reliable or more valid data that have superseded his outmoded or partial or dubious information. Doubtless we overestimate rather enormously the degree to which most of us "keep up-to-date." Among the many touchstones against which the data cited by any writer are to be evaluated are, certainly, their dates of publication, especially in any field, such as the one represented by this book, in which the amount of research activity and the rate of methodological and technical refinement, have been and continue to be relatively great.

It is to be ventured, then, only with due qualifications that there would seem to be maximal opportunity for agreement on relatively descriptive, as contrasted with inferential and theoretical, levels of discourse. In the present case, so far as different investigators report in sufficiently unambiguous terms their observations of what speakers do when they are said to be stuttering, there would seem to be reasonable likelihood of arriving at agreement as to what has been observed—or, at least, as to what it is that has been called "stuttering." What is of overshadowing importance is the fact that only to the degree that agreement is achieved on this level can disagreement on higher levels of abstraction be examined or considered meaningfully. If it is not clear what men are disagreeing about, disciplined discourse concerning their differences would seem to be out of the question.

There is a special interest in the class of statements characterized previously as "statements descriptive of what speakers, classified as stutterers, do other than what is called 'stuttering' that allegedly distinguishes them from what is done by speakers who are not classified as stutterers." With respect to such matters as "rate of development of speech," or "diadochocinesis," or "handedness," or various cardiovascular, biochemical, and physiological measures, or "perseveration," or behavior represented in measures of various facets of so-called emotional and social adjustment, and other forms of behavior or modes of functioning "other than what is called 'stuttering,' " the investigator must be concerned not only with the reliability and validity of his measures, but also with their relevance to the problem of stuttering. Statements in this general class appear to rank next to those of theoretical generalization in providing sources of disagreement. They may tax severely the reader's capacity for differentiating dependable description from what might be called pseudo description (seemingly descriptive statements that represent analogies or suppositions rather than observations), irrelevant description, partial or dubious or outmoded reports, and statements of inference on relatively high levels of abstraction.

It is on the relatively high levels of inference and explanatory generalization that the more extreme and influential types of disagreement occur. This is intimated by Bloodstein's classification of the major divergent points of view with respect to stuttering referred to in the opening paragraphs of this paper. It would appear to be particularly significant, however, that while on the very high levels of abstraction the disagreements that occur tend to imply more or less global divergences, there apparently is not a lush abundance of diverse fundamental theories concerning stuttering. Indeed, the various distinguishable interpretative patterns appear to be reducible not merely to Bloodstein's set of three but to only two basic theories.

Two Basic Theories of Stuttering

According to one of these fundamental theories the problem that we call "stuttering" primarily involves speech and the speaker; according to the other the problem primarily involves perception and evaluation as carried out in a framework of interaction involving a speaker and his listeners. According to the latter view, as the problem develops beyond its beginning stages, in which it appears to be primarily a matter of the evaluative perception of a speaker by others, it comes also to involve significantly the speaker's perceptual and evaluative reactions to his own speech.

The speech theory of stuttering, as we may call the first of these two basic views of the problem, has been presented traditionally, and again in this book, in two forms. According to the one, the speaker is characterized by some sort of bodily fault; according to the other, he is possessed of a psychical flaw. In either case, the imperfection may be assumed to be congenital or acquired. An impressive variety of possible or conceivable factors or conditions, both psychic and organic, many of which are represented in this book, particularly in the chapters by Glauber and West, have been hypothesized or asserted to be distinctively characteristic of persons classified as stutterers, and to be causally related, directly or indirectly, to whatever may be referred to as stuttering. Most of the operationally meaningful assertions of this sort so far made have been subjected to more or less rigorous and relevant laboratory testing, and the present writer, with due reference to his own particular perceptual and evaluative filters, feels constrained to offer as his own most scientifically defensible tentative report that none of them has been confirmed.[7]

The interaction theory of stuttering, as we may generally designate the second of the two basic explanatory approaches previously indicated, appears to lend itself to a very considerable variety of modes of elaboration.

[7] Documentation for this opinion is to be found in a variety of sources, particularly relevant reports of research in the *Journal of Speech and Hearing Disorders* and the *Journal of Speech and Hearing Research*, published by the American Speech and Hearing Association. Of the present writer's publications, those which contain the most pertinent investigative reports are *Stuttering in Children and Adults: Thirty Years of Research at the University of Iowa*, edited by the writer with the assistance of Ralph Leutenegger, Minneapolis, University of Minnesota Press, 1955, and "Stuttering," Chapter 5 of *Speech Handicapped School Children*, by Wendell Johnson, S. F. Brown, J. F. Curtis, C. W. Edney, and J. Keaster, New York, Harper & Brothers, 2nd ed., 1956. A comprehensive report by the writer and his associates of detailed investigation of the beginning and development of the problem of stuttering in 246 cases is scheduled for early publication under the title of *The Onset of Stuttering* by the University of Minnesota Press.

These modes may be thought of as distributed along a continuum, ranging from those in which primary emphasis is placed upon those aspects of the speaker's behavior that are regarded as stuttering, to those in which primary emphasis is put upon the perceptual and evaluational reactions made by one or more listeners (including the speaker himself) to whatever the speaker may be doing when he speaks. Thus, theories of the origin or onset of stuttering tend to range from the view that it is the child's change in the direction of speaking more nonfluently that triggers the disturbed, and disturbing, reactions to his speech by the mother or some other important listener, on the one hand, to, on the other, the view that there need be no increase in the child's nonfluency, but that rather it is the altered perceptual set of the listener that is crucial in triggering the disturbing interaction between listener and speaker.

Moreover, once the problem has arisen its development may be explained with major emphasis on the patterning of the stuttering behavior, or "avoidance reactions," or with major emphasis on the reactions made to this behavior—reactions considered as perceptual and judgmental, neuromuscular and symbolized, presumably unexpressed and overt. And the greater stress may be placed on such reactions made by the speaker to his own relevant speech behavior or on those made to it by other persons. Also, the relevant behavior of both speaker and listener may be variously explained with reference to theories of learning, with differing assumptions respecting such notions as conditioning, reënforcement, drive, and habit, and with distinctive approaches to the matter of conflict among these and other variables. Obviously, explanations in terms of learning theory may be focused in different ways upon the learning done by the speaker and the listener, respectively, and upon the relation of their interaction to the learning done by each of them. Different explanations may also reflect more and less attention to the neurophysiological, psychological, and sociological contexts in which the interaction between speaker and listener occurs.

It is clear that there is leeway for tremendous variation among interpretations constructed on this general base. This means, of course, that the possibilities of the further development of this explanatory approach to the problem of stuttering are relatively broad in scope. Meanwhile due reflection on this interaction theory and its implications serves to make readily apparent the many-faceted dissimilarity between it and the more traditional speech theory of stuttering. As between those who favor the one and those who prefer the other basic orientation, the opportunities for disagreement are abundant, and for reasons that are many and wonderful.

To Agree or Disagree?

There is far more, certainly, to the story of the six men and the elephant —and to the story of the six men and the stuttering—than can ever be encompassed by the assumption that each observed a different aspect of what they had all come to see. Indeed, the beloved parable, so representative of the folk-thinking of our culture, seems only to appear less and less plausible with each passing moment of thoughtful contemplation of its charming naïveté.

Not only do men disagree in their reports of observations of the "same" events, and in the interpretations they spin of what they say they have observed, but they also disagree about the value of agreeing. It is by no means to be taken for granted that agreement is always worth the price that must be paid for it. The price can be as outrageous as loss of freedom, as exorbitant as the abandonment of imagination. The joy of contemplating a world in which everyone agrees with you must end by giving way to the nightmare in which no one agrees with you—until you come to think as all others do.

Disagreement can come high, too, of course. Cherished for its own sake it is surely valueless. Whenever scientific integrity would serve to diminish disagreement, it is to be maintained only at an awful sacrifice. There is much disagreement, however, that is but the obverse of the unceasing variation of the human kind. It is commonly the by-product of individuals seeking self-realization. And when it is the disguise of creativity it deepens wonder.

The possibilities of exercising creativity in refining our understanding of the problem of stuttering are far from exhausted, and therefore there are kinds of disagreement among those seeking to comprehend the problem that can hardly be other than reassuring to the duly perceptive. They are evidence of continuing investigation, even, in certain instances, of the outcroppings of constructive ingenuity. So long as this continues to be true, there would seem to be cause for glad anticipation of the future, and so for present joy within reason. An unacceptable point of view need occasion dismay only in the absence of a more congenial position with which it is incompatible. This granted, the reader may venture into the pages ahead with assurance of finding, in varying proportions, both stimulation and contentment.

STUTTERING AS AN ANTICIPATORY STRUGGLE REACTION

OLIVER BLOODSTEIN, Ph.D.

Assistant Professor of Speech at Brooklyn College and Supervisor of its Community Speech and Hearing Center. Fellow of the American Speech and Hearing Association; contributor to professional journals including the Journal of Speech and Hearing Disorders, ETC, *and the* General Semantics Bulletin; *former Associate Editor for the* Journal of Speech and Hearing Disorders *and Associate Editor for the* Journal of Speech and Hearing Research.

Stuttering as an Anticipatory Struggle Reaction

The Background of the Problem

The Moment of Stuttering

BREAKS IN the normal flow of speech probably occur for many reasons. Stuttering, in the usual clinical meaning of the term, is a distinctive type of speech interruption. It appears more frequently in boys than girls, tends to "run" in families, begins for the most part in the early childhood years, and is especially rampant during this time in the form of episodes of varying duration. It follows a roughly predictable course of development when persistent over a period of time, and in its developed form it has a complex symptomatology and a tendency to vary consistently in response to specific sounds, words, situations, and listeners by which it is differentiated without great difficulty from other kinds of nonfluency. There is, moreover, one attribute of this disorder which typifies it above all: the person who exhibits it knows precisely what word he wants to say; he is simply unable for the moment to say it.

What the onlooker observes is the so-called stuttering "block." This may take somewhat varied forms—repetition, prolongation, or complete cessation of sound. But these distinctions must not be drawn too fine, being somewhat obscured by the overriding effort and hurry which tend to characterize stuttering in its developed form. There is perhaps one dominant feature of developed stuttering, and that is a strenuous attack on the stuttered sound. Whether explosive or long-continued, silent or audible, interrupted or maintained, there is nearly always that pressure or stoppage of the articulators which Van Riper conveniently terms a "hard contact" (45:384).[1]

If we ask what this block or hard contact "is" we may currently choose among perhaps three major explanations. One, which may be termed the "repressed-need" hypothesis, states that the stutterer blocks because he unconsciously wishes to block, principally in order to satisfy infantile erotic or aggressive desires. The second is the "breakdown" hypothesis, which represents the stuttering block as a temporary failure in the smooth, integrated performance of a complex neuromuscular activity in certain individuals who are emotionally or constitutionally predisposed to such breakdown under conditions of stress. The third, which appears to the writer to be far more cogent than either of the others and will be accepted as essentially valid for the purpose of this discussion of stuttering, may be called the "anticipatory struggle" hypothesis. Stated in the most general way possible, the theory is that the stutterer exerts himself in his speech attempts in varied and complex ways on the assumption that he must do so in order to carry them out successfully. In recent years this explanation has become especially well known in a form in which it has been advanced by Wendell Johnson, namely, that stuttering is an avoidance reaction performed in the fearful anticipation of speech interruption, or, essentially, that it is the effort not to stutter (22:216 ff.).

As research findings on the moment of stuttering have gradually accumulated, in large part under the impetus given to this type of investigation by Johnson and his students and associates at the State University of Iowa, the evidence has tended more and more strongly to support the anticipatory struggle hypothesis. This evidence may be summarized briefly as follows. The occurrence of stuttering is generally preceded by anticipation of stuttering (**28**). In successive oral readings of a passage the stutterer tends to block fairly consistently on the same words (**24**). The words on which he is most likely to stutter are those on which he remembers past stuttering (**25, 26, 27**) or which he evaluates as especially important, conspicuous, or difficult because of their length, position in the sentence, grammatical function, or initial sound (**9**). There is more stuttering under the threat of electric shock as a penalty for stuttering (**44**). There is less stuttering whenever the stutterer appears to have less anxiety about stuttering and less desire to avoid it (**3**). The implications of these findings are corroborated by a variety of clinical observations.[2] To cite a particularly

[1] Boldface numbers refer to references at ends of articles; lightface numbers, to chapters or pages in references.

[2] Those referred to here are only a few of the pertinent studies. For a more detailed review of research on the moment of stuttering see W. Johnson (ed.), *Stuttering in Children and Adults: Thirty Years of Research at the University of Iowa,* Minneapolis, University of Minnesota Press, 1955, pp. 13–24.

revealing example, it is familiar to most speech clinicians that some stutterers who are unable to say words beginning with *f* have no difficulty when the sound is spelled *ph*. The writer knows of one stutterer who blocks consistently on words beginning with *th,* although he mispronounces this as *t* or *d,* on which he rarely stutters otherwise. Finally, there is something to be learned about stuttering from apparently analogous difficulties which are observed to occur in typing, writing, and the playing of musical instruments.

All of these observations seem to reinforce a view of stuttering as basically the result of certain attitudes, predictions, or preconceptions which the stutterer entertains about his speech. More specifically, he appears to acquire a belief in the difficulty of words and sounds and to struggle against an imagined obstacle in the process of articulating them. It is to be particularly noted that the essentials of such a view may be expressed in many different ways. It has been embodied from time to time in conceptions that stuttering blocks may be precipitated by faulty autosuggestion (8), fear of normal nonfluencies (22:241–247), or fear of "primary stuttering" (6). Alternative statements of such a view in the rigorous terms of modern behavior science have been formulated by Sheehan and Wischner (40, 50, 51). It is intended to imply not that there are no important differences among these conceptions, but only that they may be regarded as illustrations of a single general principle. A convincing formulation of the anticipatory struggle hypothesis is given by Van Riper in his discussion of the "preparatory set" in stuttering. Van Riper points out that in the moment before the stutterer attempts the word on which he expects and fears to stutter he firmly "preforms" the first sound with his articulators, tenses his speech muscles in whole or part, and readies himself to produce a fixed articulatory position rather than a normal movement leading into the next sound. Once he has prepared himself to attack the word in this manner, however, he has made it practically impossible for himself to say it without blocking (45:429 ff.).

Stuttering, then, may be regarded as a habit of making elaborate preparations for speech on the assumption that it is a difficult and treacherous process. In his very anxiety to articulate words or syllables adequately the stutterer makes certain that he will fail to do so, like the frightened and inexperienced swimmer whose struggles to stay afloat serve to drag him down. In a word, stuttering is the speech difficulty of a person who tries to speak not wisely but too well.

Primary and Secondary Stuttering

A more difficult, and from certain points of view more crucial, question is that of the precise conditions under which children first adopt the peculiar and troublesome assumption that they must lay siege to their sounds and syllables. The cause of stuttering is widely conceded to be obscure. That we are far from hopelessly ignorant of its beginnings, however, is apparent from the amount of agreement which exists with regard to certain basic concepts. One of the most significant of these is the distinction between early and late forms of the disorder. By the early 1900's the observation had been made repeatedly by Bluemel and others that stuttering at its inception is often quite different from stuttering as seen in most older children and adults. In the first place, the earliest symptoms of stuttering to be identified as such were reported to be for the most part merely simple, effortless repetitions and prolongations; and second, the young child when first regarded as a stutterer appeared to be essentially unaware of any abnormality in his speech. Clearly, the more advanced symptoms of fear and tension arise when the child reacts to his repetitions and prolongations and exerts himself to speak without them. To these contrasting types of speech behavior Bluemel gave the names "primary" and "secondary" stuttering (6).

It has since become rather widely taken for granted among speech therapists that stuttering develops in two distinct stages. Recently various dissatisfactions with this view have arisen, and in succeeding pages it will be seen to be an abstraction which fits the facts only in the most general way. But one thing of almost epochal value remains of this conception after due account is taken of what must be discarded and revised, and that is a simple and believable explanation of the tension and anxiety of developed stuttering, as well as all of its varied associated symptoms. It is, ironically, the very efforts of parents or other adults to help the child overcome the "primary" symptoms of repetition and prolongation which most often serve to transform them into a serious speech difficulty. The average parent's natural impulse is to slow the child down, to ask him to "think" before he speaks, or to have him "say it over again." Since the child tends to speak fluently as long as he is doing these things, the parent is encouraged to continue reminding him to do them. But the helpful effect of these admonitions rarely lasts until the next time he has anything to say, something few parents seem to discover for themselves, and in time they may cause something unlooked-for to happen. A degree of effort, the earliest "secondary" symptom of stuttering, may begin to creep into the child's speech attempts. He is simply beginning to act on the assumption which his parents have done their best to teach him, that fluency is a highly valued kind of behavior which is difficult for him to maintain. As a result, there is added interruption in his speech and a new pitch of urgency in his mother's exhortations to "talk slowly" and "stop and start over."

So he tries all the harder; and the harder he tries, the more convinced he becomes that he is basically unable to talk without stuttering, and so the more he stutters. As a result of specific unpleasant experiences his conviction that fluent speech is difficult soon begins to take the form of a more or less specialized anticipation of difficulty on certain sounds, words, and other features of the speech sequence under particular conditions and environmental circumstances.[3] In his efforts to avoid or terminate his blocks he may acquire typical postponement, starting, release, or other devices which still further complicate his stuttering (43; 45:379–383). He may learn ways to avoid certain words and certain speaking situations, and he may develop more or less intense feelings of embarrassment and apprehension about his speech.

This, then, is the manner in which stuttering has been thought to grow from a transient childhood tendency toward simple, unconscious speech repetitions into a serious and complex disorder. The point to be emphasized is that there has been widespread agreement among qualified workers in the field of speech disorders about the essential validity of this account. Various authorities have modified it in various ways, have differed about the importance of the parents' part in the process, and have disagreed in particular about the nature and origin of the "primary" symptoms. But the basic inference that the advanced symptoms of stuttering result from efforts at concealment and avoidance of simpler interruptions in speech has come to have a strong influence on modern thinking about the disorder.

The "Diagnosogenic" Theory of Stuttering

A second significant advance in our understanding of the conditions under which children acquire anticipatory struggle reactions was made when Wendell Johnson pointed out that fluency is a relative matter. If abnormal efforts to speak smoothly could develop as a reaction to unusual amounts of speech repetition, then they could arise in more fluent children as well, as a result of unusually high standards of fluency in the environment. Johnson's answer to the question of what causes primary stuttering was simply that there is no such thing. He asserted that the simple interruptions which have been termed primary stuttering are, by and large, merely part of the normal speech hesitancy of early childhood, and that the reason some children become stutterers while others do not is to be found less often in the speech of the children than in the evaluations placed upon their speech by parents or other adults.

[3] Van Riper has presented convincing illustrations of the manner in which these anticipations develop and spread (45:376–379).

Johnson's theory was first advanced in 1942 in his report of a study of young stuttering and nonstuttering children which he and a number of co-workers had conducted at the University of Iowa (23). Information had been gathered about the birth conditions, disease history, family background, laterality, language development, and other aspects of maturation of these children. When the data were finally tabulated and compared they offered no new clue to suggest why the onset of stuttering had recently occurred in some cases and not in others. Beyond the familiar finding that the stutterers had more stuttering relatives, which was open to several interpretations, the two groups appeared to be composed of essentially the same children. Johnson had something unexpected to report, however. As these children continued to come to him for study he was struck by what was at first a puzzling observation. *It was difficult to tell some of the stutterers apart from some of the nonstutterers by listening to the way they spoke.* To be sure, the stuttering children hesitated and repeated, but so did the nonstuttering children, in some cases in approximately the same way. Johnson began to obtain parents' descriptions of their children's speech interruptions at the moment when they had first begun to regard them as stutterers. In over 90 percent of the cases what they described appeared to him to be indistinguishable from interruptions frequently noticed in the speech of the nonstuttering children. What did differentiate these two groups, then, if even their speech characteristics were originally so similar? Johnson's conclusion was that the difference lay for the most part in the diagnosis.

In his systematic formulation of it, Johnson's theory states: (1) that stuttering is in most cases first diagnosed by a layman, usually one or both parents; (2) that what these laymen appear to diagnose as stuttering are, by and large, the normal hesitations which are characteristic of the speech of most young children; and (3) that stuttering as a disorder develops not before the diagnosis but after it and is caused to a large extent by the diagnosis and the attitudes and reactions with which it tends to be associated. A child who has been labeled a stutterer is likely to be worried about and helped and admonished until he begins to adopt the evaluations placed upon his speech by his parents and to exhibit the symptoms of tension and anxiety which distinguish stuttering from normal nonfluency. What sort of adult tends to foster such misevaluations in a normal child? Johnson believes it is likely to be an overanxious or obsessively perfectionistic person whose child-training policies reflect unrealistically high and rigid standards of politeness, cleanliness, obedience, and other behavior. In some cases the parents' exaggerated concern about their child's nonfluencies may be due to the knowledge that close relatives stutter, which serves in part to explain the tendency for stuttering to recur in successive generations of the same family. In brief, stuttering is regarded by Johnson as the child's effort to avoid normal nonfluencies. It is a "hesitation to hesitate" to which children generally normal in every other respect are especially prone in a society which places a very high premium on fluent speech (21:ch. 17).

The ingenious simplicity of this theory has attracted to it many clinical and research workers. What evidence is there by means of which it may be checked? Johnson's hypothesis—that "*on the date of original diagnosis,* stuttering children may speak in a manner that is not always to be clearly differentiated from that of other children of like age who have not been diagnosed as stutterers" (23)—is not an easy one to put to a rigorous scientific test. Certain implications of the theory, however, may be verified without great difficulty. Chief among them is the assumption that the normal speech of young children tends to be marked by many hesitations and breaks in fluency. From research on children's speech repetitions by Davis it may be inferred that these actually do occur very frequently—at the average rate of a few each minute in the running conversational speech of 2- to 5-year-old boys and girls (13). Davis found repetitions of all types, but whole phrases were repeated especially often, words less often, and syllables comparatively rarely. Van Riper takes these results as evidence that, while word and phrase repetitions are normal for young children, frequent syllable repetition is not, and he suggests that syllable repetition is one of the distinguishing features of "primary" stuttering (45:352). It is probably true that syllable repetition is more readily identified as an abnormality by listeners than other types of speech interruption (7). If so, it probably more often elicits social penalties and, consequently, more often leads to anticipatory struggle reactions. This should perhaps not be taken to mean, however, that ordinary children with normal speech characteristics may not also rather easily be regarded as stutterers under certain conditions or by certain adults. Several studies conducted in recent years at Brooklyn College have shown that normal-speaking children are frequently diagnosed as stutterers on the basis of their recorded speech by listeners who have been instructed to indicate "whether or not the child is a stutterer." One of these studies is of particular interest because it demonstrated that parents of stuttering children were more frequently inclined to make such diagnoses than were other adults (5). This is not, of course, evidence of the *effect* of high standards of fluency as imposed by parents, since we have no way of knowing which came first in these cases, the high standards of the parents or the stuttering of their children. It is possible, at least, that the mother of a stuttering child is not only deeply troubled by his speech difficulty but also made more readily disposed, for various reasons, to label someone else's normal child a stutterer. It does, however, appear to be a convincing illustration of the ease with which certain individuals may be induced to hear abnormalities in essentially average speech. As long as listeners may differ so markedly in their definitions of defective fluency, for whatever reason, it is quite difficult to attach any absolute meaning to the term "primary stuttering." Given high enough parental standards, even the smallest amount and most ordinary kind of hesitation would appear capable of setting off the parental reactions which tend to bring about stuttering in its developed form.

If the influence of parental standards of fluency cannot be ignored, it is logical that unusual degrees of nonfluency must be given their due as well. True, these might rarely lead to anything more serious if no one regarded them as unusual, but it is easy enough to imagine repetitions occurring so often in a child's speech that they would alarm the great majority of parents. What we ought to call such large amounts of repetition is perhaps not the most vital question, although "primary stuttering" is probably not a helpful term if it is readily taken to imply that repetition of this sort may be sharply differentiated from more normal degrees of nonfluency, or that it is either a necessary or a sufficient condition for the onset of the struggle reactions which characterize stuttering as a relatively serious speech disorder.

A more crucial question appears to be the relative weight which is to be assigned to the child's fluency, on the one hand, and to the manner in which parents or other adults evaluate that fluency, on the other. Is the origin of stuttering in its developed form largely a matter of the child's repetitions and the constitutional or environmental reasons for them? Or is it largely a matter of the parental standards?

An Initial Hypothesis

It should by now be apparent that "What causes stuttering?" is not an entirely sensible question as stated. Whoever answers it must first specify exactly what he means by "the beginning of stuttering," and that is not so simple, for reasons which have to do only partly with the difficulty of making certain types of observation. Whether or not stuttering begins in the form of easy, unconscious repetitions is a question which cannot be answered by observation at all, and actually has little to do with the scientific study of speech disorders. This point is exceptionally important. We can observe the occurrence, frequency, and attributes of repetitions, their relationship to norms, the conditions under which they arise, the effects they produce, and what they are called by listeners of various types, but not whether they "are stuttering."

It will be well, therefore, to put the emphasis from the outset of this discussion on a somewhat different question: Under what conditions do children begin to exhibit strenuous blockages and other struggle reactions in their speech? To this question current theory, as we have seen, suggests the answer that they are a joint product of two factors. One is the amount of hesitancy which the child exhibits. The other, given special emphasis by Wendell Johnson, is the degree of tolerance with which this hesitancy is reacted to, generally by the parents. From this point of view the onset of stuttering, in the sense of hard contacts and anticipatory struggle reactions, is a matter of the relative potency of these two factors and the conditions under which each of them may vary.

Standards of Fluency. High standards of fluency may be supposed for the most part to be manifested as an aspect of that general perfectionism and overconcern which appears to be so significant a feature of the stutterer's parental environment. Few characteristics of stuttering have so frequently been commented upon in recent years as its tendency to be associated with environmental pressures upon children to live up to high standards of behavior. Evidence of this comes to us in three forms. First, stuttering abounds everywhere among those people who are most competitive in their social organization and who train their children most strictly in the observance of complex codes of behavior (30, 33, 41). Second, in our own culture stuttering appears to have its highest incidence in segments of the population which are socioeconomically the most upward-moving (34). Third, there is a tendency for parents of stutterers as a group to be more exacting than average in their child-training policies (12, 14, 32). It is probably safe to assume that we are dealing here essentially with a single fact in three different aspects.

Degree of Nonfluency. What of the fluency factor? Its importance can hardly be discounted. But where does it come from, this increased nonfluency which is unquestionably a large part of the reason that some children learn to struggle with their speech attempts? Is it merely an extreme degree of the same sort of hesitancy which is to be heard in the speech of the average child? If so, there is much to be learned about the development of stuttering from research on normal nonfluency. If not, more unusual causes must be imagined. Both Johnson and Van Riper have given substantial emphasis to certain common environmental circumstances in this connection, for example, frequent competition with others for the opportunity to speak, the need to verbalize new or exciting experiences or to communicate under conditions of conflict or emotion, and the like (22:294 ff.; 45:344). The most reasonable surmise on the basis of all our present knowledge would seem to be that any tendency toward excessive nonfluency at all, *no matter what its form or its cause,* is capable of leading to habitual anticipatory struggle reactions, particularly if it occurs in an atmosphere of strong disapproval of nonfluency. After all, neither the mother when she is alarmed by the speech hesitancy nor the child when he reacts to the alarm by straining to speak more fluently is concerned with distinctions with respect to the causes of speech interruptions. It is the simple *fact* of nonfluency which appears to cause the trouble.

A variety of interesting observations combine to support this view. One of these is the occurrence of stuttering now and then as an apparent side effect of aphasia. By its very nature, aphasia in its expressive forms often tends to result in slow and exceedingly nonfluent utterance. Most persons who exhibit a degree of expressive aphasia obviously do not stutter in the sense in which the word is used here. But is there any reason why these nonfluencies should not sometimes be evaluated by the aphasic in ways which occasion hard contacts, releases, postponements, or other symptoms of developed stuttering? In some cases they apparently are. Peacher mentions a brain-injured patient who "developed stuttering as a secondary manifestation in his attempts to obviate a very evident motor dysphasia" (36). Other instances in which stuttering appeared as an aftermath of transient aphasic disturbances are cited by Eisenson (16). In this connection one recalls with new interest familiar accounts of onset of stuttering after a severe blow on the head followed by temporary loss of speech. One example was the case of a 19-year-old stutterer seen at the Brooklyn College Speech and Hearing Center, who also had severe difficulty in reading and spelling. All of his difficulties, including the stuttering, apparently dated from the age of 9 when he suffered a concussion of the brain with loss of consciousness on falling from a tree. Upon his return to school after the injury his grades immediately began to drop. He attended a vocational high school and at the time of his examination was a skilled cabinetmaker, although his reading ability was approximately at the third-grade level. His speech problem was a severe stutter accompanied by characteristic symptoms of tongue protrusion, clicking of the teeth, and speaking on residual air.

So much for aphasic nonfluency as a potential, if rare, contributing cause of stuttering. Most stutterers do not appear to be aphasic, even in a special, subclinical sense, if their scores on verbal tests of intelligence are any indication. Neither are they cerebral-palsied. Yet the frequency with which reports of stuttering are heard of among the cerebral-palsied is arresting. Lack of statistical evidence makes it impossible to be sure that our occasional clinical encounters with cerebral-palsied stutterers are not purely accidental. If there were none but a chance relationship between the two conditions, however, the cerebral-palsied stutterer would literally be one in a million or rarer, and the likelihood of meeting him even in the speech clinic or cerebral-palsy center would be extremely small. Furthermore, the cerebral-palsied child with labored and arrhythmic speech has every reason to learn to stutter if our working hypothesis is correct. It is true that there must be other factors operating as well before he acquires the disorder, or else stuttering would be found in most cerebral-palsied individuals. But it seems implausible that his stuttering, when it does manifest itself, has nothing whatever to do with his neuromuscular difficulties.

Still a third case in point is afforded by certain types of mental retardates, particularly mongols, among whom stuttering is reported to be very common (18, 39). What is meant by "stuttering" in these cases? A description is given by Cabañas, who found that the speech blocking of a group of mongols did not appear to be associated with anticipations, avoidance devices, or memory of past interruptions. Cabañas considered it to be unlike "true stuttering" and preferred to use the term "cluttering" for what he observed (11). It is possible, then, that mongols who appear to stutter do not for the most part do so in quite the sense in which that word is used here. It would hardly be surprising, however, if the more intelligent of them occasionally developed symptoms of struggle and avoidance as a reaction to speech interruptions of the type which Cabañas reports. From the descriptions of speech clinicians who have worked with the educable mentally retarded, as well as from occasional personal observation, the writer has gained the impression that relatively developed stuttering in the usual sense of the term is not at all uncommon among such children.

As a final illustration, even the nonfluencies caused by delayed speech feedback appear capable of provoking stuttering reactions. It is well known that when normal speakers attempt to talk against the echo of their own voices reproduced with a fraction of a second's delay, certain vocal disturbances including marked hesitation may result. In an article on this effect Tiffany and Hanley have this to say concerning one of their subjects:

> This subject had experienced increasing difficulty with the sidetone readings, particularly on one word—pony. Following the delayed sidetone readings, he continued to experience great difficulty with this word even though no sidetone delay was present. He exhibited stuttering-like symptoms, as though the experimental readings had produced a kind of specific anxiety for this word.

He not only appeared to be more non-fluent than before the sidetone experience but also appeared to show tension and avoidance behavior consistent with accepted descriptions of stuttering patterns [42].

An incident of this sort goes far to confirm the struggle hypothesis, it demonstrates that struggle symptoms may arise as a reaction to nonfluency, and it supports the view that the nonfluency may have practically any conceivable origin.

The Hypothesis in Summary. To sum up what we have said so far, stuttering, in the sense of anticipatory forcing and avoidance behavior, might be regarded as due in most cases to the coincidence of two factors, an unusual degree of nonfluency from any source whatever and an environment which is exceptionally intolerant of nonfluency. It is to be emphasized that this is merely a working assumption, clearly suggested by previous theory and research, which we will attempt, in succeeding pages, to evaluate in the light of clinical findings. As will be seen, it is an assumption which leaves various questions unanswered and certain observations unaccounted for. Before we are done we shall need to broaden and modify this hypothesis to make it accord more adequately with the facts.

A Clinical Study of the Onset of Stuttering

The purpose of the following discussion is to suggest some inferences about the conditions under which stuttering has its onset. These inferences have been drawn in large part from a study of the case records of a group of 108 children who were examined by the writer at the Brooklyn College Speech and Hearing Center from 1950 to 1955.

The group consisted of 90 boys and 18 girls from 2 to 6 years of age and represented substantially all of the stutterers in this age range seen during that period. In a certain number of these cases the parent was clearly unable to date the onset of stuttering with accuracy, and for this reason it is not possible to state with exactness the average length of time which had elapsed between the onset of the disorder as first noticed by the parent and the occasion on which the child was initially seen at the Speech and Hearing Center. The interval may rather confidently be said to have ranged from three weeks to approximately four years, eight months. With a strong possibility of error of several months, it could be stated that its average duration was about one year and ten months. The information secured about this group has been freely supplemented as needed by data on older stuttering children, some few hundred of whom were seen during the same five-year period.

The Early Symptoms of Stuttering

Although clinical observations such as these must be viewed with the usual cautions, one conclusion to which they may be said to point fairly unequivocally is that there is little basis for assuming the existence of a "primary" stage of stuttering as something to be distinguished more or less sharply from a "secondary" form of the disorder. This conception, which has served to clarify so many aspects of stuttering in its advanced forms, must apparently be severely altered and refined if it is to accord with observation.

In the first place, the fine line which divides children with simple, unconscious repetitions and prolongations from those with tense, complicated forcings appears to be fictitious. The 108 Brooklyn youngsters who were the principal subjects of this study were simply not to be sorted into two categories. They appeared to exhibit only widely varying degrees of muscular tension in their efforts to speak, and widely varying degrees of awareness or anxiety as reflected in their observable reactions and the parents' accounts of their behavior. It is quite true that an outstanding speech symptom of a large number of these children—in a few cases evidently the only symptom—was a frank repetition of syllables and monosyllabic words, typically at the beginnings of sentences, which has frequently been identified as a characteristic feature of early stuttering. For the most part, however, even these less-complicated speech interruptions tended to have a definite suggestion of hurry and tension, an observation which has also been made by Glasner (17). In addition, they were often accompanied by hard contacts, strenuous prolongations, and unmistakable release devices, usually consisting of sudden exhalations. When symptoms of struggle and strain were not evident during the clinical interview itself they were often vividly and, from the point of view of the writer, convincingly reported by the mother. Furthermore, children whose symptoms were largely repetitive were frequently said to have passed through an earlier phase of more or less severe forcing. The development of stuttering, in other words, was by no means always a simple matter of *relatively* easy hesitations giving way to *relatively* labored blocks. The course which the disorder took in its early stages was actually an extremely variable one, often marked by fluctuations in complexity, periods of relative fluency, and transitions from more complicated and strenuous to simpler and easier symptoms rather than the other way about. In short, if many of the repetitions of these children would have been difficult to distinguish from normal nonfluencies, in essential confirmation of Johnson's findings, it is equally and perhaps as significantly true that in almost every case the symptomatology as a whole would have been impossible to separate qualitatively and categorically from that of developed stuttering.

In the second place, it is doubtful whether the earliest symptoms of stuttering to be identified as such by the parents were in all cases merely effortless, unconscious repetitions, "excessive" or otherwise. For the majority of the group they undoubtedly were. Others, however, appeared to have forced and struggled from the start. These children either never passed through a stage of relatively simple speech repetitions noticeable to others or did so months or years afterward, when the initial violence of their stuttering seemed to boil away. This is not to say that they were perfectly fluent before they suddenly began to force and strain. But whatever nonfluencies they may have had did not appear, at least in retrospect, to strike the parents as "stuttering."

In view of the confidence with which early stuttering is often assumed to be synonymous with "primary" stuttering, it is of some importance that roughly half the children who were seen fairly soon—a matter of weeks or several months—after the reported date of onset exhibited some hard contacts, often accompanied by facial tensions and other complications similar to those of relatively advanced stuttering, and in many of these cases there was distinct evidence of occasional awareness or even concern on the part of the child. Of two cases who were brought for examination only three weeks after the parent had first noticed speech difficulty, one was a boy of 3 who had been reacting to his stuttering by saying, "Mommie, why can't I *talk?*" and the other was a 2½-year-old boy whose mother told that "when he first started he became so annoyed that he hit himself on the mouth and stopped talking for three days."

Somewhat more to the point, however, are the first symptoms of stuttering as recalled by the parent. In more than one-fourth of the cases the earliest-noticed signs of stuttering appeared to have been something more than merely repetitions or prolongations. In many of these instances the parents described the initial symptoms by saying, "There was effort from the first," "The forcing was very severe then," "His whole body got tense," or "He became red in the face and choked up completely." A 3-year-old girl whose stuttering in the clinic consisted of hard contacts and silent intervals was said to have begun to stutter nine months before with "gasping" and refusals to talk. The mother could not remember her ever merely repeating. A 3-year-old boy, said to have been stuttering for about a month when he arrived at the Speech and Hearing Center, was reported to have begun by forcing, blinking his eyes, and clenching his fists. These symptoms were now gradually giving way to repetitions. "It was like a dog barking" was the way in which the mother characterized the initial symptoms in still another case.

What can these reports mean? May the child himself have reacted in these cases to certain repetitions in his speech of which his parents were unaware? If so, this would hardly justify a concept of "primary" stuttering. It would merely serve to divert our attention from the standards of fluency of the parents to those of the child and to raise questions about the sort of child who would react with concern and avoidance to hesitations so slight that everyone else, including his parents, overlooked them. Another possibility is that these were cases in which the child reacted with unusual promptness to the onset of "primary" symptoms and that this phase of the disorder was consequently so brief that the parents had forgotten it by the time they reached the speech clinic. This interpretation is supported by the case of the 2½-year-old stutterer cited above who was seen three weeks after stuttering had first been noticed by his mother. She related that his difficulty had consisted at first of simple repetitions, but that only two or three days later he began to produce hard contacts to which he reacted by "screaming, 'I can't talk!' " Whether or not we accept either of these explanations, however, a primary stage of stuttering would appear in certain cases to be a hypothetical and at best a highly transitory phenomenon.

It must be carefully emphasized that these observations, at first sight so puzzling because of their apparent irreconcilability either with a concept of primary stuttering or with strictly "diagnosogenic" view of the disorder, are not in complete agreement with previous findings. Johnson, in a study of 46 cases after a median interval of 5 months, 18 days following reported onset, apparently found no cases in which symptoms of effort and strain were identified by the parents as the earliest indications of stuttering (23). Darley, examining 50 cases after a longer average interval, appears to have found 11 instances in which at least one parent described the initial stutterings as "blocks" or more complicated symptoms, but in only three instances did both parents agree on this description. In six cases both parents agreed that the earliest symptoms were accompanied by "tension," although in three of these cases only one parent described this tension as "much" or "excessive" (12). Johnson cautions that "care must be exercised . . . in obtaining data of this type, since the nature of stuttering a week, or even a shorter period, after 'onset' may be quite different from stuttering at 'onset'—that is, at the particular moment when someone first decided that a given child was 'stuttering' " (23).

It is evident that there is more than one way to explain those cases in the Brooklyn group whose stuttering seemed to come to the parents' attention initially in the form of interruptions more complex than effortless repetitions and prolongations. In later pages an additional interpretation perhaps more satisfactory than any which we have considered will be suggested. For the time being the observations reported here should serve to emphasize once more that in order to account for something it is first necessary to describe it. The great diversity of views on the onset of stuttering is perhaps not surprising when we consider that there has apparently never been adequate agreement on precisely what it is that we have been speculating about.

Conditions Associated with the Onset of Stuttering

It is probable that almost any qualified observer who studied the histories of the 108 children in the group and then stood back to ascertain their most prominent common features would have observed three things which distinguished them as a group from any comparable series of youngsters. These were a restrictive parental environment, a family background of stuttering, and a personal history of delayed speech, immature articulation, or other speech difficulty besides stuttering.

Parental Pressure or Overconcern. In the majority of cases the parental environment appeared to be in large measure exacting, overanxious, or in other ways unduly prone to penalize children for failing to live up to certain ideals of behavior. Such a description is a matter of degree, and it would have been meaningless to try to determine exactly how many cases did or did not fall into this category. It may not be too misleading to say that in about two-thirds of the cases the evidence seemed incontestable. It should be kept in mind that observations of this kind are especially difficult to make on an objective basis and that they lack the scientific rigor afforded by a control group. It will be recalled, however, that similar descriptions of the stutterer's home environment have been given by various workers (see p. 11).

In many cases the parents would have been best described as obsessively perfectionistic. There was evidence, in these cases, of strict, demanding, nagging parental discipline, with the imposition of many restrictions in the home and heavy pressures to live up to adult standards of conduct. A few mothers voluntarily described themselves as perfectionists. Some gave accounts of plainly coercive feeding, weaning, and toilet training. One mother began attempts to toilet-train her child when he was 4 months old. Others told with apparent pride of rigid prescriptions with regard to cleanliness, manners, obedience, and the performance of various aspects of the daily routine. "I would like him to be perfect," was one mother's comment. Frequently, these parental reactions could be observed directly in the interview situation. One 7-year-old girl was reminded so often to sit up straight, take her hand away from her mouth, and say "yes" instead of "yeah" that it was actually somewhat difficult to converse with her. Occasionally the chief source or pressure seemed to be an adult other than the mother, for example, an aunt living in the home who exercised stern discipline, or an overly meticulous housekeeper who cared for the child while the mother went to business. In one case it was apparently the father, a talented and perfectionistic musician, to whom the child was recalled to have said on one occasion, "Daddy, why is it everything I do is wrong?"

In quite a few instances the effects of these pressures were most clearly seen in the behavior of the children themselves. They were often described as "good" children. Many of them appeared to be unusually meticulous and to have exceptionally high goals. One boy of 6 reacted to the request that he copy a circle by saying, "I can't make it as round as that." In building a tower of blocks he used extreme care to make the corners of each block coincide with those of the one beneath, and in making several folds in a piece of paper he took pains to see that the edges met accurately. His mother described him as very clean and well behaved, and an assistant in whose charge he was placed during part of the interview remarked about his extraordinary politeness. The compulsive orderliness shown by this boy was to some degree a feature of about one-fourth of the case histories of the group. As typical examples, one child before going to bed at night needed to have his shoes in a special place, the room and closet doors closed, and the chairs placed just so, while another child became upset if the arrangement of his toys was disturbed in the slightest or if he was accidentally wet or dirtied. In the records of somewhat older stutterers this type of report is less common, but in their place there is frequent mention of meticulosity, high aspirations, and strong desires to excel. A 10-year-old girl was said to be capable of destroying 10 or 15 sheets of paper in doing her homework. A boy of the same age often arose at 6 o'clock in the morning to study. Another boy, 9 years of age, was said to be a "perfectionist" about his schoolwork. It was recalled that as a small child he would cry when dirty and that he was completely toilet-trained at 8 months. The parent was generally at a loss to explain the child's need for perfection. "We never expect it of him," was a frequent comment.

In many cases excessive protectiveness would have been a more suitable description of the dominant parental attitude than perfectionism. Observations by Rotter and others that stutterers often tend to be unusually sheltered were clearly borne out in many cases (1:115–121; 38). Mothers often spoke freely of themselves as overprotective. Their great anxiety and concern frequently seemed to have to do with much more than the child's speech alone. Many of these boys and girls were generally hovered over and worried about, and their food, rest, and other aspects of their health and development watched with overwhelming intensity. One boy of 5½ years had only recently been allowed to play out of his mother's sight. Another, aged 6 years and 11 months, enjoyed being fed while he watched television. A child whose mother had died when he was an infant was cared for by a grandmother and two aunts. The grandmother remarked, "We feel so sorry for him that we do things for him we don't need to."

In corroboration of this finding, a large number of the children were relatively dependent and immature in behavior. In one-third of the cases there were reports of unnecessary demands for help with dressing, washing, and feeding, or other evidence of social immaturity. During the clinical interview it was not unusual for a child of 6 to refuse to leave his mother, or for a child of 4 to attempt to toy with papers on the examiner's desk or to insist on taking home the crayons with which he had been allowed to play.

The overprotective parents overlapped somewhat as a group with those who tended to be obsessively perfectionistic. As an illustration, one mother explained her son's social immaturity by saying that she was rarely satisfied with the way he "did things" and was consequently inclined to help him too much. It is possible that the most severe effects on the child were often those produced by a dominating type of protectiveness or by extremely anxious high expectations, because this kind of environment would appear to undermine the child's capacity to fulfill its unrealistic demands at the same time that it pushes and prods him to outdo himself. An instructive example was the case of a 4-year-old boy who was separated from his mother only with difficulty during the interview. She explained that he clung to her continually and confessed that she had "overprotected him at one time." The boy, however, was expected to "fight his own battles and not come crying," and his father had taken the practical step of teaching him to fight with boxing gloves. The same child was determined to learn to read and write, a fact which his mother attributed with misgiving to her pride in his precocious ability to read and spell a few words.

These, then, were the outstanding features of the home environment in well over half the group. As might be expected, many of these children seemed to show the effects of this environment in their behavior. Not only did they frequently exhibit somewhat compulsive or dependent tendencies, as already seen, but about one-third were feeding problems, about one-fifth were enuretic, and about one-third had exaggerated fears or night terrors, or were chronic worriers. Most of these problems, of course, are fairly common among children. So is a certain amount of overconcern among parents. Of even greater moment, however, as we attempt to assess the significance of these findings, is the fact that some stutterers in this group seemed to have none of such traits or symptoms, and some of the parents were not anxious or demanding at all. A certain number of these parents made positive impressions of substance, warmth, and understanding, and it would have been difficult not to respond to them as essentially adequate and unusually sane adult individuals. Their children, furthermore, often gave the appearance of being friendly, spontaneous, and self-possessed, in addition to merely being free of so-called "nervous" symptoms.

It is quite consistent with our initial assumptions about the onset of stuttering that this should have been so. The stuttering of these children probably did not result directly from neurotic family backgrounds any more than it was caused by maleness, which characterized so large a majority of them. If obsessive perfectionism and protective overconcern were fairly common features of the home environment in these cases it was in all probability because they served as an important source of unusual pressures on speech. They were not, however, the only source, as will be seen.

Family Background of Stuttering. The tendency of so many of these children to have stuttering relatives was to be expected, and the proportion of children, about half of the group, whose histories revealed it was the usual one. Such family backgrounds were noted both with and without evidence of parental overprotection or overconcern.

The Brooklyn case studies unfortunately add little to our knowledge of the reasons for this familial tendency. Some of them almost certainly illustrated the influence of familial stuttering on parents' reactions to speech interruptions in their children, as observed by Wendell Johnson. Among those parents who seemed the most anxious and perfectionistic about fluency were some who freely admitted that they were so concerned because they stuttered themselves or came from "stuttering" families. One, the mother of an 8-year-old boy, recalled the occasion on which she had first heard him "stutter," at age 1½. He had said the word "h-hug," repeating the first sound only once, but she had been disturbed by it because there was stuttering in her family. Another boy was brought to the Center at the age of 3 years, chiefly because his parents regarded his normal "baby talk" as an articulatory defect, but they were also alarmed by the hesitations in his speech and explained that two of the boy's uncles were stutterers. His language, articulation, and fluency were all easily regarded as normal for a child his age. In still a third case the mother began the interview by confiding with emotion that she was the cause of her child's speech difficulty. A stutterer herself, she had often thought with horror of the possibility that her children would stutter. When she became pregnant the idea became virtually an obsession. "Other pregnant women," she said, "worry about whether their babies will be deformed or mentally retarded. With me, it was whether he would be a stutterer." The child's first clumsy and hesitant attempts to speak seemed to justify her most pessimistic forebodings. In a panic, she did everything she could think of to help him speak without hesitations, interrupting, advising, insisting, rewarding, and punishing until, as she put it much later, she "had him all tied up in knots."

On the other hand, some parents who came from stuttering families did not seem anxious about their children's speech at all. A familiar example was the parent, usually the father, who had "outgrown" his own stuttering. In one instance a mother who had stuttered as a child was certain that her 8-year-old son would "grow out of it" just as she had. She had brought him to be examined on the insistence of the school nurse. Another case in point was that of a 4-year-old stutterer who was brought because of retarded speech development and defective articulation, he having only recently begun to speak in sentences. The mother referred to his stutter in passing and mentioned that his father stuttered as well. But when the examiner referred to the stuttering later with the intention of offering some help she brushed aside the implication that she might be concerned about it. She explained that her daughter, now 7, had also stuttered for a time shortly after beginning to speak. On the advice of a pediatrician she had fiercely ignored the girl's stuttering and had bullied her friends and relatives into doing the same. It had disappeared in short order, and she was confident that under the same regime her son would stop stuttering as well. In such cases the learning of anticipatory struggle reactions in one generation after the next of the same family would seem to have more to do with the speech of the children than with the speech attitudes of the parents.

May unusual degrees of nonfluency sometimes exist as a family trait? Experience suggests that it may. Occasionally, parents who asserted that there was no stuttering in the family had so many pauses, repetitions, and other breaks in fluency in their own speech that they aroused the suspicion that they had not been entirely candid. A few were questioned on this point somewhat persistently. Their answers left the conviction that they had never thought of themselves as stutterers. One mother was aware of her tendency to be nonfluent. Furthermore, she said that her father when living had also been apt to "hesitate at times." Yet neither was known to have been regarded by anyone as a stutterer, and neither apparently exhibited stuttering in the specific sense to which the term is confined here.

How it is handed down from parent to child remains one of the mysteries of stuttering. It is as yet impossible to tell whether the principal agent is the child's speech or the parent's standards, nor can we answer the overlapping question of whether the transmission of stuttering is primarily genetic or primarily social. All that we can say with confidence is that the familial factor in the onset of stuttering is a very powerful one. In the face of the very high familial incidence of stuttering, coupled with its high concordance in identical twins (35),[4] there is perhaps not adequate reason to reject the simple and natural inference that heredity plays a considerable part. These issues are not, of course, to be drawn too sharply. One may be fairly sure that stuttering is no exception to the universal rule that both hereditary and environmental influences are intricately involved in virtually everything that we are and do. It is to be stressed, nevertheless, that the questions raised here are not only fundamentally meaningful, but also in large part rather readily answerable from a practical point of view. Research is needed on stuttering children who were adopted at birth. We know that a great number of these children, being stutterers, have a family history of stuttering. But where is this stuttering for the most part to be found, in their biological or their adoptive families? Certainly, a good portion of what we want to know might be learned from the answer to this question.

Delayed Speech and Infantile Articulation. We now come to the third peculiarity of these stutterers. Fully one-third of the children in the group were described by their parents as "late talkers"; they were said to have persisted for a relatively long time in "baby talk" or were "difficult to understand" before they began to stutter. This occurred either with or without signs of parental overconcern, and with or without a family history of stuttering. Some disagreement has existed on the subject of the stutterer's speech development. By and large, the Brooklyn cases corroborated past research findings of speech retardation among stutterers (2; 12: 90; 31).

[4] Some contradictory evidence is cited by Odny I. Graf, "Incidence of stuttering among twins," in W. Johnson (ed.), *Stuttering in Children and Adults, op. cit.*, pp. 381–386.

What is meant in this instance by delayed speech? Children are known to differ considerably in their rates of language development, and normalcy permits a wide range of variation. Strictly speaking, few of the stutterers referred to by their parents as late talkers were probably far outside what would ordinarily be considered normal limits. The typical child has begun to say his first words by the time he is about a year old and to speak in simple sentences by about age 2. With a few exceptions, all that could be said in deprecation of the speech development of these stutterers is that they were somewhat slower than average; many of them had not said their first words until age 1½ or 2 and their first sentences until 2½ or 3.

In several cases, moreover, what the parent referred to as late talking turned out on further questioning to be merely average or actually superior speech development by any reasonable standards. One boy who had been a source of anxiety to his parents for a time because they considered his speech development retarded had acquired sentences *at 1½ years of age*. In another case the mother of a girl only 2 years and 10 months of age worried about the child's inability to pronounce speech sounds which normal children sometimes do not learn until age 6 years or so. In cases of this kind the mother's report of her child's slowness in speech seemed to be nothing but an ominous reflection of her own unrealistically high standards.

That many of these children had actually made somewhat slow progress in developing speech and language skills, however, is hardly to be doubted. Frequently other people besides the mother had evidently regarded the child as delayed in speech or defective in articulation. That is, relatives or neighbors had commented, playmates had teased, or strangers had had great difficulty in understanding. In some cases there was a history of delayed speech in other members of the family. In many cases the late persistence of infantile errors of articulation was observed in the clinical interview and served as partial corroboration of the parent's report of delayed onset of speech. Several of these children, in fact, were referred primarily because of articulatory difficulties, their stuttering being mild or occasional.[5] Furthermore, there were a few instances in which the child had been examined earlier—many months before the onset of stuttering—because of failure to speak at the expected time or because of infantile articulation. For example, one boy was brought to the Center at age 3

[5] An unusually large number of articulatory defects among stutterers has been reported in previous studies. See M. D. Schindler, "A study of educational adjustments of stuttering and nonstuttering children," p. 355, and F. L. Darley, "The relationship of parental attitudes and adjustments to the development of stuttering," in W. Johnson (ed.), *Stuttering in Children and Adults, op. cit.*, p. 90.

years because he was saying only a few single words. When he was seen again at age 5 language was fully developed, but he had begun to repeat and prolong many of his sounds and exhibited a few typical associated mannerisms. Finally, five children in the group began to stutter *while attending the Center for help with their articulation,* an interesting and significant fact which brings to mind Rigmor Knutsen's observation, reported by Van Riper, of the frequent onset of stuttering in Norwegian children treated for delayed speech (45:346).

What are the implications of these facts? In the first place, the effect of a parental evaluation of retarded speech may be an intensified alertness to all aspects of the child's utterance, including his repetitions. It is not a long step from worrying about a child's language or articulation to worrying about his fluency. Delayed speech, or what the parent thinks is delayed speech, may therefore be a potential source of abnormal anxiety about children's speech hesitations. From this point of view the mother's belief that the child is behind in speech development is more significant than how far behind he actually is. Experience at the Center seemed to show that such beliefs may arise because of unquestionable speech retardation on the part of the child, because of invidious comparisons with precocious siblings, or for no other reason than the parent's general perfectionism.

In the second place, there is the possible effect of delayed speech on fluency itself. It is perhaps not unreasonable to expect a child who matures late in other aspects of language use to be slow in developing adult fluency as well. Frequent hesitation, as we now know, is a normal occurrence in the speech of young children, and in most family gatherings it tends to escape serious notice. But the same nonfluencies which are ordinarily passed over in a child of 2½ would seem likely to have a somewhat different ring to many parents if the child were 4 or 5.[6] It is evident that the tendency of many of these stutterers to be slow in speaking may be explained on the basis of either of these two factors. There is, however, still a third possibility which may be of far greater importance than either of these.

An Altered Hypothesis About the Onset of Stuttering

Perhaps the most significant inference to be drawn from the evidence just presented is that in a large number of cases the child had acquired

[6] Davis actually discovered no relationship between the amount of speech repetition of normal children and their language levels (13). This is not quite the same, however, as saying that the child who is somewhat grossly retarded in language development may not be excessively repetitive in comparison with normal children his age.

a reputation as a defective speaker which *antedated* the onset of his stuttering. If this is true, it would appear to suggest some changes in our initial hypothesis. Anticipatory struggle reactions arise, as we have seen, from the child's conviction that he must exert himself if he is to speak adequately. How does the stutterer learn his belief in the difficulty of speech? We have been assuming that it is entirely a matter of how hesitantly he speaks and how severely he is badgered about his breaks in fluency. But speech offers many other things to worry about besides fluency—for example, vocabulary, grammar, pronunciation, rate, and articulation. It is hardly possible to doubt that the child who falls behind in these or any other aspects of language development may find communication something of a struggle at times. If he is subjected as well to parental attempts to hurry his speech development the suggestion that speech requires laborious preparations and special effort may be powerfully established.[7]

We should take stock of precisely what it means to be a little behind in speech development in a society such as ours. It is a society which is terribly conscious of speech, as almost any speech therapist can testify. If we accepted for remedial work all children whose parents thought they needed it, speech clinics would be overrun by essentially normal children whose basic problem is that they do not speak as well as the child next door. If this is so, it is not difficult to imagine the social pressures to which parents are exposed when their children are somewhat seriously delayed in speech. The humiliating remarks of the neighbors, the helpfully meant confidences of friends and relatives, and the "cruelty" of other children often become almost impossible to endure. The harassed parents tend to harass the child, and the youngster is apt to find his backward speech a focus of intense concern. Even after he has begun to speak, his parents may continue to be agitated by the errors of articulation which are so frequently an aftermath of delayed onset of speech. To make matters worse, parents often naively assume that a lisp or infantile *r* is due to carelessness, a "lazy" tongue, or excessively rapid rate, and the child may be urged to "slow down" or "be careful" about the way he speaks. Such children may in time become essentially fearful of speaking. When they are brought to the speech clinic the examiner's invitations to converse may draw forth no more than a whispered word or two, and in some cases all of the mother's bribery and commands may not be enough to

[7] Van Riper has observed that many children begin to stutter "if, driven by their parents, they try too swiftly to master the art of talking in phrases and sentences." Both Van Riper and Curtis have called attention to cases in which delayed speech or defective articulation appeared to prepare the way for the development of stuttering reactions. See 45:345–349, and J. F. Curtis, "Disorders of articulation," 22:ch. 3.

make them speak at all. In general, this is the reaction of a child who has been coached, corrected, and criticized so often that he goes about virtually in a continual state of stage fright. It is not difficult to understand why some of these children so profoundly doubt their ability to get their words out acceptably that they begin to buffet and beat their way through speech. In one revealing case of defective articulation recently seen by the author, the mother described how the child, who had never been considered a stutterer, began to force grotesquely on the word "ship" when she tried to help him to articulate it.

The foregoing appears to the writer to be, on the whole, the most plausible explanation for the large number of young stutterers in the Brooklyn group who were late talkers, or who could not "speak clearly" or "make themselves understood" before they began to stutter. In these cases the mother frequently reported that the child had been made upset, impatient, or resentful by her attempts to improve his articulation. A number of parents commented specifically that the onset of stuttering had occurred soon after the child had begun to exhibit these reactions. One girl of 5 years, originally a late talker, had been exposed to the combined efforts of her mother, her sister, and a neighbor to help her overcome her "baby talk." When seen at the Speech and Hearing Center because she had begun to have trouble "getting her words out," she was badly frightened and refused to speak. Significantly, she stuttered *only on those sounds which she misarticulated,* according to information offered by the mother. A similar observation was made by another parent. The child had acquired his first words late, at age 3. Some time afterward the mother noticed that he was not "forming his sounds right," particularly the *l* and the *g*. Directing him to watch her mouth as she said them, she devoted herself to the task of teaching him these two sounds. She first regarded him as a stutterer when, at age 5, he was observed to repeat the sounds *l* and *g* frequently in initial position in words. By the time he appeared at the Center about five months later, the boy was repeating and prolonging a good many other sounds as well and had acquired the habit of releasing himself from blocks by means of a rapid expulsion of breath.

Oral Reading Difficulties as a Source of Stuttering. If the words with which the stutterer has difficulty may sometimes provide a clue to the etiology of stuttering, it will be worth while to record an interesting observation made on somewhat older stuttering children. When, as has often happened, these children have stuttered in oral reading, they have almost invariably blocked on the unfamiliar or "hard" word, of whose identity or pronunciation they were evidently uncertain. Many a 9- or 10-year-old who has read "Arthur, the Young Rat" aloud during the initial clinical interview has stuttered on little besides "zealous," "flighty," and "shirker." Furthermore, it has been instructive to see how, on occasion, a child's efforts to "sound out" the strange word have apparently turned into a genuine stuttering block. The importance of this is most readily seen in relation to certain other observations. In the first place, in a certain number of cases stuttering seems to begin in the classroom during the early grades. Secondly, some stutterers block only in oral reading. We occasionally discover adults who speak fluently and spontaneously in vital interpersonal relationships, yet have had since early elementary-school days a troublesome stutter when reading aloud. Finally, the very fact that the majority of stutterers have some difficulty in oral reading even though, as usually performed, it differs sharply from the normal pattern of communicative speech to which stuttering is otherwise almost wholly confined, appears to reflect the stutterer's experiences in the classroom and is perhaps additional evidence that such experiences may be enough to precipitate the disorder in some cases.

These facts serve to call to our attention that nonfluency, delayed speech, and immature articulation are not the only sources from which children may, under certain conditions, receive the malignant impression that talking involves the overcoming of obstacles. The danger probably exists in any situation in which a child is repeatedly expected to speak in a manner somehow beyond his depth, in which he continually makes mistakes, and in which the consequences of an error are, from his point of view, grave and dreadful. For some children the oral-reading situation as it is to be found in certain classrooms fulfills these requirements exceptionally well. Some of these children may have reading problems per se. Others may merely have somewhat poor verbal ability or limited skill at pronunciation, which the oral-reading situation serves to make conspicuous. Even among adults one occasionally sees cases in which stuttering exists together with a gross verbal poverty and articulatory ineptness, and appears to be related to a lifelong sense of inadequacy at pronouncing somewhat long and difficult words. In still other cases the essential factor appears to be the interaction of a timid, withdrawing child and a severe, impatient, or aggressive teacher. One rather sensitive and insecure child began to stutter in the second grade in the classroom of a teacher who terrorized him by her scoldings. Probably as important as the teacher's irascibility in this case was her demand for speed in oral reading and her astonishing insistence that there was to be no pausing except at periods.

Cluttering in Relation to Stuttering. Abnormalities of rate or phrasing are probably still another source of difficulty. Of particular importance, as has long been observed by Deso Weiss, is cluttering, a familiar type of rapid, indistinct, staccato utterance whose cause does not appear to be reliably known, although it is evidently quite common in children. Weiss believes that stuttering symptoms frequently appear as the result of the child's efforts to overcome his tendency to clutter (48). It is perhaps not without some significance that one of the most common complaints with which children of practically all ages are brought to a community speech clinic is that the child "talks too fast and swallows his words." This is a potential source of serious concern to parents. Experience affords definite evidence that it gives rise to stuttering in some cases. One girl of 7 began to force and repeat at age 5½, but prior to that she "had always been a rapid speaker" and had been urged continually to speak more slowly. A boy of 6 "began by just jumbling up and talking very fast before he actually stuttered." In still another case a first-grade teacher noticed that the child "spoke too fast" and began to remind her systematically to talk slowly. The mother did this at home as well, on the advice of the teacher. Six months later this girl appeared at the Center exhibiting rapid sound repetitions with gasping and frequent retrials. Rapid, cluttered speech was also observed during the interview. The same combination of symptoms may sometimes be seen in adults. What experienced speech clinician has not seen individuals who seem both to stutter and to clutter? A noteworthy case of this kind was a college student, aged 18, who had been stuttering for only two years when he came for help. As far back as he could remember he had spoken very rapidly. As he grew older his family nagged him about his rapid speech with mounting intensity. "They didn't let me alone," he said. As an adolescent he finally made diligent attempts to talk slowly, but these proved of little use. Then he began to have great blocks which contracted his face and hunched his body. During the course of his therapy it was found that the rapid, staccato utterance had persisted. His clinician observed it even during occasional periods of complete freedom from stuttering of several days' duration.

Conclusions Regarding the Onset of Stuttering

The Multiple Etiology of Stuttering

We may be fairly certain that if the conditions which produce anticipatory struggle reactions in children were not varied and complex they would long ago have obtruded themselves upon us. The clinical study reported here disclosed three elements which appear to contribute to the onset of stuttering—parental pressures, slow or otherwise imperfect speech development, and a family background of stuttering. They are certainly not the only contributing causes, but they seem to be exceedingly important ones. Of seventy children in the Brooklyn group whose histories were detailed enough to permit a practically unequivocal judgment about the presence or absence of each of these three characteristics, only six cases appeared to present none of them. Twenty-four case records revealed one characteristic; twenty-nine, two of them; and eleven, all three. The following is a more detailed analysis of the occurrence of these factors among the seventy cases.

All three factors combined	11
Parental pressures and familial stuttering	10
Parental pressures and abnormal speech development	12
Familial stuttering and abnormal speech development	7
Parental pressures alone	9
Familial stuttering alone	8
Abnormal speech development alone	7
None	6

We have already taken passing note of a rather significant fact about these three features of the stutterers' histories, namely, that they occurred independently of each other. If, for argument's sake, we had found slow speech development in practically all cases which disclosed evidence of parental overconcern and, by and large, in no others, it would have been a fair assumption that only one of these two factors had had to do directly with the onset of stuttering. If, on the other hand, delayed speech and parental overconcern had almost never appeared in the same history we might have inferred that either one alone was quite enough to produce stuttering. We actually find no interdependence at all among these factors; statistical analysis shows that any one is about as likely to occur with as without any other. Perhaps it is not far-fetched to conclude that while each of these three circumstances is by itself somewhat conducive to stuttering, *the majority of cases come about to a large extent through the accidental concurrence of at least two of them.* A supposition of this sort goes far to explain why none of these conditions is to be found in all stutterers' case histories, and why so many children never become stutterers although they have demanding home environments, family histories of stuttering, or difficult speech development.

Viewed in this manner, stuttering is in most cases a joint product of more than one factor. Yet even this surely oversimplifies its complex etiology. It is likely that many more circumstances than can be recorded in a single clinical interview or even a series of interviews combine in a given case to instill the assumption that speech is difficult and struggle reactions mandatory. Those we have discussed are merely the most obvious and perhaps the most important ones.

The Role of Repetitions in the Onset of Stuttering

Before we pursue this question further it should be emphasized that we have finished our review of clinical evidence with a somewhat altered conception of the onset of stuttering. In the last analysis, neither excessive demands for fluency nor the occurrence of many repetitions in the child's speech are absolutely necessary in order for struggle reactions to develop. The essential condition for stuttering is simply the child's belief that communication is an arduous process and that he must put his back to it. Have we come so far on the theory that stuttering results from pressures to avoid nonfluency only to repudiate this idea in the end? Not at all. It is quite possible that this is actually the way in which many stutterers first learn to make their turbulent speech attempts. The writer recalls vividly certain college students who became acutely alarmed by repetitions in their speech. These persons generally have had no history of stuttering, and their breaks in fluency have proved to be rare and almost imperceptible. Their anxieties appear to be transient symptoms of the exaggerated value which individuals perhaps somewhat perfectionistic about speech to begin with may attach to fluency in a highly competitive, verbal, academic environment, and they serve to emphasize how readily speech hesitation may become a source of extreme concern in our society.

At the same time, how are we to account for the occasional onset of articulatory-pressure symptoms in the apparent absence of simpler hesitations or of any evidence that simple hesitation had been a matter of previous awareness or concern either to the child or to anyone else—assuming that such observations are sometimes valid? What are we to make of the case of a 7-year-old boy, brought for examination because of infantile articulatory substitutions, not stuttering, whose mother remarked at the close of the interview, "Every now and then he suddenly exhausts all his breath when he speaks. What is that?" The boy had apparently never been regarded by anyone as a stutterer and his speech appeared to be quite free from hesitation. Finally, how are we to interpret those cases in which stuttering evidently appears as a reaction to communicative inadequacies other than speech repetitions? The most plausible answer appears to be that while stuttering begins as a fluency anxiety in many cases, this is not the most general way to describe its onset. Stated more broadly, stuttering at its onset is what a child does on the assumption that he will not be able to say the word without hesitating on it, mispronouncing it, misarticulating its most conspicuous sounds, saying it too rapidly, or failing on it in any other way.

At this point, however, an unexpected difficulty arises to complicate our explanation of those relatively effortless and spontaneous syllable repetitions which antecede the occurrence of more strenuous symptoms in so many cases. The occurrence and the avoidance of repetition are clearly two different things. Yet, as we have seen before, observation reveals no clear-cut distinction on the basis of which we may say that here is merely a repetition, and here is an attempt to avoid it. All that we find as we study the repetitions, prolongations, and blockages which so-called stuttering children display is that they vary by fine degrees from relative effortlessness and spontaneity to extremes of tension. Not only are tension and awareness probably characteristic in some measure of practically all children regarded as stutterers, but careful attention to the speech of many presumably normal young children shows that a perceptible amount, and occasionally quite a bit, of effort and strain creep into even their hesitations. Nor must we forget that sound repetitions are often to be found in the complicated, advanced symptomatologies of the most severe adult stutterers. To be guided simply and innocently by what appear to be the logical implications of the facts, we would have to come to the surprising conclusion that when repetitions appear prior to more strenuous blockage reactions in a child's speech *they are likely to represent merely a less severe degree of the very same anticipatory struggle behavior.*

The Consistency Effect in the Repetitions of Young Stutterers. This conclusion appears to be strongly supported by an interesting observation. In 1937, Johnson and Knott, in one of the more significant of modern studies of stuttering, found that adult stutterers block to a very marked degree on the same words in successive oral readings of a given passage (24). This so-called "consistency" effect may reasonably be regarded as the essence of stuttering. It epitomizes a disorder which typically occurs in response to specific words, as distinct from more normal kinds of nonfluency which may involve indecision about what to say, and it may be demonstrated in virtually all persons ordinarily regarded as stutterers. Consequently, it seems of some importance that the consistency effect has revealed itself regularly in the very youngest children referred to the Center as stutterers, when they repeat simple sentences dictated by the examiner. It is of the greatest possible interest, furthermore, that it is quite uniformly exhibited even by youngsters whose presenting symptoms consist almost entirely of repetitions of words and syllables. The last statement is based on a small number of observations and needs to be checked with special care by further research. If true, it would seem to mean that not only complicated forcings but seemingly carefree repetitions as well may under certain conditions be precipitated by such attributes of words as their position in the sentence, initial sound, grammatical function, and the like, or by memories of recent difficulty on particular words. It would follow that there are types of repetition which primarily reflect the child's difficulty "getting the word out" rather than framing his thoughts, knowing what to say, or maintaining his composure, and are consequently similar in their essential nature to stuttering symptoms as we ordinarily understand them.[8]

If this is so, we can hardly continue to think of stuttering at its inception as principally a struggle to avoid repetitions. This is not to say that speech interruption of a given degree of tension and complexity does not give way to even more tense and elaborate symptoms through efforts to avoid it, or that stuttering does not in time begin to vary with variations in the child's desire not to stutter. It would simply appear that by the time certain types of repetition in a child's speech come with relative frequency *there has already taken place in most cases a significant process of avoidance of some real or imagined speech difficulty.* Such repetitions are to be distinguished, of course, from speech hesitancy of an essentially more normal kind.[9] The latter consists for the most part merely of repeated phrases, pauses, interjections, corrections, and incomplete expressions. These presumably would exhibit little or no consistency effect, are characteristic to some degree of the speech of almost all young children, and are not stutterings in the sense in which the term is used here. If it is not always easy to differentiate between a child who does and a child who does not hesitate in a manner indicative of anticipatory struggle, it should be borne in mind that struggle reactions are also probably far more common in children in a mild and transient form than has generally been supposed, the attitudes and values which tend to create stutterers being, after all, integral features of the society in which we live. Research shows that of the average group of adults or adolescents as many as 10 to 14 percent recall that they stuttered *at one time or another* in childhood (19, 46,

[8] These observations are substantiated by parents who sometimes notice that the child is most likely to repeat the *b*'s and *w*'s or some other specific sounds. Mention has been made (see p. 27) of a child who was said to have repeated the *l* and *g* when he began to stutter. That this boy was evidently reacting to articulatory difficulty on those sounds would seem to imply with particular clarity that repetitions may represent struggle reactions. Additional weight is lent to this assumption by parents' reports of the conditions under which repetitions are absent. These conditions—singing, unison speaking, solitude, and so forth—appear to be the very same ones under which stuttering in its more complex and severe forms is likely to disappear.

[9] Van Riper has called attention to the basic difference between syllable repetition and other types of simple nonfluency (45:352).

47). How many more briefly exhibited stuttering reactions which were overlooked or forgotten can only be guessed. It does not seem at all unlikely that the majority of young children at one time or another repeat or force slightly for reasons which would justify the use of the term "stuttering" for what they do. Egland's finding that unfamiliar polysyllabic words evoked a high frequency of syllable repetition in normal-speaking youngsters as well as in children who had come to be regarded as stutterers would appear to be an extremely significant illustration of this (15).

The hypothesis that syllabic repetitions are in and of themselves anticipatory struggle reactions seems for several reasons to be a particularly useful one. It does away with the abstract separation of stuttering symptoms into two categories where only fine degrees of difference in strength of avoidance appear to exist. It offers a firm basis for applying the term "stuttering" to certain unusual repetitions of syllables and monosyllabic words which are a conspicuous feature of the speech of many children referred for help as stutterers at early ages. At the same time it helps to explain perhaps more plausibly than other assumptions the reports of children who apparently began to stutter without ever exhibiting a comparatively frank repetitive pattern. For with avoidance a matter of degree it is not unreasonable to expect unusually powerful provocations to produce violent initial struggle reactions. Lastly, it permits us to avoid some misleading assumptions about the nature of blockages or "hard contacts." The old concept of primary and secondary stuttering, with its notion that the blockages are produced solely by the effort to avoid repetitions or easy prolongations, has probably embodied for most speech therapists the curious bit of unconscious fancy that the stutterer wrestles with and subdues the repetition or prolongation, as though taking it by the horns or riding on its back. No such thing occurs, of course, even in the most figurative sense. It may be that the stutterer often forces out his words chiefly because he believes that he would repeat or hesitate in some way if he did not. But once we have put it this way it can be appreciated that he could just as readily learn to force in this manner in the belief that he would distort a sound, mispronounce a word, or fail to speak acceptably in some other way if he did not.

Summary of Factors Influencing the Onset of Stuttering

In summary, we may say that the question of what causes stuttering as we have now defined it is essentially the question of why some children learn to behave on the basis of two assumptions—the conviction that they will not speak properly and the belief that they must.

The Anticipation of Failure. What are the outstanding conditions which make for the first of these assumptions? The answer seems to be, any obstacle to communication which may create the impression that speech is difficult. Among these obstacles are delayed language development, common defects of articulation, reading difficulties, pronunciation problems, and "cluttered" speech. Probably of major importance as well is speech hesitancy of an essentially normal kind.

There are unquestionably many other conditions which may lend an aura of formidability to the act of speaking. The writer is personally acquainted with three adult persons with cleft palate who stutter. We cannot rule out mere coincidence in these cases, but we may say that if the hypothesis which has been developed in these pages is correct a somewhat increased likelihood of stuttering is no more than we should expect where special pains are required in order to be understood and speech may become a matter for shame and concern in the early years. There is still another possible case in point in the occasional accounts, familiar to almost every speech therapist, of the onset of stuttering following a period of speechlessness after a severe shock. For example, one child in the Brooklyn group witnessed a bad automobile accident at age 3. When his mother found him two hours later he was apparently making an unsuccessful attempt to say "mama." Despite her frightened efforts to help him, or perhaps in part because of them, the boy stopped talking completely for three weeks. When his speech came back it came with strenuous hard contacts and rapid sound repetitions. Assuming the authenticity of such accounts, and it is certainly hard to doubt it in all cases, why do episodes of this kind sometimes terminate in stuttering? Part of the answer may be that for some children the experience of profound helplessness to give words to the inexpressible is enough to make them so utterly doubt their capacity for speech that for a time they become totally blocked, with more ordinary forms of stuttering as an aftermath. Nearly every speech therapist has seen stutterers having such severe difficulty that they are literally speechless, appearing to be unable even to struggle.

A somewhat unusual illustration of the development of struggle reactions in the absence of fear or avoidance of any form of underlying nonfluency was afforded by an intelligent and well-educated young woman who began to stutter at age 24. When first interviewed eight months after the appearance of her speech disturbance *she was unaware that she was a stutterer, believing her difficulty to be a form of voice disorder.* The earliest symptom of which she had been conscious was a "tightening" of her throat at times during speech. In an apparent effort to overcome this she soon began to make use of an explosive exhalation. This was the chief symptom to be observed when she came for help. It occurred only on words beginning with plosive consonants or with *h,* and she was acutely aware of such words as difficult to say. For the most part her symptoms came and went in response to the same conditions under which stuttering varies typically. She had vivid anticipations, and in repeated readings of the same passage the loci of her blockages showed almost perfect consistency. There appeared to be a combination of underlying causes for her glottal struggle behavior. Her father had always placed a great deal of emphasis on the ability to speak well in public, he himself feeling severely handicapped in this regard by a foreign accent. This might not have been of great importance had it not been for the fact that she possessed a weak, tremulous voice which made it difficult for her to make herself heard in almost any type of audience situation. To make matters worse, she had been the target of much sniping criticism by such persons as her older sister and her fiancé because she articulated too precisely, expressed herself at times too lengthily and pedantically, and used a somewhat artificial pattern of stress and inflection. Because she was, as she herself said, a perfectionist in almost everything she did, she reacted to her feeling of inadequacy at speech in a characteristic manner. As a challenge to her ability to learn to speak in public she accepted a type of public-relations position in which it was often necessary for her to address groups of people. Obeying a harsh conscience, she had persisted in this work for three years at the time of her initial interview, despite the fact that public speaking was more difficult and distasteful to her than ever. It was impossible to say precisely what single event finally served to push her over the brink of stuttering, but it is a tenable interpretation of the facts presented that there were a number of different influences in this case which gradually led to the difficulty.

While some of the contributing causes of stuttering illustrated by these cases are rare, they all exemplify the same principle—namely, that not hesitancy alone but anything at all which tends to shake a child's faith in his ability to speak may result in an appreciable danger that stuttering will arise sooner or later. Paradoxically, this danger may even lie in speech which becomes a focus of attention because it is so extraordinarily good. There are perhaps rather significant implications when parents wistfully report that the child "was an extremely early talker," or "spoke beautifully before he stuttered," or that "at 1 year he knew 20 nursery rhymes." Such comments may offer a clue to a situation in which the speech process came to be invested with the hobbling threat of failure because the child's good speech was so intensely valued.

The Child's Acquisition of High Standards of Speech. This leads us directly to the second assumption or attitude underlying stuttering. Generally speaking, we may be sure that the factors which have just been discussed are rarely enough to produce stuttering by themselves. What appears to be needed in addition is the child's exaggerated conscience about speech. On the basis of accumulated evidence there seems little reason to doubt that certain parental attitudes and adjustments, whose relationship to the onset of stuttering has been pointed out by Wendell Johnson, are chiefly to blame for this. Specifically, the stutterer's parents are likely to be largely dominating, overprotective, anxious, or obsessively perfectionistic. Whatever its most precise description in a specific case, the point about this parental environment is that it tends to favor the imposition of excessively high standards of speech and the acquisition of these by the child. It may well be that such standards are sometimes enough to precipitate stuttering, as Van Riper has observed (see footnote 7). Certainly it is conceivable that even the most articulate child who is subjected to pressures to exceed his speech or language capabilities may learn to evaluate his speech attempts as failures and acquire that assumption of basic inadequacy at speaking which appears to underlie the tendency to stutter.

An instructive illustration of the manner in which high standards of speech may be related to a broader pattern of parental anxieties was provided by the mother of a 4-year-old stutterer. By her own admission her handling of the boy was inconsistent and vacillating; she confessed intense feelings of anxiety about the child and inadequacy as a parent, and there were many family problems about which she had already been advised to seek psychological guidance. She was tortured by her son's habit of creeping on the furniture and other normally disorderly behavior, and she was concerned not only about his stuttering but about his slight lisp as well. One of her more significant comments was, "Since my childhood I liked people to speak well. If a girl had grammatical errors or anything like that in her speech I didn't want her as a friend. My great fear was that my child wouldn't talk well." While the majority of stutterers do not appear to come from quite such unwholesome home environments, this case serves to emphasize the important point that among the conditions which appear to lead to stuttering are some which are also conducive to severe adjustment difficulties.

This is not, however, the only reason for which children are subjected to severe demands for skill at speaking. A factor which has already been mentioned and which has been given considerable emphasis by Johnson is a "climate of anxiety" about speech which prevails in certain families in which cases of stuttering have been common. Perhaps an equally important factor is the dominating presence in the home of an adult model whose effective or beautiful speech is regarded with pride as an unusual gift. One is frequently struck by the father, often a minister, rabbi, teacher, or attorney, whose articulateness is in blunt contrast to the speech of the boy he brings for examination. Even if exceptionally good speech was never asked of this boy, either expressly or by virtue of certain values which he encountered in the home, one can be reasonably sure that he inflicted on himself all of the consequences of such demands merely in the natural process of competing with the older members of the household, particularly his father, who of all these figures was the most powerful and with whom the boy's personal identification was perhaps the strongest. There are no doubt many other reasons for which children come to have an abnormal need for approval of their speech. One boy in the Brooklyn group was obliged to live up to standards set by a fraternal twin brother who was said to have overshadowed him from the start in various aspects of development, including language.[10] Another case was that of a boy whose parents had accepted with difficulty the knowledge that he was slightly retarded mentally, and tended to make a great fuss about all of his intellectual and verbal achievements.

Some Final Observations

Stuttering, then, is a child's conscientious effort to speak acceptably despite a deep conviction that he cannot do so. It germinates readily in an environment which is in some manner critical or anxious about speech, and is frequently set off by certain provocations in the form of unusual nonfluency, inferior language skill, articulatory substitutions, pronunciation errors, or any other difficulties which may leave a child in doubt as to his basic ability to communicate properly. We may call stuttering a severe form of speech consciousness. It serves to remind us that as a natural consequence of its deep social implications speech is far more vulnerable as an object of fear and self-consciousness than other modes of human behavior. The great tendency of stuttering to begin during the period of language development when speech is subject to so many kinds of failure is therefore no accident, as has so frequently been remarked. The puzzling sex ratio in stuttering, too, appears to find a convincing explanation from this point of view. It is no wonder that far fewer girls stutter when they tend to be superior to boys not only in fluency but in

[10] The influence of unequal competition between fraternal twins on the development of stuttering has been commented on by H. Schuell, "Sex differences in relation to stuttering: I," *Journal of Speech Disorders,* XI, 1946.

vocabulary, sentence structure, articulation, reading ability, and most other verbal skills as well.

If the processes by which children learn these skills are hazardous from the point of view of stuttering this seems to be especially true in surroundings where standards are high and pressures severe. In themselves the speech defects and language deficiencies which frequently appear to precipitate stuttering are slight enough by almost any reasonable, objective criterion. What stuttering seems to reflect in the final analysis is a society which promotes intense competition for status and prestige, and capriciously accepts the most trivial refinements of speech as valid symbols of their attainment.

The Treatment of Stuttering

The remedial procedures to be described here are based upon a way of treating stuttering which has become widely known among speech therapists in the last 20 years, and which was developed chiefly by Bryngelson, Johnson, and Van Riper (10; 22:ch. 5; 45:ch. 9). For the most part, this method consists of a rather specialized process of modification of the stutterer's anxieties, attitudes, and expectations about speech, based upon systematically planned observations and experiences, carried out with careful regard for many features of behavior which the individual exhibits as a person rather than merely as a speech defective, and supervised ideally by a qualified speech clinician with a broad background in clinical psychology and special training in adjustment counseling. This therapy may be adapted with little change to accord with the viewpoint about stuttering which has been presented in this chapter.

As we have seen, there would appear to be two fundamental beliefs underlying and maintaining anticipatory struggle behavior. One is the stutterer's belief that he will have difficulty with his speech. The other is the knowledge that he must not. In most cases it seems wise to direct remedial work toward the elimination of both of these assumptions.

Eliminating the Anticipation of Stuttering

The difficulty which the stutterer struggles to avoid is a purely hypothetical one. That is, if he simply went ahead on the assumption that he would have no difficulty he would speak quite normally. As Johnson has pointed out, the very things which the stutterer does in order to avoid speech difficulty are the things which make it so difficult for him to go on

(22:216 ff.). The resulting abnormal interruptions in his speech thus serve as a powerful vindication of his struggle behavior, in all probability the reason that the suggestions which precipitate stuttering in children often seem to take hold so rapidly and sometimes persist so tenaciously. What this appears to mean is that, whatever the nature of the anticipations which originally touched off the struggle reactions, once stuttering has established itself as a recurring type of behavior the immediate reason for the behavior is the anticipation of stuttering itself. All of this as well as much more that it implies can be succinctly summed up by saying that if the stutterer could forget that he is a stutterer he would have no further difficulty with his speech.

Historically speaking, it is with the anticipation of stuttering that therapists were until recently almost wholly concerned in one manner or another. Furthermore, it is probably still safe to say that practically any method of treating stuttering which proves successful does so in large measure because it teaches the stutterer that his blocks are not inevitable. If the traditional methods so often failed to produce more than temporary fluency, it was because they depended either upon the stutterer's uncritical acceptance of the assurance that he could speak without stuttering—that is, upon suggestion—or upon his escape from the preoccupation with impending disaster by the exercise of unusual ways of talking or other temporary distractions which continued to be effective only as long as they retained their novelty. There are in use at the present time perhaps two promising methods of attacking the anticipation of stuttering directly on a sound basis.

Changing Semantic Reactions. One of these methods, developed by Johnson and recently extended and applied by Williams, is based upon semantic reorientation (22:283–287; 49). Certain students who have been concerned with the broad significance of language have noted that the age-old structure of language embodies the stratified remains, as it were, of primitive conceptions about the physical world. Korzybski, in particular, developed at length the implication that we unwittingly come to believe a great deal of nonsense because of certain habits of formulating our evaluations of sensory data which language forces upon us. While we can hardly remodel the basic structure of our language to make it accord better with reality, Korzybski believed that we could avoid a great many misconceptions by training ourselves to make a sharper distinction between the words we use and the experiences which they are designed to symbolize (29). Johnson and Williams point out that the expectancies which perpetuate stuttering appear to represent this type of misconception. That is, they are fostered in part by the language which the stutterer uses in talking to himself and others about his difficulty. In the first place, his verbalizations frequently appear to express a kind of belief which may be reduced to the statement "I am a stutterer." Now, stuttering is nothing more than a type of behavior. To say "I will stutter on 'hello' when I answer the telephone" is one thing, and involves its own particular brand of insidiousness. But to say "I am a stutterer" is to utter a fundamental untruth of the most sinister nature. For it is as much as to say "I am that sort of person," or "Stuttering is something which is in me and of me." What possible outlook could more strongly imply the inevitability of stuttering and therefore more deeply entrench its anticipation? Part of the task of therapy, then, is to train the stutterer to appreciate that there are no stutterers, but only stutterings. He will learn this most effectively if it is reinforced by observation and experience. For this reason it may be helpful to suggest that he practice fluent speech regularly in the clinic or at home, by talking in time to rhythms if necessary, or by using some other "distraction" (22:284). Once he has thoroughly absorbed the lesson that he is basically able to speak without difficulty, it may become somewhat easier for him to "date" his stutterings—that is, to adopt the attitude, "I stuttered that time. The next time? Well, let's wait and see."

It is, of course, difficult to stutter for any appreciable length of time without becoming convinced that one is fundamentally unable to speak in any other way. The stutterer often divulges this conviction even more clearly in the manner in which he describes his stutterings. To begin with, he is frequently quite vague about the details of his struggle behavior. Although usually all too vividly aware that he is "stuttering," he may perform his stutterings so emotionally, hurriedly, and automatically that he finds it difficult to say precisely what activities they consist of. This vagueness is in itself subtly conducive to continued expectation of stuttering, since one can scarcely imagine what it would be like to stop without knowing what one is stopping. When he does become aware of specific features of the stuttering experience, however, he is likely to report them in a remarkable way. He may say, "My tongue sticks to the roof of my mouth," "My lips come together tightly," "My throat closes," or "The word won't come out." The implication of these descriptions is that the lips, the tongue, and the throat have separate identities of their own—in other words, that it is not the stutterer himself who is responsible for his difficulty but a being inside of him who is beyond his control. It would be difficult to imagine a more revealing expression of his feeling of helplessness, or one which was better calculated to promote the expectation of further stuttering. It must be an objective of therapy to get rid of these fundamentally animistic notions. From this point of view, there are important advantages in helping the stutterer to make a detailed study of his symptoms. In the course of this analysis much is to be gained by training him to discontinue the use of the word "stuttering" and to talk descriptively and factually about his habit of pressing his lips together or closing his throat, and all of the various ways in which he stops the onward progress of his speech (22:287). The point which he must learn to appreciate is that if we are to get rid of the assumptions which underlie stuttering it is helpful to remove some of the verbal undergrowth in which they hide. Williams has demonstrated that once the stutterer does so it is often possible for him to learn to speak freely and spontaneously on the assumption that there is nothing to prevent him from merely going ahead and talking except the things which he himself does to keep the words from "coming out" (49).

Changing the Preparatory Set. A second method, suggested by Van Riper, attempts a more direct approach to the process of anticipation. It is based on the observation that the stutterer's silent rehearsals during the crucial moment of anticipation appear to determine the occurrence, length, and the very form of the block. The stutterer about to say a feared word is like a runner on his mark, poised in such readiness to perform a given pattern of reactions that at the expected signal no other behavior is possible. It is in this moment just prior to the block that an excellent opportunity for modifying the stuttering behavior presents itself. If the stutterer can learn to adopt a different form of preparatory set it may be possible for him to say the word with little or no abnormality even in situations in which he has a certain amount of fear.[11]

The new preparatory set has essentially three aspects. First, the stutterer must prepare himself to say the feared word with his articulators in a state of rest. Typically, he establishes a self-defeating focus of tension in his speech musculature even before the attempt at evoking the word. Second, he must get set to say the first sound of the feared word as a movement leading into the rest of the word. In normal speech each sound is in constant transition as it blends with the succeeding one. But to the average stutterer the first sound of a feared word is quite distinctive. The word is difficult because it is a *g* word or an *s* word, and its initial sound may impose itself for the moment like a large and threatening emanation upon the entire speech situation. Under these circumstances the stutterer makes ready to produce not a movement but a fixed articulatory position, and it

[11] Even such devices as "cancellations" and "pull-outs" with which Van Riper has been experimenting recently appear to have alteration of the stutterer's preparatory sets as their ultimate goal. See his detailed treatment of the subject in **45**:421–443.

is hardly any wonder that the resulting attack on the word is abnormal. Third, he must assume a set to produce audible sound simultaneously with his attempt on the feared word. The stutterer may tend ordinarily to "preform" the initial vowel or consonant, placing his articulators mutely in position for the sound before he initiates voice or expiration.

In the writer's experience, the stutterer who is able to change his preparatory behavior for the moment in the manner just described is likely to speak without stuttering or with markedly less stuttering, and to do so in a natural and spontaneous way. To maintain the new preparatory sets outside of the clinic is much more difficult, of course. To some extent the effectiveness of the method appears to depend upon how well we are able to communicate exactly what we mean by relaxing a "focus of tension" or avoiding a "fixed articulatory position." For some stutterers a few brief instructions may be enough. In other cases much practice is needed in order to translate these abstractions into a muscular "understanding." The writer has found it helpful to employ a somewhat cursory form of Jacobson's "progressive" relaxation for this purpose (20). Jacobson's method is one by means of which a person may be trained to localize and voluntarily dissipate minute amounts of tension in each of his skeletal muscle groups in turn, and to do this progressively until he is in a state of relatively complete relaxation. For the purpose of stuttering therapy it is probably not necessary or desirable to teach the case how to relax the limbs or torso, except perhaps as a brief demonstration of the principle to be learned. What is required is simply that the stutterer learn to relax that rigid stance of the tongue, jaw, and lips with which he readies himself for supposedly difficult words or sounds. To this end Jacobson's basic technique of producing the tension purposely in varying degrees and studying the associated muscle sensations seems excellently suited. It is possible to study all of the various articulatory contacts in this manner. In some cases it may be enough to focus attention on one or two which represent the stutterer's major sites of difficulty. In addition to learning certain basic features of differential relaxation, the stutterer should have some knowledge of descriptive phonetics as a basis for this type of remedial work. It is never desirable, of course, to reduce stuttering therapy to something suggesting mechanical drills. It may be difficult, however, for a person not trained in phonetics to tell precisely what he is doing with his speech organs when he articulates a sound. If the knowledge that *d* is a lingua-alveolar sound will give him a more vivid understanding of some of his strenuous anticipatory reactions, then no important principle of clinical work would appear to be upheld by sheltering him from this realization.

Reducing Fear of the Consequences of Stuttering

If these measures were enough to convince the stutterer that he could speak normally, no further therapy would be needed. It is extremely difficult, however, to eliminate anticipation of stuttering unless something is also done to neutralize some of the punishing consequences of stuttering as the individual perceives them. He may tell himself with conviction that he will not stutter. But as long as he continues to regard stuttering as something utterly intolerable the most trifling suggestion of impending difficulty may be enough to evoke the old struggle reactions. Attempts to overcome stuttering by eliminating anticipation can generally be successful only when there has been some lessening of the stutterer's emotionalized desire to keep from stuttering. Experience shows that not only are such attempts likely to fail otherwise, but they may also produce a great deal of anxiety.

Various ways have been devised to teach the stutterer how to tolerate his speech handicap more adequately. Here too, however, some extremely important qualifications must be kept in view. We should never imagine it possible for the stutterer to rid himself of all of his fear of stuttering, nor should we fill him with feelings of guilt about the apprehensions which he will almost inevitably have. To do so is to demonstrate a lack of empathic understanding of the stutterer's problem. We live in a society which is peculiarly forbidding in its attitude toward what it considers incompetence at speech. There would be far fewer stutterers if this were not the case. Fortunately, it is not necessary to erase every remaining vestige of fear in order to eliminate stuttering. We observe the converse of this when the stutterer reports that in the speech clinic, in the midst of other stutterers and precisely at the moment when he is enjoying to the fullest a feeling of liberation from the fear of speaking, he may occasionally find himself having the most severe difficulty with his speech. The explanation appears to lie in the extent to which he is reminded of his speech problem while in the clinic. The immediate cause of stuttering is not fear of stuttering. It is the unconscious assumption that under certain conditions certain words must be attacked in certain particular ways if they are to be said at all. This is an assumption which the stutterer is probably as likely to act on under conditions of relatively objective expectation of stuttering as under conditions of fear. It is true, of course, that in most ordinary circumstances the absence of fear of stuttering means the absence of any occasion to expect it. In addition, the more calm and detached the expectation of stuttering, the greater the opportunity to learn to react to it consciously and purposefully in alternative ways. There can be no doubt that the stutterer's sometimes desperate awareness that he must not have speech difficulty is a maintaining factor of as much importance as his knowledge that he will. There are good reasons for doing everything possible to reduce his fear, and in particular to help him overcome his more extreme reactions of agitation and panic.

Learning to Speak About Stuttering Freely and Frankly to Others. This feature of stuttering therapy has been given particular emphasis by Bryngelson (10). It is one which appears to hold the key to all others, in the sense that little further progress can usually be achieved if the stutterer is unable to carry it through successfully. If he cannot admit frankly to others that he stutters, it is on the face of it a significant indication that he himself is basically unable to accept the fact. Self-acceptance, in turn, is a most vital part of any type of personal adjustment. Until the stutterer is able to accept his speech problem unemotionally in the privacy of his own self-evaluations everything else must be subordinated to that goal.

This work may be broken down into several somewhat distinct aspects.

1. *The stutterer must freely admit his problem to those of his associates who may not be aware of it.* The average stutterer intensely desires to be regarded as a normal speaker. So zealously may he dedicate himself to this end that some of his closest associates may be among those who do not know that he stutters. By standing constant guard over their speech, stutterers have been known to conceal their difficulty from wife, husband, or children for many years. It is not at all unusual to find that it has been kept from coming to the attention of casual acquaintances or even a fiancée. Sometimes, it is true, these persons turn out to have known all along. But the result, as far as the stutterer is concerned, is the same. The threat of exposure is a constant source of anxiety which may tend to bring about a general attrition of morale. Furthermore, sooner or later the pretense is almost bound to crumble in a cloud of mortification in spite of every trick to avoid stuttering which the stutterer knows.

2. *He should cultivate the ability to discuss his stuttering casually and objectively with others.* Most of the time the listener is quite well aware of the speaker's stuttering, but even when it is most obvious they may both adopt an attitude of profound obtuseness, acting as though there were nothing extraordinary at all about the stutterer's struggles to speak. The situation becomes tense and unnatural for both. This is the essence of the problem which the stutterer may have in social adjustment. In many respects it is like the problem which any handicapped person may have in establishing normal social relationships. If the handicapped person is some-

times rejected socially it is partly because he stirs in us an uneasy feeling of inadequacy. We are not certain exactly how to treat him, and we feel especially obliged to weigh beforehand what we say to him. This is by no means true of all such individuals, however, and it is instructive that when we encounter a handicapped person who appears to inspire others with a desire to know him better, and whose associates seem genuinely oblivious to his handicap, we usually find a person who in one manner or another conveys to us the information that it would not hurt or embarrass him if someone were to broach the subject of his clubfoot, spastic paralysis, or artificial limb. It is this knowledge which the stutterer must somehow convey about his speech handicap. The surest, most direct way is to bring up the subject himself from time to time as the occasion calls for it, so that it may be talked about, disposed of, and forgotten. The average stutterer who has protected this sensitive area for many years finds difficulty in exposing it in this way until he has had some practice at it. Some of this practice may be obtained under the direct supervision of the clinician. Many stutterers will gain what amounts substantially to their first experience at talking about their problem before an audience of other stutterers in the speech clinic. Later, it may be possible for the clinician to accompany the stutterer while he initiates conversations with strangers on the pretext of making a survey of public reaction to stuttering or opinion about its cause and treatment. If the therapy is conducted in a school setting, a very effective method is to arrange for stutterers to visit several classes in small groups for the purpose of giving brief talks about stuttering. Some topics which they might plan to touch on are: how it feels to have a block, how listeners react to my stuttering, tricks I have used to avoid stuttering, conditions under which I can talk fluently, or memorable experiences as a stutterer. Under the spur of questions from the audience they will find to their surprise that the subject of their stuttering is practically inexhaustible. Other experiences will need to be obtained outside the clinician's surveillance through the medium of "assignments" to discuss their remedial work, or bring up the subject of their stuttering in some other way, with relatives and friends with whom they are in daily association.

If possible, the stutterer should collect a repertoire of amusing anecdotes about his own stuttering or even stuttering jokes, and acquire the ability to tell them skillfully and with enjoyment. Many stutterers, including some who learn to become quite objective about their speech, seem basically unable to see any humor in it, a failing for which they may perhaps be pardoned. Nevertheless, there is probably no more reliable way of establishing a reputation as a stutterer who is not easily embarrassed about his speech than by developing a sense of humor about it.

3. *He should learn to announce that he stutters on entering particularly difficult and feared speaking situations.* One college student began her first oral presentation in an introductory speech course by saying, "We've been asked to talk about something on which we're experts. I'm going to talk about stuttering. I've been doing it for about 17 years, and I think I'm an expert at it." She had little further anxiety in this class. The point is that once the stutterer establishes a general understanding that he may have trouble with his speech there is no longer any need to dread the awful hush of shocked surprise which is the great terror of such a situation. In many cases the stutterer would be happy enough to make such an announcement as a means of making a situation of this kind more tolerable, but feels the need to be shown how. If he can do it in a whimsical or good-humored way, so much the better. But even the slightly acid statement "I stutter. I don't have any apologies to make for it, but it may take me a while to get started sometimes" goes a long way to win him respect and acceptance as a stutterer.

4. *When he encounters exceptional difficulty in speaking he should be prepared to make an appropriate remark which will help him to "pass it off" lightly.* "There will be a slight delay in transmission due to technical operating difficulties" or "We will have a brief intermission between words" are examples which have been tested successfully. One of the most troublesome fears of many a stutterer is that in a formal social situation, before an audience, or on some other crucial occasion he may suffer the humiliation of becoming so completely blocked that he is unable to go on. He may rarely or never have had such an experience, but the possibility may be enough to make every word a crisis in such a situation. Once he is armed with a weapon against this extremity, though he may never need to use it the knowledge that he has it may be all that he needs in order to face these situations in security.

Learning to Evaluate Listener Reactions Realistically. Whatever the punishing consequences of stuttering, they must practically always have something to do, ultimately, with a listener—that is, with the manner in which a listener reacts or is believed to react to the stuttering, with the attitudes which the listener seems to adopt, and with the inferences which he draws or seems to draw about the speaker. If stuttering is painful it is because it is painful to be laughed at, pitied, or thought a fool. Surprising as it may seem, this punishment may often be reduced very markedly without changing the behavior at all. One of the best opportunities for modifying the consequences of stuttering as they appear to the stutterer is to be found in the disparity which tends to exist between the listener's attitude and what it is imagined to be. It is difficult for the average stutterer, so sensitized by past experience to unfavorable reactions, to avoid exaggerating them and observing them even where they do not happen to be. Careful study of listener reactions by the stutterer with the help of the clinician will frequently do a great deal to keep these tendencies at a minimum. Johnson has pointed out that one of the outstanding things to be learned from such observations is the distinction between descriptions of and inferences about these reactions. "He looks down when I start to talk to him" is a description. Its accuracy can be checked independently by another observer, and there are means by which one can determine how often listeners behave in accordance with such a description. On the other hand, "He becomes embarrassed when I speak to him" or "He feels sorry for me" or "He gets annoyed" are inferences. Too frequently the stutterer behaves as though such inferences were descriptions. That is, he does not appear to feel any need to test his assumptions, or to regard them as anything other than simple fact. The peculiar viciousness of this identification is that it permits the stutterer to go on indefinitely believing that his listeners are "amused," "impatient," "embarrassed," "shocked," or practically anything else he pleases. Once acquired, there is no means of checking and rejecting such an inference which a person is likely to stumble on by himself. It can be made to fit almost any listener, any facial expression, any behavior, any circumstance. The stutterer must be taught, therefore, to distinguish clearly between inferences and descriptions. He should next be trained to reserve his inferences about his listeners' reactions and to make statements about them which are essentially descriptive—to learn to say, in other words, that listeners look away, smile, frown, attempt to help him with difficult words, or the like. Such assertions can be verified objectively, and he should then be given every opportunity to find out by means of observation how frequently his listeners actually do these things. Experiences of this kind are excellently calculated to make him question a good many of his assumptions.

Another way to teach the stutterer to be more cautious about the inferences he draws is to give him the chance to compare them with those of other observers. An effective method when working with a group of stutterers is to arrange for a nonstutterer to be interviewed for several minutes by one member of the group while the others jot down their interpretations of the listener's reactions. As a rule, such interpretations will show little agreement. A motion-picture film of listeners' facial reactions to stuttering may also be used conveniently for this purpose (4).

In the foregoing discussion we have been concerned solely with the stutterer's exaggerations and misconceptions of his listeners' reactions. When all is said and done, however, we cannot deny that listeners occasionally do interrupt the stutterer, attempt to hurry him, or give other evidence of reacting strongly to stuttering, and this is a fact which we are obliged to help the stutterer to face. Malreactions should be discussed objectively as troublesome but wholly expected occurrences, and they should be examined above all from the point of view of the possible reasons for them. Once the stutterer begins to ask exactly why an occasional listener appears to find it so difficult to tolerate his hesitations he may decide that it is the listener who is in need of help. This is an extremely liberating realization, but one which does not come naturally to the average stutterer. Although he may condemn the listener bitterly for his malreactions they correspond so closely to his own unfavorable appraisals of himself that he is usually all too ready to accept them without question as essentially warranted by his own behavior.

Overcoming Avoidance. Precisely because of his fear of stuttering, the stutterer tends to make his difficulty more handicapping than it needs to be. He may do so by declining responsibilities requiring speech, by avoiding social situations, by speaking as little as possible in situations which he cannot avoid, and when he must speak, by resorting to word substitutions and circumlocutions which distort his meaning and to devices of postponement, starting, and release which hamper his utterance and intensify his blocks. The more handicapping he makes his stuttering, furthermore, the more threatening and fearful it becomes, and so the more he avoids it in all of the ways in which it is possible to do so. This process can be reversed. One of the primary concerns of therapy is to develop in the stutterer a conscience which prevents him from avoiding stuttering. This is not always as difficult as it might appear. The typical stutterer is rather easily convinced that he should not cringe before the world in an attitude of apology merely because he stutters. From there it is not far to fostering in him a sense of pride in his ability to get along without avoidances. Many stutterers before very long reach a point at which they derive a feeling of achievement from every feared speaking situation entered voluntarily, every feared word attempted, and every block which they have with a minimum of embarrassment, struggle, and associated mannerisms for avoiding stuttering. One immediate consequence of this is that the stutterer talks more, does more, and shows a rapid general improvement in his capacity for constructive relationships with others. This is often one of the earliest substantial results of therapy.

There are, generally speaking, two useful methods for working on the elimination of avoidances. One is to take aim directly at the stutterer's most difficult and feared speaking situations, especially those which he meets frequently in the normal course of his activities. It is here that the most important, sometimes essentially the only, features of his problem are concentrated. These situations will differ from case to case. Typical examples are the classroom, the telephone, and various social situations. In the individual case these may usually be narrowed down to a particular classroom, to telephone conversations with certain people, or, perhaps, to the weekly fraternity meetings which are mined from beginning to end with the threat of stuttering. These may be marked off as the arenas in which he will face his stuttering and overcome his avoidances, and in some cases it may be desirable to conduct the therapy as a whole almost entirely on the basis of its relationship to these particular situations.

The second way to help the stutterer cope with his avoidant tendencies is to arrange for him to have stuttering experiences far in excess of those demanded by his ordinary daily routine. For this purpose the stutterer may stop people in the street to ask them for directions, price articles in stores, ring people's doorbells to inquire whether so-and-so lives there, or seek out any of a hundred other possible speaking situations. Not only the number but also the character of these situations can often be prearranged to advantage. It is possible to contrive situations which are especially efficient as clinical exercises because they contain the concentrated venom of certain stuttering experiences. For example, the stutterer may plan ten situations in which he will begin a sentence with "what," "why," "when," or "where" because these words are huge obstacles which he usually avoids by means of an adroit circumlocution. Or he may make three telephone calls in the course of which he stops in the middle of a sentence and remains silent until the other person hangs up—because this is exactly the eventuality which he dreads most when he speaks on the telephone. Furthermore, because it would be difficult to do anything more antipodal to avoiding stuttering than performing it deliberately, it may be helpful for him to learn to block on purpose in some of his situations. Such "stuttering" should, of course, be carried out in the spirit of a test of his ability to assume an objective attitude toward his speech interruptions, and should therefore consist of simple repetitions or prolongations with a minimum of hurry or tension.

Whatever methods are used to eliminate avoidances and teach the stutterer that stuttering is not so fearful, the projects or assignments which he undertakes should be specific, clearly defined, and capable of evaluation in terms of relative success or failure, a rule which applies to other phases of stuttering therapy as well. In addition, it is of the utmost importance to keep in mind two related principles having broad application to the planning and evaluation of the stutterer's work in outside situations. The first is never to assume that simply because we have told the stutterer clearly and repeatedly what we believe he must do and why, he has an adequate understanding of what we mean. The second is never to assume that once we have listened to the stutterer's account of the experiences he has had, the observations he has made, and the things he has accomplished or failed to accomplish, we have a rough idea of what he was talking about. Anyone who ignores these precepts will almost certainly receive some jarring surprises before he learns to demonstrate to the stutterer as far as possible what he means and to observe the stutterer as far as possible as he does it. Stuttering therapy cannot be confined comfortably to an office. The clinician who tries to do so will soon discover that such therapy tends to become vague, abstract, and fundamentally out of touch with the realities of the stutterer's problem.

Improving Social and Emotional Adjustment. It will be unusually difficult for the stutterer to reduce his fear of stuttering if he is an unusually anxious, inadequate, insecure person. For this reason stuttering therapy does not exclude broader forms of personal guidance when necessary. The immediate question which must be answered in the case of each stutterer is whether his emotional difficulties warrant the specialized attention of a trained psychotherapist. The decision to refer a stutterer for such help must be made with care and in itself requires a basic knowledge of personality problems. On one hand, it is dangerously negligent to allow a clinically neurotic person to trail his anxieties, depressions, hysterias, or compulsions ineffectually to one speech-therapy session after the next without making such a referral. On the other hand, too many referrals for psychotherapy reveal a degree of naïveté about emotional disorders and perhaps a certain amount of panic on the part of a speech clinician faced with somewhat difficult cases. It must always be kept in mind that personal problems are universal and that most people have the capacity to cope with them without assistance. There are certain emotional storms, in particular, which are characteristic of various temporary stages of maturity or common life situations, and none more violent than those surrounding the acceptance of adult roles in adolescence and young adulthood—that very same period during which stuttering in its developed form is most frequently treated.

If there are any emotional problems with which the speech clinician can often be of very direct help, it is with problems of social adjustment which are due in large measure to the stuttering itself. While every reduction in the fear of stuttering will itself tend to result in a capacity for more active social participation, the reverse is also true. The more adequate an individual feels in social relationships the less reason he has to fear stuttering. For this reason no effort should be spared in helping the stutterer to acquire new social assets and to find opportunities for capitalizing on them. The clinician should do everything possible to see that the stutterer knows how to conduct himself in all of the usual social situations and has no reason to feel ashamed of his personal appearance. The writer recalls one 12-year-old girl whose ability to face and handle her stuttering problem underwent a substantial improvement after her clinician had taught her how to dress, wear her hair, and lower herself into a chair in a graceful and feminine manner. Other stutterers have been helped similarly by suggestions that they learn to dance, or to see a doctor about a problem of excessive weight.

The Clinician-Stutterer Relationship

Any attempt to help a stutterer with his speech involves a relationship between two people. This relationship may either be left to chance or deliberately molded to conform to a specific conception of what it should be like. Too often it is merely allowed to develop as it will. Depending on the individual or the occasion, the clinician may assume the role of a teacher who demands the stutterer's work when due; a priest who hears his confessions, encourages, and guides him; a big brother who fights his battles for him; or a friend with whom he exchanges confidences and good-natured abuse. In the author's opinion there is one kind of relationship which is far more suitable for stuttering therapy than any other, and that is what might appropriately be termed a clinical relationship. While it is difficult to give this term any highly exact meaning, we may understand it to refer in a general way to relationships of the type existing in a successfully maintained psychotherapeutic situation between patient and therapist. Psychotherapeutic relationships vary, but most of them appear to have certain significant features in common. There are perhaps few descriptions of the clinical relationship so directly applicable to remedial work with stutterers as that found in Rogers' account of "nondirective" or "client-centered" psychotherapy, and it is upon Rogers' work that this discussion is very largely based (37).

Our behavior toward the stutterer in the clinical situation and the general relationship which we establish with him should be governed by at least five basic principles.

1. *All good therapy is based upon a belief in the individual's innate capacity for emotional growth.* This is far from a euphonious banality. A good many of the mistakes made by inexperienced speech clinicians appear

to stem from the assumption that the stutterer is essentially a blank whose entire program of speech rehabilitation it is the clinician's terrifying responsibility to direct in minute and inexhaustible detail. One of the greatest rewards of experience is the sense of relaxed detachment made possible by the knowledge that the stutterer, if he is given time, can usually be counted on to exercise in his own behalf all of the human qualities of initiative, motivation, resourcefulness, and potentiality for improvement, and that he, not the clinician, is the leading actor in the scene. It is this knowledge, moreover, which makes feasible one of the most satisfactory methods of conducting stuttering therapy—that of working intensively on a few carefully chosen situations which represent the stutterer's special problem at the moment. If he can once enjoy a sense of accomplishment and success, say in the classroom or at his fraternity meeting, whether it is in the matter of alluding casually to his stuttering, volunteering to speak, using feared words, effectively altering some of his preparatory sets, or doing anything else which helps him to handle the situation adequately or gain a feeling of acceptance as a stutterer, we need have little fear that he will fail to seek a repetition of his triumph in other difficult situations as they arise. The converse of this is to try to prepare the stutterer deliberately for every fearful contingency, an attempt which is impossible on the face of it and aims at so much that it makes direct contact with almost nothing.

2. *To be effective, therapy must be conducted in a permissive atmosphere.* In the first place, it is obviously desirable for the stutterer to be able to express all of his feelings about his problem and his reactions in the course of therapy, no matter how embarrassing, shocking, or ridiculous they may seem to him to be. For this reason the clinician must receive everything which the stutterer tells him in a manner which indicates his complete and uncritical acceptance. But permissiveness should not stop here. The stutterer must be made to understand that there is nothing in the course of clinical work which he will be required to do in the sense that he is required to do class assignments or schoolwork. This is especially important when therapy is administered in a school setting, where the clinic is something to which one is assigned and the clinician gives every appearance of being a teacher. This rule, though perhaps contrary to a certain amount of practice, is of the utmost importance if the most valuable advantages of a truly clinical relationship are to be gained.

What of the assignments which we "give" the stutterer? It follows from what we have said that these should be assignments which the stutterer is willing and eager to carry out, and that as far as possible they should represent his own choice, based upon a thorough knowledge of the courses of action which are open to him. In particular, the wise clinician will learn to take advantage in one form or another of every suggestion which comes from the stutterer himself, even when he knows that by certain criteria other ways of proceeding would be preferable.

3. *Therapy should stress the clarification of attitudes and feelings of the person being helped, in preference to persuasion, reasoning, advice, or reassurance.* It is quite true that in treating stuttering the therapist must communicate a large amount of sheer information. But a point is frequently reached in the clinical session at which further explanation no longer finds a gap in the stutterer's knowledge and is merely a somewhat impulsive response to his objections, fears, resistance, or other emotional reactions. At this point sound therapeutic principles demand that the clinician do less talking and the stutterer more. *Much of the time the clinician will find that his most valuable articles of equipment are the phrases "What do you mean," "Give me an example," or "Tell me more about that."* There are several reasons for the great usefulness of these phrases. In the first place, there are very many occasions when the only alternative to using them is to argue with the case, a practice which may be said categorically to have little place in stuttering therapy. Second, the clinician who asks for further explanation will often find to his astonishment that he actually had not understood what the stutterer was trying to say. Third, what the stutterer usually needs more than anything else on such occasions is the opportunity to clarify his own feelings. The clinician must learn that when, after a substantial period of therapy, the stutterer says with emotion, "Do you think I should tell my girl friend I stutter?" the chances are that he is not really asking to be told the answer. He is probably saying, "I'm all confused. I can't make up my mind to do it. I have to talk this over." And the best reply which the clinician can make is, "Tell me some of the things that run through your mind when you think about it."

4. *Good therapy is "client-centered."* That is, it is based upon the individual's own values, not the therapist's. It is concerned with the individual's problems as he himself sees them, not with the problems which a therapist thinks he ought to have. This means, among other things, that the stutterer is the only one qualified to judge whether, when, and for how long his stuttering warrants clinical attention, and to point out the specific aspects of his problem for which he needs help. From this point of view it is exceptionally important for the speech therapist to listen carefully to the manner in which the stutterer describes his difficulties. If the only problem of any real concern to him is that he stutters when reading aloud at school, then it is poor therapy to seize upon his speech in making introductions because the therapist has observed that he stutters "badly"

in this situation. The issue can perhaps be made particularly clear by referring to a somewhat different type of choice which arises in clinical work when the stutterer has an additional speech deviation, for example, an articulatory defect. Shall we attempt to help him with it? It is surprising how cogently arguments can be advanced on both sides without regard for virtually the only relevant question: Does the stutterer want this assistance? If he does not, then pressing it upon him constitutes an unwarranted attempt to burden him with a problem which is more suitably to be regarded as ours than his. If he does, it is questionable whose problem we solve by withholding such help from him. On the same principle, if a stutterer desires therapy we should never decline to help him on the grounds that his stuttering is too slight. It is not the business of a speech therapist to determine, in spite of the stutterer's opinion to the contrary, that he does not have a problem.

5. *To develop a genuinely clinical relationship with the case the therapist must have as much understanding as possible of the complex motivations which may underlie human behavior.* A hypothetical illustration will serve to make clear why this is so. Let us suppose that in the course of a clinical session the stutterer repeatedly makes comments which may be interpreted as subtly critical of the therapist. Any properly disciplined speech therapist will, of course, do his best to react objectively. But suppose that the therapist has previously recognized in the stutterer's behavior a group of traits to which students of personality refer as an "obsessive-compulsive" personality make-up. He will have realized that he is dealing with a person who almost certainly possesses severely repressed, strongly aggressive feelings, and from whom hostile behavior is disguised forms must probably be expected. There can hardly be any greater insurance against the possibility that he will react to the stutterer's thrusts as occasions to defend himself or reflections on his ability to establish rapport.

There are without doubt still other useful principles of broad clinical practice to be derived from a study of psychotherapy. The foregoing are a few which seem especially pertinent to the speech treatment of stutterers. While they apply in a pervasive manner to the clinician-stutterer relationship as a whole, their importance is given particular emphasis by certain specific clinical problems. Of these, the problem of resistance is so integral a part of therapy that it deserves some special consideration here.

Handling Resistance to Therapy. At the outset of his clinical practice the speech therapist is likely to be somewhat baffled and dismayed when the stutterer delays, makes excuses, or refuses to comply with suggestions. Yet such behavior is exactly what we should expect when we ask the stutterer to do so many things which he has been trying so hard for so long not to do. It is not the fact of resistance which should concern us but the form which the resistance takes.

The most common and least serious form of resistance is an open admission of fear. This is usually a reaction to a specific assignment which the stutterer knows he must carry out, and it may come after a genuine effort to do so. This simple, acute form of resistance in most cases merely calls for patience on the part of the clinician and an accepting attitude toward the stutterer's feelings while it runs its course. Some help may be given him by proper planning of therapy. For example, in most cases he should not be expected to do very much stuttering in a given situation before he has learned to announce freely and confidently that he stutters. Another very substantial help from this point of view is group therapy. The example set by cases more advanced in therapy is often very stimulating. Furthermore, if the emphasis is placed on coöperative activities it is possible to generate in a group a kind of morale which can be obtained in no other way. In the final analysis, however, the stutterer whose clinical progress is impeded by acute fear is like a person standing for the first time on the high diving board. No one can make his decision for him, but if he must dive, then sooner or later he will. Or, if the reasons are not sufficiently compelling, he will not, and if this is his decision he should not be privately regarded as though he were beneath contempt. It is not for any clinician to say that avoidance and concealment, whatever their drawbacks, may not be the best possible adjustment for a given stutterer *at a particular time.*

A second form of resistance more difficult to deal with is characterized by rationalization. Too insecure in his own self-esteem to appreciate how helpless and afraid he is, he comes to believe that there are other reasons for his failure to pursue an active program of clinical work. For example, he may feel that he does not have the time, that he does not approve of the method, or that his stuttering does not actually "bother him that much." What are we to do about assertions of this sort? The answer is that, although we will certainly wish to ask the stutterer to explain these reasons more fully, there is nothing for us to do but appear to accept them at face value. In the first place, rationalization is a self-protective device. We cannot and dare not try to remove it by storm. Perhaps the most direct approach permissible is to introduce the subject of rationalization as a topic for group discussion in the hope that certain members of the group will be assisted to gain insight into their own rationalizations more rapidly when they are ready to do so. In the second place, we cannot be so sure that the stutterer's reason for not participating more fully in therapy is wholly a rationalization. At least we cannot be sure of the precise point at which semirationalization shades into half-truth. So that if we simply ask him to "tell us more" we may discover that what seemed to be resistance was chiefly an inability to budget his time efficiently or a lack of information. Nor do we know at once how tightly the stutterer is prepared to cling to his rationalizations, if this is what they are. We may find that the process of explaining his assertions to us was all that he needed to recognize them as rationalizations. Or, finally, we may be strengthened in our suspicion that we are confronted with an organized defense against the threatening aspects of speech therapy. If so, we must keep in mind that the situation is far from hopeless if we are not insistent on definite signs of recovery by the second Wednesday in May. Clinical experience shows that in time, either as we succeed in reducing the stutterer's fears somewhat or as he becomes more mature and adequate as a person, his defense may become less urgently needed and he may gradually find more time to work on his problem or see more sense in the clinical procedures.

The third form of resistance consists of the behavior often referred to as "intellectualization." This is usually the most difficult of all to overcome, partly because it appears in the guise of acceptance. The intellectualizer, frequently an intelligent and articulate person, may quickly absorb an abstract understanding of stuttering therapy and compliantly verbalize many of the attitudes expected of him. But his glibness proves to be no more than an effective evasion of active clinical work. It is his obvious pleasure to prolong the clinical hour in talk. The greater part of his friendly chatter may be related more or less directly to his speech difficulty, and much of it may consist superficially of the most hang-head self-excoriation. But the intellectualizer feels nothing—this is the essence of his problem. The stutterer who begins therapy in a mood of angry intransigence rarely presents any serious difficulty. In most cases all that is necessary is to put an accepting face on his hostility and wait for the hurricane to blow itself out in a rain of lachrymose emotion; his very spontaneity of feeling offers the most favorable forecast of the future. But the agreeable countenance of intellectualization is not sun, rain, wind, frost, or fog. Incapable of frank and unambiguous emotion, the intellectualizing person is often somewhat repressed, overcontrolled, and peculiarly resistive to change.

These are the essential patterns of resistance which stutterers for the most part exhibit. It cannot be denied that they may occasionally offer obstacles so great that for the time being failure, or what appears to be failure, must be accepted as unavoidable. The stutterer's anxiety may be too great, or perhaps there are more complicated and neurotic reasons for his resistance. It is necessary, however, to add an extremely important word about failure. As a word for the outcome of speech therapy, "failure" suffers from the same vagueness and is subject to the same extensive qualifications as the word "cure." It is quite true that stutterers sometimes fall short by measurable degrees of certain more or less clearly definable goals in therapy. But these are our own goals, the ones we have chosen for the stutterer. We must always keep in view the familiar clinical phenomenon of the stutterer who, having kicked and fought his resistive way through a period of therapy and having appeared to gain essentially nothing from the experience, returns weeks, months, or years later, a remarkably changed person, to tell us of his gratitude for all we "did for him." Whenever we hastily assume that therapy has been a "failure" we do not consider the arbitrary, personal nature of the criteria which we use to make such a judgment, nor do we take into account the enormous capacity for change, maturation, and adjustment which nearly all human beings appear to demonstrate when given sufficient time.

The Treatment of Stuttering in Young Children

Stuttering manifests itself in various developmental stages. The techniques of treatment which have been discussed up to this point are suitable chiefly for the completely developed form of the disorder in which it is most serious and least likely to disappear without clinical help. This advanced form of stuttering is found for the most part in adults and adolescents. Generally speaking, the same type of therapy may be used with the majority of older preadolescents as well, provided we are prepared to adapt it by means of certain fairly obvious modifications to some of the peculiarities of less-advanced patterns of stuttering behavior. For example, one child who has complex blockages and recognizes his stuttering to be, in theory, a personal problem exhibits so little avoidance and so few evidences of fear in the ordinary sense that therapy may for all practical purposes be confined to the elimination of his disruptive preparatory sets. Another child may have an abundance of fear but no vivid awareness of one word or situation as more difficult than another, and clinical work must be planned accordingly. In still other cases we may need to take into account that there are no highly conscious anticipations of stuttering on specific words.

A vastly different type of clinical approach, on the other hand, is ordinarily demanded by the youngster of preschool or early elementary-school age whose stuttering is in the incipient stage. At this stage most workers are agreed that the foremost object of therapy is the prevention of more advanced forms of the disorder, that to this end our chief concern must usually be with alterations in the home environment, and that we must therefore do our work for the most part with the parents.

This raises the question of the earliest age at which it is advisable to work directly with a stuttering child. To adhere strictly to a principle to which we have already given allegiance, the best answer would seem to be that the decision as to whom to work with depends not primarily on the child's age but on who has the problem. If, as is frequently the situation, it is chiefly the mother who is distressed by the stuttering, then it is the mother who must receive help. If, on the other hand, the child himself appears to be chronically worried and unhappy about the way he speaks and is quite well aware that he has been taken to the speech therapist for help with this problem, it is probably not only safe to accept him for therapy but unwise to tell him that he does not "need" to come to the speech clinic or to allow him to be dismissed mysteriously from the picture with some impromptu excuse. By the same reasoning, there are many instances in which it is desirable to work with both the parent and the child.

The ensuing discussion, however, will be restricted essentially to the parent's problem and what the parent may be helped to do about it. For the sake of this discussion it will be well to review beforehand certain salient features of the speech symptoms about which the parent of the young stutterer comes for advice. It will be recalled that in the great majority of cases these appear to be true struggle reactions, reflecting the child's growing belief in the difficulty of speech. That is, abnormal forcing is usually to be observed during the clinical examination, or is reported to occur during "bad" periods, or is recalled as an earlier development, and even when the symptoms appear to consist almost wholly of simple syllable repetitions these tend to possess a tenseness of release and an element of hurry and above all to exhibit an ominous consistency with respect to their distribution in successive repetitions of the same utterance. On the other hand, we should not overlook the significance of certain broad distinctions which exist between stuttering at its inception and stuttering as a fully developed disorder. At this early stage there is a virtual absence of starters, postponements, and other clearly defined devices for concealing blocks, of vivid anticipations, of specific sound and word fears, of avoidance of words and situations, and in fact of most of the reactions and attitudes which are ordinarily regarded as important aspects of developed stuttering. Moreover, it tends to come and go, and minor eruptions of incipient forms of stuttering are probably exceedingly common in early childhood. We may conclude from this that what we most vitally need to know about the young child who is brought to us for examination is perhaps not the cause of his stuttering but rather the factors which threaten to turn it into a chronic disorder and the manner in which these may be circumvented.

Removing Environmental Pressures. By far the most important of these factors are almost certainly anxieties and pressures imposed upon the child in ways which were discussed earlier in this chapter. They arise in the great majority of cases from the child's home environment, having their source for the most part in the behavior of the parent who comes to us for help. The removal of these pressures may be divided into a number of somewhat different aspects for purposes of systematic discussion.

1. *Any effort to change some of the parent's behavior must start with the removal of guilt about the child's stuttering.* The mother who brings her stuttering youngster to the clinic is likely to have a crushing sense that she herself was somehow implicated in the development of his speech difficulty. "What did I do wrong?" is a question which in one form or another she may ask as anxiously as "Will he outgrow it?" While she must be helped to accept a sizable share of responsibility for the child's speech improvement, there is hardly a more effective way of intensifying her anxieties than to corroborate her suspicion that his stuttering resulted from abnormalities in her relationship with him. On the other hand, our confidence in her basic adequacy as a parent will leave her better able to accept suggestions for specific changes in her behavior. We may not be able to tell her with conviction that she had nothing to do with her child's stuttering. But we can, in the author's opinion, truthfully tell her that stuttering seems to be brought about by a combination of many factors or conditions varying somewhat from case to case, and we can truthfully tell her that stuttering children appear to be found in every conceivable type of family environment, not excluding some which seem in many ways unusually wholesome and favorable.

2. *We must insist on the removal of all speech pressures.* This is perhaps the central concern of therapy, toward which everything else is in some way directed. The parents must put a stop to any tendency which they may have to correct the child's articulation, pronunciation, or choice of words, his speaking rate, or any other real or imagined flaw in his communication, and in particular, of course, his stuttering. A somewhat special question which this may raise is what to do about the youngster with definite infantile errors of articulation when the mother is deeply concerned about these. Perhaps the best way of making certain that she does not agitate the child about these errors is to accept him for articulatory therapy. If we do, however, the remedial operation should be regarded as a rather delicate one. Pains must be taken to see that the acquisition of new articula-

tory habits never becomes a struggle. This means that we should limit ourselves with unusual strictness to auditory stimulation in teaching the new sounds, avoiding any technique which draws attention to movements or positions of the articulators. Furthermore, attempts to transfer the sounds to conversation should be deferred with more than ordinary care until there is not the slightest doubt about the child's ability to use them easily in connected speech.

In many, in fact the majority of cases, there will be no speech difficulty other than stuttering. Furthermore, even when some other speech difficulty originally served as a provocation to stuttering, the parent's anxieties will usually have concentrated themselves long since upon the struggle behavior itself. Consequently, removal of speech pressures is in most cases essentially a matter of eliminating parental reactions to the child's stuttering. For this purpose it is not enough merely to advise the parent to ignore the stuttering or avoid bringing it to the child's attention. It is well to devote some time to a discussion of the many ways in which it is possible to tell a child to "stop that awful stuttering." Many parents do not appear to be aware that they are doing this when they praise the child for speaking fluently, promise him a bicycle for his birthday if he stops stuttering, finish a difficult word for him, or stop what they are doing to look at him when he becomes blocked. Some parents do not even seem to realize that they are doing this when they tell the child to speak more slowly, "Stop and start over again," or "think" before he speaks.

Merely to tell the parent that she must not do any of these things is not enough, however. Few parents can probably hide their feelings from the child for long if they are profoundly distressed, and every effort should be made to reduce their anxiety about the stuttering. There are at least three things which can be done to decrease the mother's anxieties. First, she must be given a certain amount of basic information about stuttering. She must know that the disorder appears in many stages, and that her own child's speech difficulty represents a very rudimentary form, different in symptomatology and far removed in development from stuttering in an advanced state. She may be told that in this rudimentary form stuttering affects a great many normal children for brief periods. We may not tell her, of course, that her child will certainly outgrow his stuttering, although we know how fervently she wants to hear this, but we may tell her that any young child who stutters has an excellent chance of outgrowing it to begin with, and that his chances will be vastly improved if the problem is handled wisely at home. Second, it is a good plan in most cases to give the mother something positive and concrete to do for the child which will allow her to feel that she is actively helping him to overcome his difficulty.

Some useful practices which the mother may institute at home will shortly be described. Here it may be said that a certain part of the benefit of these probably lies in their effect on the mother. We must bear in mind that a parent who is overwrought about her child's stuttering may find it very disquieting to be told that beyond doing her best to make no issue of it there is nothing for her to do but wait and hope. Third, the mother should be advised to come back at intervals if there continues to be no improvement in the child's speech. Each time she returns we may review the advisability of beginning a program of clinical therapy with the child himself or of arranging to see the mother regularly for a period of intensive guidance. One of the chief purposes of the advice to bring the child for reëxamination, however, is to let the parent know that we are willing to assume a definite share of the responsibility for the child's improvement. She should never be permitted to feel that she is being left to face her difficulties entirely alone.

3. *When necessary, the parents should be helped to understand in what respects they might be less restrictive and demanding in their attitudes toward the child's behavior as a whole.* As we have seen, the pressures which are imposed upon a child's speech are often to be found in a setting of general high standards or overconcern. Parents may tend to be overly critical of the child's developing physical and intellectual abilities, expect too much in such matters as cleanliness, manners, and obedience, or attempt excessive regulation of the child's eating, sleeping, and play habits. If the parent is able to be less anxious or perfectionistic about the child's general behavior this may help to make her more easygoing about his speech, and the advice to relieve the child of accumulated pressures occasionally appears to have exceptionally practical results. We must be careful, however, to apply this advice with discrimination. Some mothers of stutterers are, if anything, too weak and indecisive in their exercise of discipline and parental control. Because children deeply need to feel safe and cared for, there must be a degree of firmness in the manner in which they are handled and an imposition of certain demands and limits. It is not parental strictness in itself which warrants our concern, but the kind of strictness which insists on essentially adult qualities of responsibility, consideration, foresight, or judgment, or in various ways puts a premium on social maturity or intelligence beyond the child's capacity.

4. *In a certain number of cases intensive, prolonged psychotherapy appears to offer the only practical hope of reducing the parental pressures.* While these pressures are always to some degree complex in their motivation, there are some cases in which they seem to arise to an unusual extent from neurotic anxieties or compulsiveness, from the mother's abnormal

need to keep the child dependent upon her, from guilt about feelings of rejection, or from the desire to use the child's achievements for the sake of the parent's personal prestige. In such cases there is often little to be gained by suggesting changes in the parent's behavior until she has undergone far-reaching changes in personality.

Reinforcing the Child's Anticipation of Fluency. It is probably necessary for a child to harbor a growing sense of inadequacy at speaking fluently for a long period of time before he becomes a confirmed stutterer. In the meantime, anything designed to give him a feeling that he can speak without stuttering would appear to be a very worthwhile preventive measure. Suggestions of this kind have been offered by Johnson, Van Riper, and others (22:273–275, 294 ff.; 45:357, 358). One method which seems excellently calculated to strengthen anticipation of fluency is to see to it that the child experiences daily successful, pleasant, and rewarding speech with a minimum of stuttering. This may be done effectively by the mother herself. Most stuttering youngsters are capable of a vast amount of fluent talking. Not only do they tend to have frequent periods during which they do not stutter, but, like older stutterers, even when their difficulty is at its most severe they can often recite simple rhymes, speak rhythmically, in a whisper or in unison with someone else, echo another person's utterance, speak to their dolls or pets, talk for a puppet, or assume a role in a play without stuttering. By setting aside a half-hour or so each day for the purpose of dramatizing familiar stories, reciting poetry, playing simple word games, or capitalizing on the child's fluent speech in manifold other entertaining and interesting ways, a parent with sufficient motivation and some guidance should be able to develop an exceptionally constructive program for immunizing the child against the harmful effects of his stuttering experiences by proving to him over and over again that he is basically able to talk without stuttering. While these procedures may be used in a speech clinic, they would appear to be best carried out at home, where it is somewhat easier to avoid the implication that they are intended as remedial measures.

A second means of systematically fighting off the suggestion that speech is barbed with difficulties is to decrease in every way possible the occasions which precipitate the child's most severe stuttering. Some of the ways in which the mother may be able to do this are avoiding situations which are charged with excitement for the child, being more responsive when he tries to gain her attention, seeing to it that he needs to compete as little as possible with others in the family for the opportunity to speak, and requiring him to speak as little as possible under conditions of conflict or emotion. Each individual child requires a special study of the conditions under which his stuttering occurs. In some cases these conditions will not permit clear-cut identification, or will not be readily amenable to change. In many cases, however, the stuttering may come and go in waves of severity, and the most conspicuous difficulty may be confined to certain "bad" days. If so, it will be a good plan for the mother to be prepared at such times with some absorbing occupations which the child may pursue for the most part alone, or which necessitate a minimum of speaking.

Before closing this discussion of therapy with parents of young stutterers it may be well to comment on the question of how intensive such work should be. Ideally, it might appear that every parent should be enrolled in the speech clinic for an indefinite period of counseling. In practice, however, much briefer contacts are often justified. In the first place, the mother has frequently come merely for advice or reassurance, and the therapist will sense that she is as yet unprepared emotionally for extended clinical contacts. (This is not to mention those instances in which the parent has traveled a long distance for an interview.) Moreover, extended therapy is not always necessary. There are indications that the stuttering frequently tends to disappear after a single clinical interview. This is particularly true of very young children who have been stuttering for a short time. (Needless to say, many of these are basically transient stuttering problems which would probably have resolved themselves just as quickly had there been no interview at all.) In such cases the possibility of more prolonged counseling should be mentioned to the parent as a measure which is available if other expedients fail.

When it becomes necessary for the parent to receive continued therapy the goals and procedures are, of course, essentially the same as those of the single interview. As is true when working with older stutterers, group therapy will sometimes be found to be extremely effective with parents. Finally, there is something else to be said about parent therapy which is also true of therapy with stutterers themselves. The procedures of treatment are not unusually complex or difficult to learn. It is in the development of a therapeutic *relationship* with the parent that the clinician will find the more crucial test of his knowledge, experience, and skill.

This chapter has presented a discussion of the etiology and treatment of stuttering as an anticipatory struggle reaction. From the point of view of etiology its chief purpose has been to unify our knowledge of the disorder as far as possible on the basis of a single explanation of its origin. To some readers it may seem that more emphasis has been placed on the great diversity of factors involved, and this may serve to raise once more the persistent question of whether stuttering does not actually have many causes. Perhaps the best possible answer is that the problem is for the most part an artificial one, having more to do with words than with stuttering. It may easily be shown that the theory of stuttering presented in this chapter is both a multicausal and a unicausal one, depending merely on the level of abstraction on which we employ the term "cause."

To begin with, there are two types of multicausal theory. According to one type, stuttering may be due sometimes to one cause, sometimes to another, in another case to a third, and so on. On the lowest level of concrete particulars the onset of stuttering cannot possibly be other than multicausal in this sense, for it is clear that the complex life situations out of which stuttering grows can never exactly duplicate themselves from case to case. But it is equally clear that we can generalize about these situations, and a true explanation is achieved only by abstracting from them certain unvarying features which may be identified on a high level of abstraction as the one "cause" of stuttering. To say that stuttering is caused by different factors in different children may therefore represent merely a failure to generalize far enough. It is to be noted further that a statement of this sort is invalid on the face of it. For the theorems of speech pathology cannot violate the assumptions of physics, one of the most fundamental of which is that the events of the physical world obey discoverable laws of cause and effect. There is only one way in which we may say that stuttering is produced sometimes by one cause and sometimes by another without denying the basic lawfulness of nature. That is by hypothesizing that there are different varieties of stuttering—i.e., that the varied causes have varied effects. It is difficult to overemphasize that a theory of stuttering of this type can be no better than the accompanying theory of its differential diagnosis.

The other type of multicausal explanation holds that stuttering is a joint product of multiple contributing factors. This kind of complex etiology of stuttering can hardly be denied, and considerable stress has been placed on it in this chapter. But it must not be imagined that there is any absolute answer to the question of how many "causes" may be simultaneously involved in the onset of stuttering. For example, on the level of relatively direct observation we can point out several circumstances or aspects of the situation which probably combined to produce stuttering in some of the cases cited in this chapter, and can posit the existence of many more. But these factors are causative only because they contribute either to the child's anticipation of speech difficulty or to his need for approval of his speech, and consequently we may say on a much higher level of abstraction that stuttering has only two causes. Generalizing still further, however, we may just as validly assert that stuttering has one cause, the child's assumption that it is necessary for him to struggle in order to speak.

As for the treatment of stuttering, one of the most important inferences to be drawn from the theory presented here is that stuttering is a remediable disorder. The attitudes and assumptions from which it appears to stem may be changed, in principle, and repeated instances of disappearance of stuttering both with and without clinical assistance encourage us to continue seeking ways to make its successful treatment a matter of more common practice. It must be emphasized, however, that attitudes and assumptions are frequently extremely resistant to change, and it is not to be wondered at that stuttering often seems difficult to correct. It will undoubtedly continue to seem so until we find a way of changing habits of thinking and evaluation more productive of lasting results than simple suggestion and more powerful than anything which we now know by the names of counseling, guidance, or education.

References

1. Appelt, A., in *Stuttering: Significant Theories and Therapies*, E. F. Hahn (ed.), Stanford, Stanford University Press, 1943.
2. Berry, M. F., "Developmental history of stuttering children," *Journal of Pediatrics*, XII, 1938.
3. Bloodstein, O., "Hypothetical conditions under which stuttering is reduced or absent," *Journal of Speech and Hearing Disorders*, XV, 1950.
4. Bloodstein, O., and Bloodstein, A., "Interpretations of facial reactions to stuttering," *Journal of Speech and Hearing Disorders*, XX, 1955.
5. Bloodstein, O., Jaeger, W., and Tureen, J., "A study of the diagnosis of stuttering by parents of stutterers and non-stutterers," *Journal of Speech and Hearing Disorders*, XVII, 1952.
6. Bluemel, C. S., "Primary and secondary stammering," *Quarterly Journal of Speech*, XVIII, 1932.
7. Boehmler, R. M., "A quantitative study of the extensional definition of stuttering with special reference to the audible designata," Ph. D. dissertation, University of Iowa, 1953.
8. Boome, E. J., and Richardson, M. A., *The Nature and Treatment of Stuttering*, London, Methuen, 1931.
9. Brown, S. F., "The loci of stutterings in the speech sequence," *Journal of Speech Disorders*, X, 1945.
10. Bryngelson, B., Chapman, M. E., and Hansen, O. K., *Know Yourself: A Workbook for Those Who Stutter*, Minneapolis, Burgess Publishing Co., 1944.
11. Cabañas, R., "Some findings in speech and voice therapy among mentally deficient children," *Folia Phoniatrica*, VI, 1954.

12. Darley, F. L., "The relationship of parental attitudes and adjustments to the development of stuttering," in *Stuttering in Children and Adults*, W. Johnson (ed.), Minneapolis, University of Minnesota Press, 1955.
13. Davis, D. M., "The relation of repetitions in the speech of young children to certain measures of language maturity and situational factors," *Journal of Speech Disorders,* IV, 1939.
14. Despert, J. L., "Psychosomatic study of fifty stuttering children: I. Social, physical, and psychiatric findings," *American Journal of Orthopsychiatry.* XVI, 1946.
15. Egland, G. O., "Repetitions and prolongations in the speech of stuttering and nonstuttering children," in *Stuttering in Children and Adults,* W. Johnson (ed.), Minneapolis, University of Minnesota Press, 1955.
16. Eisenson, J., "Aphasics: observations and tentative conclusions," *Journal of Speech Disorders,* XII, 1947.
17. Glasner, P. J., "Personality characteristics and emotional problems in stutterers under the age of five," *Journal of Speech and Hearing Disorders,* XIV, 1949.
18. Gottsleben, R. H., "The incidence of stuttering in a group of mongoloids," *The Training School Bulletin,* LII, 1955.
19. Hertzman, J., "High school mental hygiene survey," *American Journal of Orthopsychiatry,* XVIII, 1948.
20. Jacobson, E., *Progressive Relaxation,* Chicago, University of Chicago Press, 1938.
21. Johnson, W., *People in Quandaries: The Semantics of Personal Adjustment,* New York, Harper, 1946.
22. Johnson, W., *et al., Speech Handicapped School Children,* rev. ed., New York, Harper, 1956.
23. Johnson, W., *et al.,* "A study of the onset and development of stuttering," *Journal of Speech Disorders,* VII, 1942. (A more complete report of this study appears in W. Johnson (ed.), *Stuttering in Children and Adults, op. cit.,* ch. 3.)
24. Johnson, W., and Knott, J. R., "Studies in the psychology of stuttering: I. The distribution of moments of stuttering in successive readings of the same material," *Journal of Speech Disorders,* II, 1937.
25. Johnson, W., Larson, R. P., and Knott, J. R., "Studies in the psychology of stuttering: III. Certain objective cues related to the precipitation of the moment of stuttering," *Journal of Speech Disorders,* II, 1937.
26. Johnson, W., and Millsapps, L. S., "Studies in the psychology of stuttering: VI. The role of cues representative of stuttering moments during oral reading," *Journal of Speech Disorders,* II, 1937.
27. Johnson, W., and Sinn, A., "Studies in the psychology of stuttering: V. Frequency of stuttering with expectation of stuttering controlled," *Journal of Speech Disorders,* II, 1937.
28. Knott, J. R., Johnson, W., and Webster, M. T., "Studies in the psychology of stuttering: II. A quantitative evaluation of expectation of stuttering in

relation to the occurrence of stuttering," *Journal of Speech Disorders*, II, 1937.

29. Korzybski, A., *Science and Sanity*, 2nd ed., New York, The International Non-Aristotelian Library Publishing Co., 1941.
30. Lemert, E. M., "Some Indians who stutter," *Journal of Speech and Hearing Disorders*, XVIII, 1953.
31. Milisen, R., and Johnson, W., "A comparative study of stutterers, former stutterers, and normal speakers whose handedness has been changed," *Archives of Speech*, I, 1936.
32. Moncur, J. P., "Parental domination in stuttering," *Journal of Speech and Hearing Disorders*, XVII, 1952.
33. Morgenstern, J. J., "Psychological and social factors in children's stammering," Ph. D. dissertation, University of Edinburgh, 1953. (Relevant parts quoted at some length in **22**, ch. 5.)
34. Morgenstern, J. J., "Socio-economic factors in stuttering," *Journal of Speech and Hearing Disorders*, XXI, 1956.
35. Nelson, S., Hunter, N., and Walter, M., "Stuttering in twin types," *Journal of Speech Disorders*, X, 1945.
36. Peacher, W. G., "Speech disorders in World War II," *Journal of Speech Disorders*, X, 1945.
37. Rogers, C. R., *Counseling and Psychotherapy*, Boston, Houghton Mifflin, 1942.
38. Rotter, J. B., "The nature and treatment of stuttering: A clinical approach," *Journal of Abnormal and Social Psychology*, XXXIX, 1944.
39. Schlanger, B. B., "Speech measurements of institutionalized mentally handicapped children," *American Journal of Mental Deficiency*, LVIII, 1953.
40. Sheehan, J. G., "Theory and treatment of stuttering as an approach-avoidance conflict," *Journal of Psychology*, XXXVI, 1953.
41. Snidecor, J. C., "Why the Indian does not stutter," *Quarterly Journal of Speech*, XXXIII, 1947.
42. Tiffany, W. R., and Hanley, C. N., "Adaptation to delayed sidetone," *Journal of Speech and Hearing Disorders*, XXI, 1956.
43. Van Riper, C., "The effect of devices for minimizing stuttering on the creation of symptoms," *Journal of Abnormal and Social Psychology*, XXXII, 1937.
44. Van Riper, C., "The effect of penalty upon the frequency of stuttering," *Journal of Genetic Psychology*, L, 1937.
45. Van Riper, C., *Speech Correction: Principles and Methods*, 3rd ed., New York, Prentice-Hall, 1954.
46. Villarreal, J. J., "The semantic aspects of stuttering in non-stutterers: Additional data," *Quarterly Journal of Speech*, XXXI, 1945.
47. Voelker, C. H., "On the semantic aspects of stuttering in non-stutterers," *Quarterly Journal of Speech*, XXVIII, 1942.

48. Weiss, D. A., "Der zusammenhang zwischen poltern und stottern," *Folia Phoniatrica,* II, 1950.
49. Williams, D. E., "A point of view about stuttering," *Journal of Speech and Hearing Disorders,* XXII, 1957.
50. Wischner, G. J., "An experimental approach to expectancy and anxiety in stuttering behavior," *Journal of Speech and Hearing Disorders,* XVII, 1952.
51. Wischner, G. J., "Stuttering behavior and learning: A preliminary theoretical formulation," *Journal of Speech and Hearing Disorders,* XV, 1950.

THE PSYCHOANALYSIS OF STUTTERING

I. PETER GLAUBER, M.D.

Practicing psychoanalyst in New York City; attending psychiatrist at the Hillside Hospital; consulting psychiatrist at the Jewish Child Care Association in New York and at Children's Village, Dobbs Ferry, New York. Fellow of the New York Academy of Medicine and the American Psychiatric Association; Diplomate of the American Board of Psychiatry and Neurology; member of the New York Psychoanalytic Society and the American Psychoanalytic Association. Formerly, Instructor in Psychiatry at the New York University College of Medicine and a Supervisor in Psychotherapy, the New York Psychoanalytic Institute Treatment Center.

The Psychoanalysis of Stuttering

Some Fundamentals of Psychoanalysis Relevant to the Understanding of Stuttering

PSYCHOANALYSIS regards stuttering broadly as a neurotic disorder in which personality disturbance is in part reflected in disturbance of speech. In order to understand how psychoanalysis conceives of speech, personality, and disturbance, it will be helpful to review briefly a number of its working hypotheses. The term "psychoanalysis" is here used in the sense of a basic science of human behavior in health and in sickness and as a method of research; toward the end of the chapter it is also used in the sense of a specialized form of psychotherapy. Psychoanalysis works with concepts of quanta of energy—the drives or instincts which, operating in an organized fashion, constitute the psychic apparatus. The drives have their source in the total physical organism but the psychic apparatus as such has no known specific physical location. Through various forms of contact the drives aim to discharge portions of that energy. The objects may be other individuals or inanimate things, as well as the self. The psychic apparatus possesses the following chief characteristics: Its energy is preponderantly a representation of visceral tensions. It is subjectively experienced mainly outside the realm of consciousness. The unconscious antedates consciousness, exists alongside it, and yields up its contents to the latter in small bits and after much inner resistance has been overcome.

Freud, the discoverer and founder of psychoanalysis, first differentiated the component drives into those of hunger and of love—(13) that is to say, the self-preservative and the sexual-procreative or race preservative. He later discovered a more fundamental duality: the sexual drives, serving and preserving the individual and the race, and the aggressive-destructive drives, similarly affecting and threatening both the individual and the race. The former express themselves more openly, the latter speak in a muted voice. The two forms of energy may be seen in open opposition, or their various expressions may coexist in a state of fusion. Certain events may lead to sudden emergence of destructive energy by defusion.[1] Some who have questioned the existence of a destructive drive as a fundamental force regard these events not as precipitating defusion but as causing its appearance *de novo* as a defensive reaction in a state of anxiety. More recent investigations point to a primary reservoir of undifferentiated drive energy which is differentiated later on. The manifestations and vicissitudes of the two drives are of fundamental importance in the understanding of meaning and motivation in human behavior.

The totality of psychoanalytic principles and working concepts of the psychic apparatus is known as its metapsychology. It has three aspects: the motivational mechanisms represent the dynamic; transformations of quantities of energy, the economic; differentiation of function, the structural aspect. As the latter has acquired increasing application and importance in recent years, I will define its component parts. The *id* is the reservoir of the drive energies in their most primitive phylogenetic and ontogenetic patterns, and it operates unconsciously. The *ego,* in considerable part derived from the id, controls executant functions and strives to integrate inner drive needs within itself and with requirements of reality and demands of conscience. The ego functions both consciously and unconsciously. The third component, the *superego,* is a derivative of the ego, uses its own energies, and may also use energy borrowed from the ego or the id. The superego is concerned with ideals or aspirations and with problems of conscience involving guilt and satisfaction, reward and punishment. It is formed and molded by parental influences; but it also contains a large collection of archaic and quite sadistic judicial patterns strongly suggestive of influences from current culture and inheritance from prehistoric times. A large portion of the superego also functions unconsciously.

There are several other fundamental principles of the psychic apparatus. One is the pleasure-pain principle, according to which all individuals strive to attain pleasure and avoid displeasure in the sense of painful frustration. A corollary to this is that it is a basic function of maturation in the personality increasingly to compromise and integrate the demands for pleasure and freedom from pain with demands of reality and propriety. Another and related principle is that of constancy of the level of psychic tension. According to Freud, "The mental apparatus endeavors to keep the quantity of excitation present in it as low as possible or at least to keep it constant" (20). This principle is important in neurosis because one facet in its causation has to do with large quantities of excitation which accumulate within

[1] Defusion in psychoanalytic theory refers to the separation or detachment of instincts operating in a state of union, so that they function independently. The more popular term "diffusion" applies to various phenomena such as the state of gaseous particles in a balloon.

the psychic apparatus but are not exposed in consciousness or in behavior. Such repressed excitation results from psychically traumatic experiences and fantasies under certain conditions.

As we are to deal here with symptoms, inhibitions, and character distortions it is well to bear in mind that these are in general defense reactions to the affect of anxiety. Thus anxiety plays a central role in neurosis. These are its main characteristics: It is the most general and significant manifestation of an unresolved mental conflict which threatens the integrity of the personality. It is a diffuse, pervasive, objectless, and severe sense of impending catastrophe to the total organism. It can be experienced as a feeling *only* after the ego has attained a certain minimal development. Prior to that stage, anxiety may be said not to exist as such; what is experienced then are gradations of physical discomfort, up to and including pain.

Two related fundamental psychic phenomena must now be mentioned. Mentally, and in a somewhat limited form, the first stage of mature sexual strivings have already been revealed before or at the beginning of school. They are experienced through fantasies and behavior indicating sexual longing for the parent of the opposite sex, accompanied by competitive and hostile wishes toward the parent of the same sex. This is the well-known oedipus complex; and though it is by now a household expression, much about its nature, manifestations, and effects remains almost universally unrecognized. This is so because both the libidinal and hostile sets of wishes are deeply repressed, and rationalized by the unconscious resistance. When the complex is out in the open it is usually highly distorted; if not, the individual is psychotic. Directly or indirectly it is a nuclear complex, determining, if resolved, such diverse phenomena as an individual's capacity to mature, to love, to succeed, to function realistically in life; and if not, the emergence of a gamut of psychopathological disorders ranging from neurosis to psychosis. Integral to this complex are the interrelated phenomena of guilt and need for punishment. The latter is experienced either as an expectation of punishment in the future or as a fact from the past; it takes on, at the depth, a specific form—the expectation of injury, damage, or—most frequently—ablation of the genital organ. Superficially, this is the well-known castration complex which rises to its greatest intensity as the oedipus complex attains its highest development. However, the castration fear represents only the final and most important developmental stage of a succession of earlier fears of damage from separation, beginning with birth, weaning, bowel and bladder training on the physical side; and on the mental, the large process of individualization or separation from the psychological state of symbiosis with the mother.

Finally, there is a vastly important phenomenon which aids the resolution of the oedipus complex and with it the disappearance of the fears of castration, thus promoting ego maturation, learning processes, and mental health. This is the mechanism of identification. By means of it, to cite the major example, the boy is able to overcome the obstacles of aggression and guilt toward his father; his now unhindered love for his father enables him to visualize himself in the role of a man like his father and like other men chosen as ideals and as models for his own aspirations.

So much for the barest outline of psychoanalytic metapsychology. Hopefully the material which follows will mitigate somewhat the liability of condensation. We turn now to some observations on the genesis of speech and ego.

The Parallel Development of Speech and Ego

Psychoanalysis has made a number of observations about speech and its development which are relevant for the understanding of stuttering. The well-known transitions from babbling, lalling, echolalia to communicative speech represent steps in change of direction from narcissistic to object-related expression. That change marks the emergence of the ego as a separate mental structure. Thus speech becomes an ego function along with perception, thinking, reality testing. But because of its very nature, speech more than any other function is the symbol of the ego (9, 13).

Before the acquisition of speech the child is able to recognize and to love objects and to fear reality. We may think of this time as the undifferentiated stage of mental functioning. But toward the end of the second year of life there are definite signs of a differentiation within the psychic apparatus—the emergence of the ego. Among a number of evidential factors such as improved locomotion and gradual attempts at sphincteric control, speech is the most significant. It is significant not only as a sign of ego emergence, but also as an instrument for its further maturation. Included in this process are advances in development of reality testing. Words permit more exact communication with others and more precise anticipation by trial actions. Such anticipations evolve into thinking and help consolidate consciousness. Thinking is an advance over the earlier so-called consciousness without words which is recognizable in later regressive states as "preconscious fantasy thinking." These early or pre-ego states play an important role in the psychopathology of stuttering. The "thinking" before ego development is characterized by the broadness of its concepts, the equation of similarities with identities and of parts with wholes, and the fact that concepts are equated by their common motor patterns.

Speech evolving as the symbol for things gradually helps to develop capacity for understanding and rationality in the handling of external reality and the instinctual drives. Speech also helps to control anxiety by causing a shift from emotional fantasy to sober reality. In the personality of the stutterer, which is frequently that of the compulsive character, we see a regression from emotion as such to the shadowy world where words and thoughts are charged with magic omnipotence. However, when this flight is not excessive it may help to master instinctual tension, as is the case with the lofty intellectual interests that make their appearance at puberty and adolescence.

The acquisition of the ability to speak is experienced as a powerful achievement. Certainly this power has realistic potentialities; however, in the psychopathology of speech we are most frequently concerned with the very earliest or pre-ego feeling of power. This is the magic omnipotence of words and thoughts to charm individuals in the environment and fate itself, to do those things that have been named or conjured up in words. Words and thoughts become magical gestures for the attainment of a multiplicity of needs, hostile and libidinal, as well as destructive reactions to frustration. This subject will be considered at greater length later on, for it is these archaic aspects of thinking and of speech as reflections of the primitive or pre-ego states that constitute essential elements in the psychopathology of the personality and of the speech of the stutterer. However, there is a particular group of words—poetry, obscene words, certain oaths, and solemn formulae—to which the original magic power always clings. These, therefore, have a special significance for the stutterer (9, 10).

The earliest thinking of an individual is in accord with the pleasure-pain principle. It is wishful and fearful mental activity, inferior to later logical, organized, and more adjusted thinking which comes with the advent of the ego and the faculty of speech. Yet this earliest thinking is relatively more adequate than immediate discharge and wish-fulfilling hallucinations. The fact is that even after speech, logical thinking, and the reality principle have been established, prelogical thinking still remains operative. Normally repressed, we see it return in states of ego regression and in other conditions. It does not serve the function of preparing for future actions but becomes instead a substitute for unpleasant reality.

Thus, the speech faculty is burdened by the possibility of serving expressions of primitive, magical id impulses and associated emotions as well as primitive ego states of perception and execution. A third burden is that at this early phase of development there emerge also the beginning forms of the superego characterized by total and magic conceptions and quite sadistic methods of execution. The expression in thoughts and words of this last agency burdens the ego as much as those of the id.

The ego is developed partly autonomously in adjustment to the needs of reality and partly from the need to resolve conflicting claims among instinctual demands, superego, and the external world. The ego's development parallels the id or instinctual development. This latter follows the pleasure-pain principle as it operates along a series of pleasure zones, each representing the pleasure-pain premium of basic biological functioning. These zones are the oral, anal, phallic, and genital functional organizations, each having a specific action pattern of discharge and requiring an object, i.e., another individual, for fulfillment or satisfactory expression. The progression from the first zone to the last is characterized by the following: increasing differentiation of the realistic self; decreasing ambivalence between love and hate with the ascendancy of the capacity to love another person; development of a more efficient, realistic, and humane conscience; finally, taming of the primitive instincts by various methods, notably sublimation or displacement of the original aims by socially more acceptable ones and of the original love objects by a larger community of individuals.

When the healthy development of the ego is impaired in certain aspects we face the prerequisites for disturbances in speech. We are now in the realm of the psychopathology of stuttering.

The Psychopathology of Stuttering

Stuttering is a symptom in a psychopathological condition classified as a pregenital conversion neurosis. "Pregenital" refers to the developmental period preceding that of the fully developed oedipal period, and to the conflicts revolving about the special problems of this period. Problems of the oedipal period, however, are invariably involved because an inability to solve them frequently leads to their regressive reorganization under the primacy of earlier levels of libido and ego functioning. In stuttering the regression may be to any one of the earlier phases. Thus, for example, a boy having many fears and conflicts about his masturbation gave up the practice and took up an earlier pleasurable preoccupation with anal activities. It was only when these were blocked that he regressed to the oral level and developed a stutter. His stutter represented phallic and anal elements distorted by the dominant oral expression.

So much for what is meant by "pregenital." What is meant by "conversion" (20)? It is simply that a conflict within the psychic sphere is transformed into a physical expression, i.e., through the functioning of a physical organ. What is a neurosis? It is suffering that is needless in terms of the requirements of external reality but is accepted unconsciously as one of the terms of an attempted settlement between contending components of the personality. Apparently an inner threat is felt as a greater evil, and the conscious suffering, or symptoms, as a lesser evil. The latter may take on many forms: besides symptoms there are inhibitions, character distortions, and disturbances of mood, such as anxiety or depression. A symptom or any other manifestation of a neurosis is, however, an unsuccessful, i.e., unstable attempt at a resolution of an unconscious conflict. This is because it is not a final resolution in the form of a genuine compromise. Because both sides of the conflict—id and superego—find expression in the symptom, there is a temporary lessening of mental tension. But the conflict is not solved, and the suffering is one indicator of that.

What is the conflict that is reflected in the symptom of stuttering? It is between a wish to speak and a fear of speaking or a wish to be mute. A genuine resolution would lead either to smooth speech or uncontested silence. When we listen to the stutterer we note both aspects. In various stutterers, or in the same one at various times, one or the other wish may predominate. Accordingly the empathic listener will note that at times he knows easily what the stutterer is saying; at other times when the dominant wish is not to communicate, the effect on the listener is almost as if the stutterer had not spoken at all, as if he had been practically completely mute.

The contents of the stutter-producing conflicts will be discussed in two different ways: first, by way of general review; second, through the contributions of specific authors, including some of the most recent findings.

In accordance with our definition of neurosis, our starting point in the psychopathology of stuttering is that the struggle to prevent preverbal or mental speech from emerging as audible speech is in fact the result of all its unrealistic, archaic, instinctual (hence unacceptable) meanings. Speech in this sense represents a concrete action, a product of the instincts before they were tamed and converted into the ego function of communication. Accordingly, speech is the self in action; the self exposed in the acting out of an instinctual drive. It may thus represent purely the id, or the primitive ego in the service of the id. It may express an attack, or a wish to be attacked, in an oral, anal, phallic manner; to exhibit one's self or to be a voyeur; to wish to hurt or to get masochistic pleasure; to be loved or to be reprimanded. It may thus also represent the primitive superego which derives a large part of its energy from the id. Thus all the components of the unconscious mind may be represented through the urge to speak.

We know from folklore that to name a thing is to master it. From the psychology of dreams (14) we have learned that to speak signifies to be alive and to love, and to be mute means to be dead or to hate. From the study of paranoia it was suggested (12) that one reason the paranoid patient believes others can read his thoughts is that his words were first given to him by his parents and that somehow words are still not quite his own possession. This relates to another archaic notion that what happens to the ego causes the same thing to happen to the object. In this way speech may become a "magical gesture": by saying something to another person the latter may be found to do the same thing, or the same thing may affect him as the speaker.

A very important meaning of speech stems from a later, anal, period of development. Here words are equatable with dangerous anal products which may kill the object. They must be held back or, like any dangerous tool, handled very cautiously. In this context belong what have already been referred to—obscene words and oaths—which may represent a merely anal assault or a violently sexual, i.e., sadistic, attack. When conflicts over such acts or fantasies are projected upon the articulatory apparatus, stuttering may result. The symptom here, as elsewhere, then represents partly the breakthrough of a forbidden expression and partly the attempt to abort it.

At a still later stage, the phallic, the speech is directly involved in the oedipal conflict. Here to speak, or to speak well, means to be potent; to be unable to speak—to be castrated. To the boy it means phallic competition with his father. In that type of situation the tongue becomes the symbol for the phallus. The castration complex is here represented by the many legends, based on unconscious fantasies, of punishment by means of the tongue being cut out.

Another significant unconscious meaning of speech is that it serves the exhibitionistic impulse. This is related to ambition (33), which has also another root to be mentioned presently. The urge to exhibit may be countered by a reaction formation resulting in an inhibition of speech. This inhibition is similar to the fear of blushing, stage fright, and fears in social situations in general. Back of the urge to exhibit is a desire for the magical influencing of the audience through the omnipotence of thoughts and words. This is not unrelated to the perverse sexual pleasure of exhibitionism. The need to exhibit one's self has a multiplicity of aims. For one thing, there is the ever-present desire for reassurance against the ubiquitous castration fears; for another, equally potent and related, the narcissistic need to be loved. Acquiring these reassurances in an environment felt to be hostile is a complicated effort fraught with doubts and dangers. Common unconscious reactions may be stated in the following terms: "I wish to influence this audience or charm them, be applauded, or else kill them. My power over them may be overwhelming. I fear it myself, or else they may fear it and retaliate. I must stop before I kill them. Or I must stop before they see through me" (10). Obviously, there are here strong motivations for proceeding with speech as well as for attempting to halt it.

The most significant zone for speech and its disorders is the oral zone. It represents a very early period of libido and ego functioning, preceding that of speech. Molded by the processes of nursing and weaning, the oral zone retains a large part of their influence during the period of speech development. This zone stands in close relation to the very earliest stirrings of the ego when it was still conceived predominantly in magical terms. The major pleasure experience here is in terms of sucking and chewing; relationships with the outside world are in terms of swallowing if the objects are "good" and spitting them out if they are "bad." There is an associated and subsidiary reflex tendency to evacuate immediately or shortly after ingestion; this also leaves lingering psychological traces. Between the world felt as so many variants of food and the final recognition of objects as human individuals, the developing child experiences his environment through a number of transitional animate and inanimate objects. This period is rich in what are known as fixation points—early instinctual and ego patterns from which the individual cannot free himself to evolve further and to which he regresses when later developmental problems prove to be too intractable. When that happens the later forms of ego and instinctual expressions fall under the primacy or dominance of the earlier fixated patterns and become distorted thereby.

The oral zone, so important in the biological economy, necessarily carries a very large pleasure premium throughout life, but especially so in the first few years. At the very beginning, oral pleasure flows from the oral and respiratory functions as the two merge in nursing. To this is soon added the satisfactions from the aural or auditory zone—the sound of mother's voice and the baby's own undifferentiated noises. The nature of these pleasures are incorporative as well as autoerotic. One leading psychoanalytic author (4), of whom more will be said later, was so impressed with this factor that for him stuttering was nothing else but a breakthrough of this early autoerotism. Incorporative wishes may have a libidinal or a hostile aim. The latter would then be equatable with killing the object. Using the articulatory apparatus may then signify that words are introjected objects, that killing the object and the words are one and the same. One result may be a speech inhibition.

Oral erogeneity, accentuated for various reasons, may lead to ambition in the field of speech. The expression of the ambition may be quite variable. In a direct way it may lead to a deep interest in languages, philology, or linguistics. A deep interest in speech may also follow in a compensatory way upon a transient speech disorder long forgotten.

Speech in the service of ambition may acquire an exaggerated importance from sources other than pure oral erogeneity. It may represent competitiveness based on the need for self-aggrandizement or narcissistic enhancement: to make more noise than the other fellow, to stand up and be counted, to show that one has a voice in all matters, etc.

A seemingly curious but quite significant need to speak much may depend upon a need to eat excessively. This in turn often represents an identification with one who wishes to eat aggressively, i.e., it is a defense against a wish to be eaten. The latter is not an uncommon and very serious regressive reaction against a host of fearsome tasks and attainments requiring a courageous, active role. Another need to eat and talk in excess is more simple: to feel on an equal footing with adults. Still another aspect of oral ambition is the imbibing of words by hearing and reading. In the last instance the need to speak may also be inhibited more directly; but in all instances the inhibitions are reactive to excesses which are felt to be dangerous.

We turn now from the manifestations of the instinctual drives as determinants of the stuttering to the stutterer's ego as a separate mental structure. In neurosis it is weaker than the id or the superego, and it yields to the demands of each in turn. Descriptively, it has elements of orderliness, severity, obstinacy, and thus resembles that found among compulsive neurotics. Theoretically, it is an ego that has to defend itself against the instincts whose expression may threaten the self and others, and must defend itself also against an unusually threatening superego. The character of the latter is often projected upon persons in authority. Stutterers frequently speak worse in the presence of such individuals because they have to struggle harder with containing their aggressions. A stutter is often produced when the speaker is placed at a disadvantage, thus indicating that he acts so in order to gratify his own severe superego. Despite the painfulness of speaking and stuttering, some stutterers can and do secondarily extract a kind of satisfaction in such situations, such as being pitied or getting gratification from keeping the audience tense and waiting. These gains are generally unconscious but may be made conscious.

This concludes the general orientation of the basic psychopathology of stuttering. An attempt will now be made to cover the theoretical skeleton just described with the flesh and blood of clinical findings, working constructs, and therapeutic approaches from significant contributions made by a number of psychoanalysts. In doing so a certain amount of repetitiveness will be unavoidable but hopefully also helpful. I have the same hope with regard to my own interpretations in rendering a dynamic image of the stutterer. Since the contributions are quite variable, not much uniformity of presentation will be possible.

Specific Contributions of Several Psychoanalytic Investigators

Freud

I shall begin with Freud, not alone out of deference to the discoverer and founder of psychoanalysis, but because his contributions in this field—a fact generally unrecognized—touch on the major aspects of the syndrome. They consist of a lengthy case presentation, several pithy theoretical statements—all to be found in his writings—and an oral statement reported to me in a personal communication.

The case presentation is that of Frau Emmy von N., one of the five case reports in his classical *Studies on Hysteria* (20) written in collaboration with Breuer. Freud treated this patient during 1888 and 1890 by the combined methods of suggestion and catharsis while she was in a state of hypnosis. It was the first time Freud ever used the method of catharsis which he learned from Breuer. The patient was a 40-year-old widow who suffered from states of confusion, various physical complaints, and a series of speech disorders. The latter consisted of a tonic stutter, a ticlike clacking sound, and a number of involuntary phrases referred to as "protective formulae." Freud observed the association between the confusional state and the stuttering; he was able to find related traumatic events compulsively repeating themselves in both. He was able markedly to influence the stutter, though not to remove it entirely, by having the patient disclose the traumatic events associated with the onset and abreact the strangulated affects. He commented on the factor of her complete sexual abstinence as disposing to the *maintenance* of the disorder. The strength of this maintenance he later attributed to the "early fixations." He further regarded her tonic stutter and her tic as two sides of the same phenomenon: the inhibition of a disturbing sound or word and the breakthrough of the same. What produced the desired inhibition he referred to as a "painful antithetical or contrasting idea." He did not at that time analyze the nature of such an idea. My own interpretation, based on current insights and substantiated by the clinical material which Freud presented, is that it represented an oral aggression toward her children. It thus fits into the classification of a pregenital conversion neurosis. From another case Freud employed to illustrate the fact of "painful antithetical ideas" it is clear that he intuitively understood the content of that idea. This was a patient who had a marked inhibition in nursing her infant despite a strong conscious desire. We know now that such blocks are caused by the opposite idea—to eat, i.e., reincorporate, the infant and undo the mother-child separation. Frau Emmy's ambivalent attitudes toward both her children, but especially one, produced the same wish. Further, he indicated in this case sketchily what he developed later more fully: the stages in symptom formation—beginning with the primitive, universal fears of catastrophe in nature and fears of animals; infantile traumata; the traumatic effects of certain fantasies; later fears; finally, the fearful precipitating events.

Freud dealt with the problem of the intractability of the stuttering symptom. He recognized the tendency of the anxiety which produces the stutter to spread and express itself through one type of fear, then through another, etc., after the fashion of the development of phobias, until the function of speaking itself becomes involved as a fearsome act.

The tendency of surface fears to spread from one to a host of situations and stimuli while the underlying anxiety remains unconscious accounts in part for another characteristic of stuttering, namely, its frequent occurrence as a monosymptomatic disorder. According to Freud the determining factors for this phenomenon include traumatic psychic associations, symbolizations—i.e., the expression of painful thoughts through suffering, associated with a fixation on certain functions of a particular organ. The last point will be taken up again.

I am not aware of any psychoanalytic references to the dynamics of stuttering as embodied in this case report or to the rich clinical material it contains elucidative of stuttering. By contrast, what has received much attention and influenced psychoanalytic thinking on the subject are two short statements Freud made almost parenthetically. In 1910, in his *Psychopathology of Everyday Life* (**18**), he made a distinction between a slip of the tongue and the stuttering occasioned by embarrassment. The latter "speech disturbances can no longer be described as speech blunders, for they do not injure the individual word, but affect the rhythm and execution of the entire speech. . . . But here, as in the former cases, it is the inner conflict that is betrayed to us through the disturbance in speech." This concludes Freud's condensed statement. It encompasses some fundamental facts which I will now elaborate. It first tells of the element of conflict between antagonistic wishes relating to speech. The wish not to speak is unconscious and is due to some unconscious meaning of a particular subject to be spoken of, or to the significance of the activity of speaking in general. In a slip of the tongue there is a resistance to the conscious intention to express a particular thought, which resistance can be discovered by the analysis of the slip. Similarly, in the very occasional stutter the analysis of the particular stimulus is the starting point for the revelation of the disturbing resistance. However, in the usual case of stuttering the very intention to speak has an objectionable significance. We can thus recognize the global nature of stuttering as contrasted with the much more constricted character of a slip of the tongue. It is a distinction worth emphasizing, as I have noticed that sometimes the same therapeutic approach was vainly applied to the stutter as to the parapraxis.

Freud's next statement appeared in 1915 in a letter to Ferenczi (31). In it he wrote that a recent analysis clearly taught him that stuttering can be caused by a displacement upon the articulatory apparatus of conflicts over excremental functions. The larger meaning of the remark can best be recognized in a statement by Fenichel: "Psychoanalysis of stutterers reveals the anal-sadistic universe of wishes as the basis of the symptom. For them, the function of speech regularly has an anal-sadistic significance. Speaking means, first, the utterance of obscene, especially anal words, and second, an aggressive act directed against the listener. One may speak in stuttering of a displacement upward of the functions of the anal sphincters" (10).

In relation to psychoanalytic therapy in stuttering generally, we find no references in Freud's writings. But in the case of Frau Emmy he was specific. We must remember that in this patient the stutter was an incidental symptom, perhaps not complained of by the patient at all. Freud was very modest about this first patient in whom he used catharsis and suggestion under hypnosis. The patient's stutter improved considerably, and he regretted that he was not able to trace fully the secondary fears to which the symptom became attached. He was further aware that, owing to the combined therapies, catharsis and suggestion, it was not possible to discern to which method the therapeutic effects were attributable, adding, however, that regarding those areas upon which he was able to do some analytic work besides, the symptoms were fully resolved. Following this case, it appears that for a long time the pregenital conversions did not occupy his attention as much as did the classical neuroses—hysteria, compulsions, etc.

From a personal communication (7) I learned that in 1913 he touched on some problems of the pregenital conversions, i.e., asthma, stuttering, and tic. Discussing a case report on asthma, he remarked that this group of disorders resembles hysteria, the prototype of the classical neuroses, but must be classified separately as a fixation neurosis. He emphasized that what is significant for this group is, first, the organ fixation. This is the result of a concentration of libidinal energy in an organ—the articulatory apparatus in stutterers. Secondly, the fixation compels the neurosis to express itself in somatic terms and thereby interferes with the physiological automatism—in this instance, speech. This thought approaches the concept of stuttering, already referred to and to be discussed further, as merely a form of oral autoerotism. However, two years later in his letter to Ferenczi just mentioned he stressed the factor of regression from the anal to the oral zone. This factor is inherent in the theory of neurotic symptom formation, even though in this quotation Freud did not mention the important fact that the regression is always drawn to an earlier point of fixation. In his oral discussion, however, he termed the fixation "infantilism," which suggests ego, as well as instinctual, arrest. This view places stuttering within the broader diagnostic category of the narcissistic neuroses, also termed character or ego-defect disorders. Psychoanalysis was not developed, at least during its classical phase, through the investigations on the narcissistic disorders. But in recent years study and investigation of this group of disorders has gained momentum. Freud himself toward the latter part of his career did pioneering work on this frontier in his studies on the ego. What is relevant here are his suggestions for the analytic therapy of this group (11), one example being his advice to relinquish the earlier more authoritative attitude for the more flexible approaches practiced by the child analyst.

The hereditary, or constitutional, factor in stuttering is mentioned frequently. Hence it is of interest to state the psychoanalytic view on constitution and heredity in general, even though it does not relate specifically to stuttering. How this factor is considered is obviously important, because both concept and therapy are affected by it. In discussing any syndrome we generally mention the constitutional factor first; but since our order here parallels the chronology in Freud, we place it last. In the last years of his life, Freud concerned himself with this problem anew, and we are fortunate that in his *Outline of Psychoanalysis* (17) and *Moses and Monotheism* (16) he left us some profound observations and explicitly stated conclusions. It is also fortunate that he begins his discussion with remarks on speech which are relevant to our discussion of its pathology.

> Thought-processes, and what may be analogous to them in the Id, are unconscious *per se* and obtain their entry into consciousness by their connection, via the function of speech, with memory traces of perceptions through touch and ear. . . . We believe . . . [from impressions of early traumata and their memory residues operating from the Id, and also from the behavior of neurotic children to their parents when under the influence of an Oedipus and castration complex] that there probably exists in the mental life of the individual not only what he has experienced himself but also what he brought with him at birth, fragments of phylogenetic origin, and archaic heritage. The question then

arises: in what does this inheritance consist, what does it contain, and what evidence of it is there?

The first and most certain answer is that it consists in certain dispositions, such as all living beings possess; that is to say, in the ability and tendency to follow a certain direction of development and to react in a particular way to certain excitations, impressions, and stimuli. Since experience shows that individuals differ in this respect, archaic inheritance includes these differences; they represent what is recognized as the constitutional element in the individual. Since all human beings go through the same experiences, at least in their earliest years, they also react to them in the same way, and this is why the doubt arose whether these reactions with all their individual differences should not be reckoned as part of that archaic heritage. This doubt must be rejected; the fact is that this similarity does not enrich our knowledge of the archaic heritage.

Meanwhile analytical search has yielded several results which give us food for thought. First of all, there is the universality of speech symbolism. Symbolic substitution of one subject through another—the same applies to actions—our children are conversant with, and it seems quite natural to them. We cannot trace the way in which they learned it and must admit that in many cases to learn it would be impossible. It is original knowledge, which the adult later on forgets. He employs, it is true, the same symbolism in his dreams, but he does not understand them unless the analyst interprets them for him, and even then he is loath to believe the translation. When he has used one of the common phrases of speech in which this symbolism is crystallized, he has to admit that its true meaning had quite escaped him. Symbolism even ignores the differences in languages; investigation would probably show that it is ubiquitous, the same with all peoples. Here there seems to be an assured case of archaic inheritance from the time when speech was developing, although one might attempt another explanation: One might say that these are thought connections between ideas which were formed during the historical development of speech and which have to be repeated every time the individual passes through such a development. This then would be a case of inheriting a thought disposition as elsewhere one inherits an instinctual disposition. . . . In fact, it [i.e., clinical material already alluded to] seems to me convincing enough to allow me to venture further and assert that the archaic heritage of mankind includes not only dispositions, but also ideational contents, memory traces of the experiences of former generations. In this way the extent as well as the significance of the archaic heritage would be enhanced in a remarkable degree. . . . This state of affairs is made more difficult, it is true, by the present attitude of biological science, which rejects the idea of acquired qualities being transmitted to descendants. I admit, in all modesty, that in spite of this I cannot picture biological development proceeding without taking this factor into account.

Freud concludes with a recapitulation. I will include it because, despite some repetition, it adds new implications and emphases.

We must conclude that the mental residue of primeval times has become a heritage which, with each new generation, needs only to be awakened, not to be reacquired. We may think here of the example of speech symbolism which certainly seems to be inborn. It originates in the time of speech-development, and it is familiar to all children without their having been specially instructed. It is the same in all peoples in spite of the differences in language. What we may still lack in certainty we may acquire from other results of psychoanalytic investigations. We learn that our children in a number of significant relationships do not react as their own experiences would lead us to expect, but instinctively, like animals; this is explicable only by phylogenetic inheritance [16].

Brill

In 1923, A. A. Brill spoke before a group of speech teachers (3) on the subject of Speech Disturbances in Nervous and Mental Diseases. His paper, in nontechnical language, touches on so many aspects of stuttering very succinctly that it may well serve as a bird's-eye view of the psychoanalytic orientation on stuttering, circa 1923, as seen through the eyes of one distinguished representative. He begins with the problems of treatment and states in broad terms that experience gradually made him less enthusiastic though not pessimistic regarding it. At a large clinic he had interviewed over 600 patients. He had treated 69 from a few months to a year and over; the ages ranged from 15 to 51. It is not explicitly stated but it is practically certain that the classical psychoanalytic treatment was not used in the clinic, though psychoanalytic understanding was utilized. Most of the patients he regarded as much improved or cured when they left. He followed them up through their yearly communications.

Elaborating further on the prognosis of the stuttering after treatment, Brill emphasized the tendency to recurrence. After 11 years, he found only 5 of the 69 patients doing entirely well. One of the 5 regressed in his speech following being drafted into the Army. Brill added that he could be very busy if he took care of all the "cured" stutterers of others. By contrast, the prognosis among young children is much better. These can usually be cured if treated properly. Like all psychoneurotic symptoms, speech disturbances can be cured more quickly and thoroughly when they have not become interwoven in the whole being of the person. Another group having a favorable treatment outlook are psychoneurotics who began stuttering at a later age; still another consists of psychopaths and mild mental defectives in whom transient speech disturbances were observed.

One question on which psychoanalysts appear to be divided is the need for supplementary speech training. Brill belonged to the group who believe in training and gave the usual rationale of that group, namely, that the patients have acquired bad "habits" of speech which need to be "untrained" or "retrained." This question will be discussed more fully in conjunction with the contributions of Coriat and myself.

Brill makes some interesting comments regarding the sex ratio of distribution—the well-known fact that there are at least four or five males to one female stutterer—adding that this is in contrast to the ratio in psychoneurosis in general. I do not believe that he meant that the two groups are in inverse ratio but rather that broadly more females than males have the classical neuroses. I do not know the current statistics about the latter, but my impression is that the difference, if any, is not marked.

Regarding the basis for the sexual distribution, Brill quotes Jespersen's theory, which he apparently accepts, that the male tends to go to extremes regarding his speech. He is both normally less fluent and shows greater preponderance in speech disturbances. The female has more control of her speech but a smaller vocabulary. The male tends to be more quiet and silent but more aggressive in his thoughts. The female talks about simpler things, encounters less criticism. Present-day competitive civilization leaves little time for speech to the male, while at the same time he must use all his mental efforts. The female, on the other hand, according to his view, has no need for involved thinking, as she is in constant close relationship with the simple human being, the child. She can cook, bake, crochet, and talk at the same time. The preponderance of speech disturbance as a psychoneurotic symptom in the male is thus only an exaggeration of his normal activity. The female's speech is more fluent and not as vulnerable as the male's. This concept may be characterized as anthropologic rather than psychoanalytic. It should be noted for comparison with my own concept based on genetic studies, to be discussed later.

In common with all psychoanalysts, Brill did not consider stuttering a symptom of a classical neurosis; he was struck by the features of introversion, some paranoid tincturing of the personality, autoerotic and narcissistic fixations.

Before concluding, he mentions two or three other significant and practical points: Speech disturbances disappear when the individual feels free to express himself fully, that is, when he can give and take emotions in a normal way. This is a way of saying that in order to be cured the stutterer must accomplish mastery over his characteristic tendency to turn upon himself—to introvert his affects and keep them dissociated from the realm of the intellect. The dissociation is a major defense of the neurosis and the overcoming of it a crucial step in the analysis.

He mentions the fundamental fact of neurosis, that the symptom unconsciously represents a morbid gain for the patient who then refuses to give it up, also doing so unconsciously; and the secondary fact that the stutterer, like other chronic neurotics, utilizes his stuttering to escape from various difficulties and stutters more when confronted with disagreeable tasks. This phenomenon of secondary gain has already been discussed.

Brill regards prophylaxis as more important than treatment. As many children begin to show signs of stuttering at an early age, study of the behavior of the parents toward the child is indicated. He advocates bringing the child in closer contact with other children, suggesting a parental tie that is unhealthy because it is too close. He cautioned against impressing the child that it has a malady, thus causing self-consciousness. He is impressed by a hereditary predisposition and by the fact that stuttering is one of the most intractable neuroses, especially in the adult chronic stutterer.

Brill's statements on therapy and prophylaxis as related here are essentially true in the light of current insights, at least in the experience of the writer. However, they are oversimplified, partly owing to the requirements of his paper and partly because they antedate the insights acquired in the intervening years.

Coriat

Among psychoanalysts perhaps no one has written more about stuttering than Coriat, beginning in 1915 and continuing for almost 30 years. The most important of his writings was his monograph, *Stammering: A Psychoanalytic Interpretation* (4), which appeared in 1927. His contributions, though reflecting in the main the psychoanalytic insights of his time, also included important ideas and emphases of his own. His contribution consisted mainly in that he placed in the forefront the dynamic factor of the oral libido, although he was not unaware of other elements in the causation. This emphasis was altogether new. He marshaled findings from various sources. He compared the reflex experiments on the newborn infant's tendencies to suck, bite, and incorporate with the oral activities in adult stutterers. These direct findings paralleled reconstructions of infantile states in the pregenital neuroses. He studied observations on the mouth activities of older nurslings who sucked after they were fed. He also compared the oral libidinal Pavlovian conditioned reflexes with the idea of the illusory nipple among stutterers. He studied his patients' associations, his clinical observations of them, and their clear, often literal, dreams and fantasies. He concluded that the basic causative factor in stuttering is the accentuated libido within the mouth. In my opinion, that contribution stands today as valid, even though his total evaluation and interpretation of that fact may be questioned as insufficiently inclusive, and despite his tendency to undervalue other factors. For him the role of oral aggression was a minor one; and he hardly treated the roles of the ego and of narcissism beyond merely mentioning them.

Coriat also regarded stuttering as one of the severest forms of psychoneurosis. He independently came close to Freud's concept of fixation neurosis, which has only recently come to light, as was mentioned earlier. To Coriat, stuttering consists essentially of a persistence into adult life of infantile nursing activities. He often reiterated that careful observation would prove that the stutterer's attempts to speak reveal motor patterns of an act of nursing at an illusory nipple. He described cannibalistic muscular patterns, anal-retentive and anal-expulsive patterns, and placed them in a secondary role. He was able to trace certain character traits of the stutterer from the oral fixations, underscoring the fact that in many instances these traits were almost as infantile as the erotism from which they emerged. In the rhythmic character of nursing he saw the root of the fluctuations in the speech and the labile emotional swings in the personality as a whole. Similarly, the obstinacy and verbal "constipation" were traceable to the anal erotism.

His great emphasis on the dominant role of the pleasure principle in the symptom in terms of the excessive libido concentration in the mouth led him to picture stuttering fundamentally as a perversion. This fact was evidenced also in his use of Abraham's phrase (1)—mouth pollutions or oral masturbation. He stated that stuttering is not a genuine conversion in a pregenital neurosis, but a neurosis in which the original pregenital tendencies have persisted from an early organization of the libido. Consequently, the beginnings of stuttering in early childhood are not of a psychoneurotic nature; it is only through the persistence of early oral and anal activities that stuttering becomes a psychoneurosis. This distinction may be analogous to the nonanalytic, descriptive approach which speaks of "primary" and "secondary" stuttering. There is no question that stuttering when fully developed fulfills the requirements of a neurosis. Coriat must have been quite aware of that, because he wrote that the motivating mechanism producing stuttering is unconscious—"The only conscious reaction being that of a morbid situation, namely anxiety and fear." In a genuine perversion those affects are not present or prominent. It is obvious Coriat saw in the stutter perverse *and* neurotic phenomena, and that he thought of these categories as not sharply distinguishable. He was aware of the double aspect of symptoms including partial attempts at instinctual gratification and prohibition. He wrote: "The symptom of the speech defect results both from a resistance barrier between thoughts and vocal expression and from a compulsive repetition of the original nursing activities, rather than from the content of the thoughts themselves." In saying this Coriat approximates Freud's distinction between the slip of the tongue and stuttering, and adds that the content of the symptom is not related to a specific thought content but to the special impulses which the unconscious equates with thoughts and words in general—notably nursing and biting wishes.

Along with other analysts, Coriat underscored the special significance of the castration complex in the female stutter. ". . . the tongue has become a displaced phallus, the inner conflict within the libidinal economy has become concentrated on the lingual organ for the purpose of unconsciously satisfying a masculine aim. The conflict is between wishes to have a phallus, to envy those that have it, to acquire it in a cannibalistic manner, and the reactions of disgust and guilt." We know now that these conflicts arise in relation to early parental ties to and separations from the mother, which become intensified at the height of the oedipal rivalry. The mother is accused as the earliest one responsible for the "fact" of castration. Unhealthy resolutions of this complex may lead either to interminable hatred of the mother or mother persons, or to homosexual attachments.

Coriat wrote clearly and emphatically about the psychoanalytic treatment of stuttering. It was a measure of his rich clinical experience and penetrating insights. In part, however, it was also due to the fact that he was confined mainly to one instinctual component—nursing pleasure—as against total instinctual and structural orientations. He advocated the use of psychoanalysis, though he was thoroughly aware of the many difficulties resulting from resistances. He was opposed to speech training, as it dealt not with the total neurosis but only one symptom, "and as such is inadequate and unscientific." Furthermore, he believed such training reinforced the oral erotism instead of relieving or lessening it. He advised directing the treatment against the resistances, which he recognized as "very severe because of the convergence of several factors. First is the narcissistic essence of the disorder; second, the reluctance to giving up the nursing pleasure in speech; third, the negativism or holding back acquired from the anal phase of development and expressed in oral terms. There is a parallelism between the difficulties encountered in analyzing the speech problem and the character traits due to the relative underdevelopment of the ego, at least as far as the oral and anal instinct gratification in early forms are concerned." He introduced a modification in the classical psychoanalytic technique, which he called "active therapy." In sum, it consisted of a marked reduction in the oral pleasures indulged in by these patients by ordering them to abstain from smoking, gum chewing, etc. This regimen by helping to crystallize the resistance to the analytic treatment aided in its resolution by demonstrating how these indulgences reinforced the oral difficulties of the stutterer.

Finally, and incidentally, Coriat pointed up something which this writer has also observed: that the psychoanalytic therapy of stutterers can be of more general scientific interest to analysts, inasmuch as in this syndrome there is often revealed what is generally hidden in other syndomes by childhood amnesias. For example, through this work the writer has been able to gain valuable insights into some problems of professional choices and inhibitions (22), certain types of sport (27), problems of homosexuality (29), and of schizoidism (26).

Glauber

Stuttering and the Early Ego State. My own interest, as embodied in a number of studies in stuttering (23) (28), relates to its more differentiated aspects, makes fuller use of the structural and economic orientations as well as of the aggressive drive, and delves especially into the genetic aspects. Until fairly recently this disorder has not been sharply distinguished from such classical neuroses as hysteria or the obsessions. More recently, however, it became generally accepted as a pregenital conversion or a narcissistic neurosis, that is, one in which primarily the executant part of the personality, the ego, is defective or insufficiently developed. Furthermore, while the general traits of the pregenital conversions have been known as such in psychoanalysis for some 40 years, it was due to the advances in the last decade that it became possible to recognize more specific content and meaning in this group of disorders. My work was involved in the adaptation and application of these advances to the field of stuttering. I shall now summarize some parts of it.

From my experience the most meaningful aspect of the pregenital conversions is the arrest in ego maturation, otherwise stated as fixation at an early ego state. The fixation is manifested in the speech symptom and in the total personality. As in general psychopathology the symptom represents an attempt, and an unsuccessful one, to bind the underlying anxiety. Anxiety emerges when an early ego state threatens to return from the unconscious and impinge upon the operation of the current ego state. This emotion is experienced by the ego when it receives a threatening signal from the superego. In the stutterer, anxiety emerges in social situations when speech is immanent because of the danger of the impinging and assertion of an early ego state (wherein speech is an id expression) upon the functioning of the current ego state (wherein speech is an ego, or sublimation expression). The early ego state represents the stage which became fixated during the process of ego emergence.

Now speech is the first intellectual symbolic expression in the child. Speech is also the first and most significant manifestation of the ego as a distinct mental structure, as well as a major tool in its development. This ego function acts as a psychosomatic automatism. It has evolved in part from the instinctual energies of the id, employing organs borrowed from the alimentary, respiratory, and the voluntary or striated muscular systems, plus the auditory sense organs. This process of transformation has been called sublimation, egotization, and neutralization. Constitutional and early traumatic factors may cause too great an adhesiveness of the early forms of expression of the instinctual energies within these organs. This is known as a fixation. Two results may flow from this: one, an interference with the full emergence of integrated and automatic, i.e., smooth, working of the symbolic function of the ego; two, a tendency within the oral apparatus to draw to itself the functions of other, later-developed, instinctual zones such as the anal and phallic zones. This latter consequence is called regression. The stutter is in part fixation and regression and in part also an attempt to defend against both. The defense is by means of an urge to mutism. Within this phase there may occur momentary amnesias in the mental speech, though during the large part of the time of this phase the stutterer is clearly conscious of the speech unit he wishes to utter. Thus when a stutterer unconsciously senses that he may want to bite or suck when he is supposed to speak, a conflict ensues the result of which contains some elements of biting or sucking as well as elements of attempts to block such expressions through amnesia, mutism, and articulatory spasms. It is possible that other elements stemming from more diffuse phobic and startle reactions may be contributory. The fixation in the speech apparatus may subserve libidinal and aggressive oral drives in their active and passive expressions. Secondarily these may be merged with onanistic, exhibitionistic, voyeuristic, and masochistic drives.

The fixation reveals itself through the archaic meanings of the stuttering symptom which flow from the id and the superego, but particularly the early ego organization. Interrelated with disturbances in individual ego functions, there are significant unconscious visual images of the total self which help further to round out the picture of the disturbance. Finally, our attention is claimed by a constellation of genetic environmental factors occurring so frequently that they may be considered typical, if not quite specific for the syndrome. Further work is necessary to determine sharper specificity.

In recent years I have been concentrating on aspects of genesis and characterology, and the extension of the range of the psychotherapeutic efficacy. Before elaborating further on these three important areas I must add some concluding remarks on the formation of the symptom. The rationale for the oral fixation will be dealt with presently. Here it may be said that it seems probable that because of the large quantity of psychic energy originally invested at the oral zone, this zone lends itself as a magnetic pole, as it were, for the return of the repressed conflicts from later-developed levels of instinctual organization, such as the anal, phallic, and genital, also such "partial" drives as the exhibitionistic and voyeuristic which may be considered as subsidiary to the oral. Thus the symptom reveals itself as the reorganized expression of genital conflicts of the oedipal phase—unconscious incestuous wishes, hostility, rivalry, and guilt; conflicts of will, pleasure of defiance and of submission regarding retaining and expelling, stemming from the period of bowel and bladder control. The equation of excremental products with oral products—words—and the projection of conflicts regarding the former upon the latter has already been mentioned. The cannibalistic wishes and the wishes for incorporation stemming from the oral zone will be considered when the characterology is discussed.

With so many contributions from different psychic levels it is evident why the symptom of stuttering is so overdetermined and hence so difficult to influence therapeutically. On the other hand, there is the seeming paradox that unlike the symptoms of a classical neurosis the stutter may relatively be more easily reversible *in early childhood* as a result of the total family constellation being normalized through therapy. The reason for this is that the ego arrest from which the symptom flows is lifted when pathological family relationships are resolved. The etiologic overdetermination is also the most important reason that stuttering is so commonly presented by patients as a monosymptomatic disorder. Also, the fact that stuttering represents an arrest of ego development at an early stage accounts for another of its special aspects. Unlike the classical neuroses, the symptoms of which precipitate during adolescence, stuttering emerges either shortly after the onset of speech or when the child begins school. It then continues without interruption through the latency period and beyond. Finally, the stutterer has many inhibitions besides the symptom, though for the most part they are totally unknown to him. In fact, inhibition invades the speech function itself, for the stutter is in essence an unsuccessful attempt at inhibition. A related and secondary line of defense takes the form of phobias for speech situations.

The oral fixation is the key factor in the neurosogenesis of stuttering.

We do not yet know all the answers to the question of how this fixation came about. Regarding inherited predisposition, we have already mentioned Freud's suggestion that the difficulty certain children have in the stage of learning to speak may represent the expression of a memory of a similar difficulty from the stage in the history of the human race when the speech faculty was in the process of emerging. In the human individual today the emergence of speech parallels the birth of the ego—at about the time that infancy comes to an end. This time marks a critical turning point in the dissolution of the psychological oneness between mother and child.

Considerations of Organic-Constitutional Factors. In the large majority of cases stuttering does not suggest an organic disorder, "organic" in the sense of altered structure and function of the speech centers in the central nervous system. It has seemed plausible to me that a certain number of stutterers belong with the group of hyperkinetic children in whom it has been postulated (32) that, owing to a series of pathogenic influences, pre- and early post-natal, a lowered threshold of susceptibility to stimuli has been established in one or several nuclei of the hypothalamus. In such cases diffuse hyperkinetic overflow in the motor pathways may also include the speech musculature. A test for such heightened susceptibility has been devised and by the use of chemotherapy the threshold of the stimulus barrier has been raised. These results would tend to substantiate such a postulate. As far as stuttering is concerned this work has hardly begun. At this writing, I am looking into this approach with a view toward testing it in a group of stuttering children. It may well be that the ego-defect disorders may be based on somatic *and* psychic causes. In one sense, the results may be identical because the causes, though differing in nature, may be identical in effect. In another sense, somatic and psychic causation may relate to each other in a circular fashion. Still another way of stating the facts is that the distinction of psychic versus somatic may be less significant than the distinction of localized versus diffuse involvement. It seems to me that this kind of orientation is more valid, meaningful, and possibly provable than the somatic concepts of cerebral dominance or delayed myelinization of unknown etiology. The facts are that in stuttering the occurrence of the causative influences is very early, the onset of the symptom is early, and its nature is relatively intractable. These observations suggest a resemblance to organic symptoms, but this does not constitute an identity.

To me it seems that on still another plane the "organic" factor in stuttering may be that which is expressed as the organ fixation. Instinctual fixation upon an organ can damage its function just as much as an actual area of brain damage. It leads to an interference in "egotization" or the full autonomous use of that function by the ego organization. It is possible that this was implied in what Freud meant by the organic factor. But it is more probable that he referred to some organic constitutional hereditary factor expressed in a weakness of the ego. But, on the other hand, is not the ego defect simply the result of, or synonymous with, the hereditary instinctual fixation upon an organ? This fixation may be equivalent to the incubation phase in the transference neuroses—the infantile neurosis. The learning to use that organ might then constitute the precipitating phase, equivalent to the second stage in the formation of the transference neuroses. We do not know whether Freud believed that this phasic difference is true in all narcissistic disorders. He certainly made it explicit in relation to schizophrenia, which is at the extreme end and the most severe form. There he said that psychology helps us to understand only the reparative, or the so-called restitutive, processes but not the first process which is pathology proper, whose cause and nature are unknown. We certainly have had that impression with regard to some schizophrenic patients. On the other hand, as regards others, it appeared that psychology could explain the basic etiology, or the first process. Similar views might hold also regarding stuttering. In this connection the problem of the stimulus barrier and the variations in its threshold offers a promising field for further investigation of this "first" process.

So much for the prenatal and phylogenetic aspects of the etiology. In what follows, the more certain field of ontogenesis will be reviewed.

Stuttering as a Uniquely Total Family Disorder. I have been impressed that regularly the oral-narcissistic fixation in the stutterer flows from the partial resolution of the primary identity with the mother. Furthermore, the meanings of this fixation may be found in the primitive struggles, aims, and self-images inherent in this symbiosis. For this reason it is essential to understand the personality of the mother of the stutterer and the rather unique mother-child relationship. The father's role is also significant, but becomes so at a later stage in the life of the child. These facts may be restated thus: the father is actually important in the maintenance of the neurosis as the mother is in its precipitation. Because of the observations, about to be elaborated, it is neither banal nor superfluous to state that the stutterer's disorder—at least the young stutterer's—is uniquely a total family disorder. Needless to say, this fact is of paramount importance in the therapy of the child stutterer.

The profile of the personality (**28**) of the mother and of the mother-child relationship is based on an extensive study of the family constellations of stutterers and material from psychoanalyses of stutterers and of their mothers. From these studies I have been impressed that the mother is a woman who never separated from, and was appersonated[2] by, her own mother. She has serious problems with her husband because of her unconscious attempts to repeat with him this state of appersonation, with its attendant mixed emotions; similarly with her children, with whom she actually does repeat this process. This mother's personality is permeated by the appersonation-separation problem with its deep, passive desire for union, the anxiety of separation, and counteracting aggression. This problem is passed on by her to her sons, less often to her daughters. On an intuitive plane, she and the child so involved with her are extremely attuned to the anxieties of each other.

Developmental Aspects. Speech arises during the second year approximately concurrently with beginning of walking and of bladder and bowel control. These are muscular-motor skills, or automatisms accomplished by developing neuromuscular finesse. These accomplishments related to the child's individualization involve feelings of separation in both child and mother. The anxiety resulting from the struggle between retaining and relinquishing oral and anal dependence, and from the reactive aggression, finally affects the coördinated functioning of the oral and respiratory apparatus producing in them repetitions and spasm. At the same time the muscular incoördination reflects the anxiety-ridden elements of the dramatic conflict as it is being acted out in the speech act.

Although the beginning of speech represents a crucial and overdetermined moment for the emergence of separation anxieties, there are several earlier and later equally important and determining moments for both mother and child. The birth process is often dramatized by the mother as a traumatic experience, and is just as often reacted to with depression. The birth of the child is experienced as if the child were an integral part of the mother's body which was performing a hostile act of separation. This struggle is repeated during the nursing period in the first year of life. The unconscious struggle here is between a wish to feed the child and a wish to eat it. Permeating the nursing process, which is then beset by difficulties, the conflict may reach a climax in the form of a severe weaning period.

Feeding difficulties, invariably traceable to a hesitant or uniquely ambivalent attitude on the part of the mother, were almost always present during the first year of the child's life. Closer scrutiny revealed the special

[2] Appersonation is an unconscious embodiment of another person as an extension, in whole or in part, of one's own identity.

characteristics of the ambivalence: alternations of aggressive feeding gestures and sudden withholding, both accompanied by anxiety. One might call this mother a "stuttering" feeder, stamping the pattern of hesitation primarily upon the oral musculature and secondarily upon the respiratory musculature of the child a short time before the same organ systems have to be adapted for the function of speech. One mother stated that her nursing difficulties stemmed from a fear that the child would eat her up. This was a projection of her own wishes and an identification with the child's own fantasies—to eat up and to be eaten. What was striking was the sense of realness with which the fear existed in the mother's mind. Nursing was acted out as a repetitive series of aggressive feeding and sudden weaning acts, reaching its climax in the final weaning from breast or bottle.

Maternal anxieties, birth, nursing, weaning, and onset of speech were felt by the mother as anxious experiences, with a special quality compounded of both separation and clutching. Also the child's taking control of his own locomotion, elimination, the development of his will in its negative and positive aspects, and of his intellect—all these landmarks of his ego development—were felt by the mother as the child's provocative acts of moving away from her. They represented images of acts of biting into and out of the idealized mother-child unity. Another important crisis is faced in the separation at the beginning of school. This period is aggravated by aspects of the oedipal conflict reaching high points of intensity.

The relationship continues to be a "sticky" one, for this mother invests more attention in this child, also more concern, preoccupation, possessiveness, and control than perhaps in all the rest of the members of the family. Regardless of the boy's age, she occupies first place in his life. An example of this tenacious tie of the mother to the child is the frequency of the mother's discontinuation of treatment of the child after it has got well under way. This is especially so if the therapist is a woman, unless in the original treatment plan proper attention is given the mother simultaneously with or prior to the child's treatment. The maternal affect most commonly shown is great anxiety; it is centered around the child's speech, his general behavior, his masturbation, his school or social life. She showers much genuine affection on him, but below the surface also lurk envy, disappointment, and hostility.

The effect upon the growing child of such a series of spoken and unspoken signs of anxiety on the part of the mother in response to the onset of each successive stage in his own ego development is the emergence, at each stage, of parallel fearful and hesitant attitudes, later augmented by feelings of guilt and pent-up aggression. The psychopathology of the stutterer in essence is based upon inadequate development of certain of his own executant, reality-oriented ego functions. Though it sometimes seemed that the young stutterer had a precocious ego development, this ego development generally referred to certain perceptive intellectual abilities, unmatched by similar development in independence, reality-testing, and in the capacity to bear frustrations.

The Effect of the Mother-Child Relation on the Speech. The speech apparatus makes use of the lips, tongue, mouth, etc., which are the first organs of contact of the infant with the mother. From this first contact, anxiety and ambivalence characterized the mother's feelings and behavior. She behaved as if she were anxious about what she and the extension of herself, her child, might do with their oral apparatus. When a child begins to speak toward the end of the second year, it is quite normal for him to repeat the first syllable. Often these normal iterations were envisaged by his mother as stuttering, and its "dire" consequence on the child's personality was soon established in her mind. This fear represented an apprehension that self-expression on the part of the child was an oral aggression upon her, the mother, with the aim of separation, and upon the world as an aggressive assertion. Paradoxically, the possibility that the child might express passive or nursing wishes was also feared. The fear also reflects the possibility that the child as his mother's "spokesman" might expose her own aggressive and passive wishes.

During this early stage of the child's learning to speak, the mother often identified the child with her husband or her brother, either of whom was frequently actually a stutterer. The child, whose oral apparatus had already been impressed with hesitations from his nursing experience, sensed that to his mother speech was overladen with forbidden content—that speech itself was in fact something of a forbidden act. Since speech is a production created by the magical act of speaking, it became for the child both a magic and forbidden object. The mother was unusually speech-conscious; speech for her had retained its archaic quality of possessing special magical power, either in aggressive acts or passive wishes. Speech, which is a self-revealing, symbolic expression of thinking and feeling which in turn are ordinarily experienced as substitutes for action, was felt by the mother more nearly as an action than a symbol. Good speech was overvalued by the mother and feared for the same irrational reasons. Speech became the tool of her own oral dependent and aggressive needs. By the feeling of oneness, as already stated, the stuttering child became the instrument of expression for her own aims, which were at once passive and aggressive.

Further Traits of the Mother: Castration Complex and Narcissistic Objects. A comprehensive profile of the mother sufficiently specific to set her apart from the mothers of children affected by the other pregenital conversions is not yet possible. However, some traits are observed very commonly and are significant. She is a "stutterer" in personality, as the father is much more frequently and overtly in his speech. This fact is the result of her own oral fixations and is evidenced in her ambivalences and notably her separation anxieties and clinging. One important result of this mother's separation anxiety is her unique castration complex, to which she cannot adjust properly. This complex, which is an important component of the unconscious mental life of all women and represents an early phase of development, deals with a sense of being damaged, inferior, less worthy as compared to men. It is an elaboration of the reaction to an awareness of the anatomical difference between the sexes, plus two additional phenomena—separation anxieties and guilt feelings, stemming from very early sources. The nonneurotic woman overcomes the wish for possessing a penis by developing her maternal wishes and strivings; the sense of physical inferiority is compensated by emphasizing feminine attractiveness; finally, the imitative, competitive, and castrating impulses toward men are transformed into feelings of mutual regard, a sense of equal worthwhileness and dignity, and mutual appreciation. We say she develops a natural sense of self: her libidinized, unconscious, visual self-representation is predominantly that of a woman, which is a very close approximation to her realistic, photographic self-image. This attainment flows from the resolution of the castration complex and from the resolution of the oedipus complex as well. Both complexes leave vestigial traces in the minds of the best-adjusted, but these are of negligible importance.

The mother of our interest has a poorly differentiated sense of self. She is part child, part tomboy, part wife-husband. Envy of and competitiveness with males are frequent traits. She generally marries a passive man, frequently after being in love with a more masculine type. The marriage is usually a sado-masochistic one, i.e., propelled mainly by a need to control and possess or by a sense of duty, and little by positive satisfactions. We would diagnose her as a narcissistic character with hysterical and compulsive features. She is often overtly anxious; much of her libido is centered on partial intrapsychic images, but not on her real self or on love objects in the outside world. Her object choice is more often bisexually balanced than predominantly heterosexual, and the relationship is generally a disturbed one. This is to a large extent not a genuine object relationship. The important fact about her personality is that love objects represent to her narcissistic part-objects. These are self-images, idealized or degraded, representing individuals—and parts of them—from her early life with whom, and with which, she is identified. Those inner selves and part-selves are unintegrated. They are experienced as multiple personalities which are not miscible and integratable. Among the reasons for this are the facts that some are idealized and some degraded, and that much hostility pervades their inner relationship. Inherent under such circumstances is that neither subject nor objects are experienced in realistic terms; rather both self and objects are viewed and felt as projections of these inner images—now one, then another. This is still another way of stating the phenomenon of fixation, now in terms of ego imagery.

I shall now mention these self-images, which of course remain unconscious. They are significant because they are intrapsychic realities in both the mother and the stuttering child, appearing in identical and complementary forms. In the baby, during the preverbal period, the self-image is that of a breast. It merges with or separates from the maternal body, thus multiplying the number of self-images. Furthermore, the sense of oneness flowing from the image of fusion with the mother is felt as a pleasurable and omnipotent source of security. This image may be called the narcissistic ego-ideal, visualized as the perfect, also the phallic mother. Conversely, in a state of separation or estrangement, the image of symbiosis is broken into its component parts: breast and, later, phallus; separated from the idealized body, and the latter damaged as a result of the separations. These disparate elements are then perceived as unattractive, impotent, yet aggressively charged, whose aim is to return to the former state of union.

These self-images are recognizable in the analysis of this mother when we deal with her separation anxieties—from her own mother and later from her child—and her wish to return to the early state of symbiosis. Because of adverse conditions in her own childhood, the early state of the symbiosis, as well as the fears of its splitting into component parts, are retained in the unconscious as unusually strong memories, while simultaneously the self-image of the realistic ego is impoverished. The shifting of the emotional investment from the self-image of an ideal ego to one of separated parts results in ambivalence, aggressiveness, and exhibitionism. Exhibitionism serves as a magical gesture—a plea for reincorporation, to allay the separation anxiety and to lessen the inner aggressiveness.

Analysis of a group of these mothers revealed disappointments in their own fathers and a characteristically strong tie to their mothers or their image of their mothers. As a result they were never freed of the strong ambivalent identifications they formed with both parents but especially with the mother. At a later time aspects of these idealized and hostile self-images were projected upon their husbands and stuttering children. A noteworthy fact about the mothers of these women is that they are inwardly dependent and anxious, subject to stubbornness and emotional outbursts into verbal barrages, though outwardly given the appearance of activity and strength. Between mother and daughter there is a lack of steady affective rapport. The effect on the mother of the stutterer is a disturbance of her basic trust in her external environment and in herself, resulting in retardation in her ego integration. The main consequences in her total personality consist of multiple inhibitions including aspects of her feminity, and repression of large quantities of rage and defiance. Further, as mentioned, she confuses her husband and child with her own phallic ideal and castrated self-images, which she projects upon them. Thus she reacts with envy or mocking as the case may be. In sum, her marriage is based on narcissistic identifications and projections.

The Father's Role and the Total Family Problem. As was already stated, the mother's preference is for a man who is of the passive-dependent type, i.e., someone who resembles the part-self with which she operates, rather than her idealized type which is the exaggerated aggressive and exhibitionistic male, patterned after some male member of her own family or an idealization of him. But the father in addition to his flight from his role as husband is also absent, or nearly so, in his father role. When he does relate closely to the boy, as is true not infrequently, it is apt to be in a mothering role in competition with his wife. Furthermore, in subtle ways he also acts as if he were a sibling himself. Often the neurotic disequilibrium of the marital couple first comes to the fore following the advent of the child, and especially after the onset of the stutter. The child's symptom and general reactions activate and bring to the surface manifestations of his own unresolved oedipal and castration anxieties. The father also appersonates the child and projects his own latent anxieties on the child, expressed in various forms. The father's neurotic attitudes toward the child manifest themselves whether there appears to be a united front in handling the child or whether that subject is a constant source of contention.

While the mother often resorts to stressing organic causes and hereditary tendencies, especially paternal, as a form of denying her contribution to the etiology, the father's denial more frequently takes the form of minimizing to outright denying of the symptom. His contention is often that the child will outgrow it, as this was frequently actually the case with him. To the writer such fathers usually seemed to be cryptic stutterers—in the way they handled their now normalized speech and in their character structure. Also, they frequently showed a complete amnesia for their own early stuttering. Their denials and wishes to maintain the status quo in the psychological climate of the family was further evidenced by their increased resistance as the therapy of the child and/or mother progressed. Thus the father makes his contribution to the maintenance of the disorder as the mother does in its initiation. He helps maintain the confusion of the parental roles in the family. By stepping over the line, so to speak, he does not help the normalizing forces, natural or therapeutic, at play in his wife. He provides her with a rationalization to "step over the line" herself and play the father role "by default." On the other hand, the possibility is always available for the father to mitigate the mother's infantile traits and assist in her emotional development. In the same way he can also help the child. Of course, the reverse possibility—of the wife stimulating the husband's emotional maturation—is also there alongside her active pursuit of treatment for the child and herself. So much for the neurosogenesis of stuttering as a total family problem. The implications for therapy will be dealt with separately.

The Self-Images of the Stutterer. The stutterer's character structure and symptom stem primarily from a fixation at an early stage of his ego organization resulting in an ego defect or deviation. Two phases of traumatic influences converge to produce the fixation. In the first, hereditary-constitutional phase, to me the most plausible concept is that certain motor centers in the cerebrum innervating the speech apparatus are ultimately affected. The exact nature and location of the primary pathology is not yet clearly established beyond the likelihood that certain sensory nuclei in the hypothalamus are involved; the effect of this seems to be a diminution in the protective barrier against stimuli, and an overreaction on the motor side. The second stage, the ontogenetic, beginning from birth if not from the prenatal period, consists of anxious, overprotective, ambivalent, maternal influences which are highlighted in a series of separations common to normal child development. There is suggestive evidence that there may be a mutual relation between the two levels of causation, and a similarity in effect amounting to a reinforcement. However that may be, the manifestations of ego fixation may be recognized either by means of their unconscious visual self-images which, together with their mental counterparts—distorted images of objects—behave like multiple personalities or, more simply, in terms of specific ego functions. The self-representations have already been discussed in connection with the personality of the mother, but they are often seen more clearly in the stutterer. Unlike the situation with the hysteric for whom the images represent different selves modeled after individuals who were loved or hated, in the stutterer they represent mainly *partial* "objects." The unbelievable fact of an individual's total ego organization being patterned after the structure and function of a part of the body of another was first discussed by Abraham (2), who named it "identification with a part-object." The identification is the result of inadequate differentiation of the child from the mother's physical self because of the mother's own needs for a sense of oneness and because of her separation anxieties, plus similar needs and anxieties on the part of the stuttering child. Fear of loss of the mother's breast results in the child's identifying itself with that organ. At the later period the idea of losing the phallus produces a similar fixation upon this organ. Fear of losing either organ may stand for the fear of losing the mother.

The stutterer therefore has three unconscious part-object "personalities": breast and phallus in a state of ablation from the body, and the "personality" in identification with the body that was damaged by castration. The fourth "personality," at the opposite pole from the other three, is that of the total person invested with libidinal energy and highly idealized. On the other hand, the feelings about the "self" within the part-objects are those of incompleteness, separatedness, helplessness, even of self-destruction. We say that these images are invested with destructive energy rather than with self-love. The goal or the aim of the "part-object personality" is to attain the attributes of and become this whole person—the narcissistic ego ideal. However, this fantasy cannot be fulfilled in reality because, among other things, it is felt to be fraught with dangers such as the fears of eating up and being eaten up. Derivative fears are those of exhibiting one's self and of being looked at, and the fear that breaking away from the narcissistic ideal will hurt the self and the object. These wishes and fears seek different forms of expression, including speech. In this conflict stuttering is produced.

Character Traits of the Stutterer. Among the chief character traits of the stutterer are inhibitions and passivity. These are the characteristics of a personality functioning unconsciously as an organ rather than a total organism. For example, at one point in the treatment a patient has steadily postponed making a telephone call, ostensibly because he disliked to stutter over the phone. Actually, his stutter resulted from a wish to delay speech indefinitely and, in this instance, to delay a call which in turn would necessitate pursuing an act of curiosity and then planning a course of action, both of which were blocked. Thus the symptom represented an inhibition in the area of speech while at the same time it reflected and fortified a larger inhibition of the total personality. Another stutterer desired a certain vocational goal which he did not obtain and for which he blamed the employer. At this time he began to behave as if he had already obtained the new position, as if in fact he were the employer. Before this it was noted that his stutter reflected attempts to block the articulation of the wish for, and fanciful act of, becoming the other person through passive identification. In both instances, despite differences in the defenses and rationalizations, there were underlying fears of being active in a realistic way, plus defensive inhibitions. Passivity is also often expressed through indecision or waiting before acting. Actually this trait signified waiting for the other person to initiate action, so that both could then act together and be as one. It was also noted that compulsive exhibitionism served as a magical gesture signifying the wish to be incorporated and become the other person. Whether expressed through quiet posturing or through frantic activity, the aim was the same: loss of self by merging and integrating with ideal image.

The futility of many types of activity—we might call them pseudo-activity—could be recognized by the fact that they were modeled after the aforementioned oral aims and oral inhibitions. For example, many stutterers in attempting to advance themselves in realistic situations made many efforts at self-improvement. However, analysis of their activity and of their failure to attain the desired results revealed some fundamental defects in the functioning of the ego and superego. For example, it is essential in solving a problem to have a clear awareness of it plus a feeling that one has a right to solve it. To have a self-image as that of a part of another person is to have a feeling in the face of a task which needs to be performed that one is being dangerously presumptive and provocative. One then feels as a usurper of authority, since the executant functions of the ego were considered to be outside of it. In the same way patients expressed themselves that they had not the "wherewithal," a term frequently used to denote independent action, mind, voice, sexual adequacy, or total self. The result was always hesitation and blocking of action, two formidable character traits in the stutterer. Other inhibitions involved the functions of imagination, volition, and creativity. However, within the sphere of executing an *assignment* in which the individual functioned as a faithful part of a larger entity, considerably greater mobility of thinking and action was available to the stutterer.

In addition to having the "wherewithal" for independent functioning, clear perception of a problem requiring solution is also essential. In these patients such clarity was obscured because many of them acted in real life, and in therapy, as if they were walking in their sleep or acting out a dream.

This state was often an amalgam between a wish for complete passivity and a wish for escape from the destructive consequences of such extreme passivity. In real life one often noted their wishful thinking and day-dreaming, associated with inhibition and general ineffectuality. It was as if they were acting out their wish to "sleep away" their lives, a combination of nursing and withdrawal. This was often demonstrated in the course of the analysis through their amnesia for the content of their therapeutic hours, their frequent actual drowsiness and occasional falling asleep. In one form or another inhibitions saddled many of the varied aspects of volition, imagination, or action. Blocking at every new step in making use of the various ego functions was in striking parallel to blocking at the beginning of words and sentences—the essence of the stutter. It seemed as if almost all activity, mental and physical, had come to bear the imprint of the aggressive drive, the force of which first emerged during nursing. Later problems from anal and phallic levels resulting in blocking and inhibition could also be recognized, though these secondary phenomena became significant for speech and personality only after they fell under the dominance of the orality, or were "oralized."

A basic mechanism of learning and of growth is that of identification. Unconsciously it is perceived as an act of incorporation which is predominantly active and selective. The process can attain its final phase—that of assimilation—only if it is experienced as a friendly and symbolic rather than literal act. However, this is rendered difficult, if not impossible, when, as in the stutterer, there is an oral fixation. Such a fixation lends both a literalness and a hostile quality to an essentially passive experience. Identification is thus experienced as being nursed, yielding, being consumed and overpowered and even annihilated. Under such circumstances, the individual often falls prey to shame or guilt, or even to fears of physical attack, the last representing the well-known homosexual panic. Thus the identification is not completed and the personality is not integrated. The individual retains an ambivalent, oscillating attitude toward another with whom he wishes to have a consistently close and warm relationship. Thus full identification for the stutterer seems to mean getting too close for comfort. He cannot complete it, has to separate and create a safe distance. In turn this separation is difficult for him to bear and maintain because it flies in the face of one of his earliest and severest traumatic experiences—separation and its accompanying anxiety. This trauma produces an excessive need for clinging—this closeness is too uncomfortable—a resultant separation and distance that is safe but unbearable—leading to clinging again, thus closing a vicious circle.

Some of the character traits of the stutterer are highlighted, and may be best described, within the context of the treatment situation. The treatment here considered is psychoanalysis or psychoanalytically oriented psychotherapy. However, more specific references to the therapy as such will be taken up later. We must return now to the ubiquitous problem of identification and separation. In fact, the two phenomena overlap. Mental identification is the greatest degree of closeness possible with another human being. At the same time actual separation is equally necessary, for in external reality one cannot literally be another person but can only emulate the role of another. At one point in treatment a certain degree of distance from and objectivity toward the material is quite essential. This implies a certain separation or distance from the therapist; thus separation becomes again a determining factor in treatment. Here again much stubborn resistance, stemming from the fixation on passivity and wishes for union, is encountered, requiring repeated working through. At this time transient symptoms may come to the fore: a tendency to drowse and fall asleep momentarily during treatment hours and a tendency toward depersonalization. This is a form of withdrawal of libido from the periphery of the ego which is in contact with reality, also termed "decathexis of the ego boundaries" (**8**).

Another trait which is highlighted in the course of the treatment is again the fact that the dominant self-image of the personality is that of a mouth. Treatment attempts to change this self-image for another which is that of a total person. But in doing this the treatment depends upon a certain degree of independent, i.e., active mental work on the part of the patient. In accordance with his character, however, the patient clings to the magical tendency to swallow isolated interpretations and regard them as final answers; for a long time he cannot synthesize interpretations into usable tools for further observation, validation, and action. His passivity further interferes with his comprehension and the application of insight by blocking the expression of affects which is crucial for acquisition of insight. Furthermore, the expressions of passivity seldom appear directly. They have to be worked out through their defense reactions, which were maintained by pleasure premiums. An individual's character is the sum total of his habitual traits, and these are based to a large extent upon stratifications of defenses. In analysis these defenses amount to the resistance to this treatment, though they are not quite identical.

The following are some of the major defense-and-resistance-reactions in the character structure of the stutterer which fall under more definite nosological classifications. The first to be considered is the schizoid defense or schizoidism. It is the most stable, comparatively the least painful, and the most frequent. It provides a defensive distance against fears in interpersonal relations. Love objects are unconsciously enjoyed through their mental representations, though actual relationships were superficial and offered a minimum of conscious pleasure. One may also characterize this as introversion; I have termed this affective state "anhedonia" (26).

The masochistic defense is the more complicated and baffling and has many motivations, two of which are outstanding. The wish for oneness with the phallic mother produces two diametrically opposite fears: the fear of complete regression into passivity—a kind of inertia or death—and the fear of identifying and being stimulated into activity and, finally, separation. Against these fears the patient would defend himself by a double identification. He would unconsciously maintain a passive attachment to a "traumatizing" mother figure, a distorted version of his actual mother, because it was she who first induced separation anxiety and passivity in him through her active feeding and sudden withdrawals; it was she who also actively dominated him by her control. He became as one with her—treated himself aggressively and harshly as he felt she would treat him—and projected this image onto others. These others then became authentic to him as his own mother. His wished-for ideal mother figures were not as authentic as she, being part of the dangerous outside world which could not be trusted. The mistrust was largely the externalization of the inner mental life. Besides, the masochistic relationship offered a vent for much pent-up aggression through complaints expressed or unexpressed. One could not feel or express one's self in that manner toward a nonfrustrating parental figure, at least not without much guilt and depression. Therefore this defense protected the patient from separation anxiety, gave him the illusion of activity, and served other needs as mentioned above. Thus it offered him much unconscious satisfaction which overbalanced the consciously felt dominations, frustrations, and failures.

Another important trait of the stutterer is his compulsiveness or compulsive "pseudo-activity." It is a kind of busy work to avoid anxiety associated with waiting or with real activity and to ascertain the wished-for incorporation, following which it was hoped endless passivity might be enjoyed under more ideal circumstances. Further, provocative behavior aims, among other goals, at caricaturing genuine productivity and avoiding it. Related to pseudo-aggression is "phallic" exhibitionism, the character trait of acting as if one's body were a phallus. These patients like to strut or to appear to be doing something for others, yet their real aim is to be incorporated by, and be fused with, the onlookers. This exhibitionism with a passive aim frequently produces phobias for speech situations. One such patient whose stuttering was hardly noticeable had a tremendous fear of saying even a few words in public. He fantasied himself in a situation where everyone would peek at him. He visualized himself standing erect, his heart and blood vessels throbbing severely. Finally, he imagined himself suddenly dropping limp and dying. It was possible for him to recognize in this imagery fantasies of sexual scenes wherein he identified with his father, particularly his father's phallus, and at the end the scene would end with punishment in the form of death. In other such fantasies he would see himself in the role of the mother figure, the scene terminating again in injury, bleeding, and death. Phallic loss was also equated with mental loss. He would then have the fantasy of becoming a patient in a mental hospital. The proof that his passive wishes were tied up with his stuttering and speech phobia came when under pressure to present a report before a business conference he was suddenly struck with an idea which broke the impasse: he would do it for his little boy's sake. What actually occurred was that he ejected his passive self and projected it upon his small son. He was then able to function through his active self-image without fear of intrusion of his passive self and wishes in what was for him an unconsciously tempting environment.

Stuttering, like any other symptom, is capable of giving a secondary gain—a satisfaction, almost always unconscious, derived from a symptom after it is formed and apart from the deeper satisfactions that have caused it to form. This gain accounts for much resistance in treatment. It also explains the basis for many stutterers not seeking treatment. A surgeon once remarked to a colleague that his patients, especially the women who admired him very much, referred to his stutter as cute. He, it might be noted, was not in treatment. In this secondary way, other emotional needs find expression, particularly anger, revenge, control, and even a quest for love.

An important problem in the character as in the therapy is the phobic avoidance, or the anticipatory anxiety about speech situations. This is frequently a serious problem and must be faced from the beginning. The phobic avoidance can be fought when the stutterer is in treatment. Patients sometimes fight it only in order to win the esteem of the therapist, rather than for the intrinsic benefit to be derived from having it resolved. Outside of treatment, it is impossible for stutterers, as for other patients with phobias, on their own consciously and regularly to resist phobias through will power. They can be resolved by means of psychoanalysis only.

Psychoanalytic Therapy for the Stutterer

We come now to the problem of therapy. Inasmuch as psychoanalysis views stuttering as a narcissistic neurosis, and because its insights strike at the roots of the disorder, its treatment should be psychoanalytically based. We are here using the term "psychoanalysis" in the sense of a basic science of human motivation and behavior rather than as the well-known specific form of psychotherapy. However, this radical therapy in its pristine form cannot be recommended for all patients who stutter. The reason for this is that not all stutterers (nor all patients with sundry neurotic symptoms—but some stutterers particularly) meet the requirements of relative maturity prerequisite for its employment. Some of these requirements include the age; sufficient motivation; sufficient capacity for making use of the therapy as an active experience; the control of "acting out" outside the therapy which is derogatory to it; the ability to relinquish secondary gains from the symptom; last, but not inconsiderable, sufficient maturity in the parents, when the patient is still under their influence, to effect requisite coöperation and avoid insurmountable obstacles. I hasten to add that for those who do not meet the requirements for the classical psychoanalytic therapy there are modified forms of this therapy generally referred to as analytically oriented psychotherapy. This differs from analysis proper in that there is here more direct ego support, the therapeutic relationship as such is essentially utilized rather than analyzed, and the therapeutic goal is generally limited to one or several broad areas. But it must be emphasized that, as the name indicates, the basic understanding of the disorder is identical in both techniques.

Exposition of the classical psychoanalytic technique is beyond the scope of this chapter. However, in recent years considerable work has been done in the adaptation and application of analytic principles to general psychotherapy. Since it has been my privilege to contribute to such work in the field of stuttering, I should like to mention it. One such adaptation I refer to as "the therapeutic team."

The Therapeutic Team: An Adaptation for the Stuttering Child. It was possible to cut a pattern from insights I gathered from the analyses of stutterers and their parents and adapt it to the therapeutic needs of the child stutterer who for one or several reasons cannot be analyzed. It may be called therapy on the clinic level, in the optimal sense of that term. Though the writer has attempted this approach in two public clinics,[3] he has given it a more intensive trial as part of his private practice. In this type of team two therapists are assigned to each case. The therapists are analysts, psychiatrists, and/or psychiatric caseworkers. Psychologists were utilized in the initial diagnostic survey. Like the psychiatrists, the casework therapists employed had been psychoanalyzed and had advanced

[3] Jewish Board of Guardians, Child Guidance Dept.; New York University College of Medicine, Speech Service of the Psychiatric Clinic.

experience in psychiatric casework. All therapists were regularly supervised by the writer. When this work began psychologists with background in clinical experience and applied psychotherapy comparable to that of psychiatric-casework therapists were few in number, though recently more have been acquiring it.

The decision to have separate therapists for mother and child from the start was based entirely on the logic of the mother's sense of oneness with her child. Experience has proved further that she was able to relinquish her child if she received a substitute for it, in treatment, in the form of her own therapist. This was especially true when the child (a boy in 80 percent of the cases) was assigned to a male therapist. Conversely, when he was given a female therapist the mother frequently interrupted the treatment. We learned further that the mother did very well with a woman therapist, because she was thereby offered a substitutive experience and a basis for a better identification to counteract her own identification with a narcissistic and masochistic woman—her own mother. The one exception was the so-called borderline type of mother, whose personality was severely damaged and who harbored a strong delusional component in her make-up. She was less difficult with a male therapist. The girl stutterer did about equally well with either male or female therapist, though here also the mother's attitude was significant. However, it was imperative that the therapist of the mother have the conviction that the mother is a neurotic individual who has a legitimate and often urgent therapeutic need in her own right. Some therapists, possessing great ability for working with children and for identifying with them, were unable to reach these mothers because they lacked such conviction and could not empathize with them.

The initial diagnostic survey began with separate and joint interviews of the child, mother, and father, totaling at least four or five hours. Projective psychological tests were given at first to mother and child; later the father was included. The main objective for obtaining the anamnestic and observational facts was to aid in choosing the most suitable treatment plan in each instance. Determining factors included severity of the neurosis, degree of flexibility and treatability of each patient, motivation, and practical elements. The following treatment plans were employed.

1. *Analysis or psychotherapy of the mother, as the only therapy.* Surprisingly, experience proved that this method was efficient for the removal of the stutter as well as for very important characterological changes in the children without direct treatment of them. It was particularly efficient for the younger children but also gave positive results in some adolescents.
2. *Analysis or psychotherapy of the mother and simultaneous psychotherapy of the child.* The children in this category ranged from ages 4 to 15.

3. *Analysis or psychotherapy of the mother and concurrent analysis or psychotherapy of the child.* Children in this series ranged in age from middle through late adolescence. Even in this group it was found that the therapy of the mother facilitated and shortened the course of treatment of the child.

In the beginning of this experience the fathers were not treated formally but were called in occasionally by the therapist of the child in relation to special problems, especially when his behavior was grossly injurious to the child or to the therapy. I will return to this aspect after discussion of the treatment of the mother.

The mother frequently came with considerable insight about certain aspects of her relationship to the stuttering child. Other mothers were able to verbalize for the first time during the diagnostic survey their recognition of the causal relation between the child's stutter and the family constellation, especially the mother-child relation. Frequently this insight came to her as a shock and surprise. Her unawareness that the stutterer was felt to be a part of her was the result both of her repressions and of her acting out. Some mothers accepted submissively the suggestion that they be treated; up to that point they had masochistically resigned themselves to their "destiny." Others, on the other hand, were quite enthusiastic that they were about to get treatment for which they were intuitively looking forward. As the treatment of the mother was mandatory, the contact was terminated at the conclusion of the survey whenever she refused to be involved in the therapy. A few exceptions were made when the children were in middle or late adolescence.

The first task in the therapy of the mother was to work through her acceptance of her mixed feelings about her own need for treatment, a need that became more apparent in the discussions of her relationship to her own mother. Next in importance was the exposing and working through of her pent-up anger and anxiety connected with unresolved deep disappointments and frustrations at the hands of her mother. She became aware of these emotions in discussions regarding her separation from her mother and also from her stuttering child. Her fear of separation was frequently covered by her masochistic submission. Much time and energy had to be spent to uncover these emotions and mental structures. This effort was preliminary to attempts in the development of a realistic sense of self and the formation of new identifications. Her own relationship to her mother was a uniquely important emotional tie, even though this principle is a truism in the most varied disorders. The presence of these strong ties was very subtly disguised because usually the control exerted was quite subtle. These ties and the fears of separation were also related to the patient's rejection of the feminine role, the envy of the male role, and to involvement of the child within the framework of her castration anxiety. She was helped to differentiate between infantile and feminine dependency. One major consequence of this is that she was helped to view her husband not as a disappointing mother image but as a real person to whom she could turn to share in the common problems of rearing their child.

We return now to the problem of bringing the husband, as a real person, into the therapeutic picture. Helping the husband became especially important at the time the mother was ready to work out her relationship with him. The marriage was generally characterized by sado-masochism and frigidity. As a result of the working through of this relationship, a psychological shift frequently took place in it so that the husband was willing to try to relate to the child and the wife in a more positive way. Two approaches were used with the husband-father. At the start of the treatment, when he was in flight as father and husband, he had been deliberately excluded from treatment. Now, to aid him, he was deliberately brought in by the boy's therapist for an occasional interview. With the shifts in the mother's and boy's personalities, positive, constructive qualities in the father were freed for promoting the treatment. He was greatly encouraged as his role was strengthened and he was given the feeling that he was the bulwark of the family, and that he was needed by the therapist to stand by in the treatment of the boy. The several interviews by the boy's therapist exploited the immediate objectives of giving the father information and explanations about the boy's behavior and about the changes that would result in his treatment. In a good many instances this approach was sufficient, but in some cases it was necessary to bring in the father for therapy for himself in a more formal way. This was inevitable when the father developed an active resistance to the treatment as a result of changes in his son and wife.

Not much need be said about the treatment of the child. As far as the presenting symptom is concerned, it was not attacked directly, as other presenting symptoms are not attacked directly in analysis or psychotherapy. Therefore speech therapy per se could not be integrated with it. However, in view of the special symptomatology and characterological features presented by the stuttering child, certain modifications in the treatment had to be introduced. Because of his marked separation anxiety an informal and completely permissive atmosphere was necessary. The therapist had himself to speak more frequently and freely and to avoid pressing the child to speak. Such permissiveness was also necessary in order to free the child's expressions of anger and aggression through play. The effect of such expressions was particularly noteworthy in the lessening of the stutter after the child acted out some biting, chewing, or smearing activities in relation to toys. The stutter reappeared later in the treatment, especially in the process of working out oedipal conflicts. Frequently the child's behavior regressed quite deeply in therapy, and yet he was able to show well-contained behavior at home.

After a couple of months, sometimes after six months, there was much less concern in the family about the stutter. In a number of instances it had disappeared before that time. The parents were frequently irritated by periods of increased aggressiveness or recurrence of enuresis. Interestingly, the smooth progress of the child's treatment was often an indication that the mother's treatment was progressing smoothly. It was also noted that her regressive behavior in treatment preceded the child's regression, and further, that by this time the mother was generally aware that she precipitated the regression in the child.

There was considerable acting out by mother and child during treatment. This was due to their basic symbiosis and because of similarities in their attitude about speech as action. The child was thus made to "speak" or act for the mother, and when he was separated by his therapy the mother acted out herself—toward her husband and toward the therapist. In this way her relationships were observed to shift during treatment. Occasionally the mother's negative reactions constituted a threat to the therapy, but it was generally not insurmountable.

One reason the mother of the stutterer is placed in the center of the therapeutic pattern is that in seeking help for her child she was really seeking it for herself. Usually this was her first indirect application for help for herself, since by that time she had had to endure two severe reactivations of her early separation anxieties: her marriage and the birth of her child. The separation of the mother and son from the state of unconscious fusion freed him and promoted a growth of his ego. The fundamental psychological shift in the family constellation is the result of a loosening of the mother's ties to narcissistic love objects and a turn toward real love objects. In this the working through of her separation anxiety was crucial (21). Inasmuch as this is a basic complex in the disorder, the mother had to be "seduced" into therapy for herself, although she came seeking it for her child. This indirect treatment of the child is frequently more efficacious than direct therapy because it deals squarely with the basic pathogenesis. An important tool in the therapy of the mother is the interpretation and the working through of transference phenomena. On the other hand, the analysis of complex symptoms and dream interpretations was avoided in the team approach.

The therapeutic team does not aim to cure stuttering per se. The aim rather is to normalize the psychological constellation of the family—the family climate—so as to free each member for further ego maturation. In these circumstances, the stutter ceases to be a family phobia. It loses the excessive charge of anxiety with which it is invested by each member of the family. It may then disappear altogether, or if the stutter reappears it is regarded as an index of some passing emotional disturbance and its intensity is thereby diminished. The family then reacts to it as lightly as to the iterations that appear in the speech of many nonstutterers.

Group Therapy Approaches. In the last few years I have had some small experience with the application of psychoanalytic principles and insights to treatment of patients in a group. One such group consisted of adult stutterers. It was surprisingly short-lived compared with the lengthy analytic therapy of individual patients, and its revelations were equally surprising. The group included 4 men within an age range of 10 years, of diverse occupations and social-economic levels. The sessions were held twice weekly and lasted for 10 weeks, after which time the group dissolved itself spontaneously and quite rapidly. The discussions were focused essentially on the historical factors leading up to their getting into treatment. When these were unearthed, found to be identical in all four patients, and their multiple meanings aired, the treatment apparently had fulfilled its purpose and was over. Undoubtedly resistance to further elaboration and individualization which appeared imminent was another factor contributing to the termination of the therapy. It was revealed that the predominant basis in each patient of this group for seeking treatment was a need to solve some problems connected with being, and the wish to become, a father. Although this was true of this group, obviously this fact cannot be generalized. But a significant aspect of stuttering is thereby demonstrable. It is meaningful only as a reflection of an underlying mental conflict or disequilibrium. When the latter threatens to emerge in consciousness the stutter worsens and/or becomes a major concern. When the threat is removed either by resolution in consciousness or by the opposite—a deeper re-repression—the stutter either lessens in intensity, disappears, or ceases to be a matter of anxious concern. On the other hand, when the patient is not ready or cannot in a foreseeable future face the conflict, he is not prepared to give up the symptom. Despite his complaints about it he needs it as a shield to protect him against something much more unpalatable or threatening. Hence not all adult stutterers are *ipso facto* to be referred for therapy or are, indeed, treatable. Therefore, for a large number of adult stutterers who cannot have analysis for a variety of reasons, a group method such as this—in contrast to those group methods which attack the symptom directly but vainly—offers considerable though less basic help in a relatively short period of time. Though some have had considerable experience with this method, it is presently still at an early stage of development.

I have also experimented with the group therapy of children who stutter. Here, however, the group approach was employed as adjunctive to individual therapy. The usefulness of the group therapy included an opportunity for a fuller expression of transference reactions, and a possibility for working through the speech phobia and the multiple meanings of the speech symptom. The group was helpful through ego bolstering as a result of identification and experience within the special milieu. This is yet another beginning approach to a therapy founded on basic psychodynamics which offers therapeutic promise for the future.

Concluding Remarks

In sum, psychoanalysis has unearthed a number of fundamental links in the chain of causation in stuttering. Considerable remains to be done in this discipline. The ego-defect group of disorders to which stuttering belongs is as yet insufficiently understood. Compared to other disorders, this group is more or less at the frontier of our knowledge. However, already the approach through the ego, or the structural orientation, furnishes us the most comprehensive view of stuttering we have had so far. Furthermore, it lends integration, and therefore more meaning, to earlier psychoanalytic findings, which to some nonanalysts may appear as conflicting theories of stuttering. Psychoanalysis, dealing with deep phenomena which operate unconsciously, aims at elucidating fundamental meanings of inhibitions and symptoms; it aims also at disclosing the nature of the disorganizing influences and the bases for their maintenance. Manifest phenomenological expressions of this disorder are obviously an indispensable part of our knowledge of it; they have a further usefulness for checking the validity of our concepts from the depth and for stimulating us to make the latter more comprehensible and comprehensive. But standing isolated from their roots, manifest phenomena offer us very little indeed for understanding, for treatment, and for prevention. They cannot substitute for the knowledge of unconscious motivations and for unconscious mental processes. Neither can the realm of the unconscious mental life be skipped over, overlooked, or denied in other ways. One can do that only at the peril of sterility in comprehending phenomena of human behavior in general and of psychosomatic disorders in particular. In its aims psychoanalysis stands altogether within the tradition of medicine.

That tradition is that in the treatment and prevention of physical, mental, and psychosomatic disorders, the pursuit of primary causation to elucidate basic concepts of disease is the first and fundamental requirement. In that pursuit and in the application of therapeutic procedures, medicine does not confine itself to physicians. It has used and will continue to use various scientists both in the search for causation and in the application of therapeutic procedures. There is only one condition for their employment—that their work must be integrated within the framework and the fundamental findings of that tradition. With the removal of the obstacles toward considering the phenomena of the unconscious mental life, we shall not be confronted, as we are now fairly regularly, with newer and ever newer theories of stuttering based upon a few isolated surface manifestations. With the removal of the prejudice against the unconscious mental life, genuine interdisciplinary progress will become possible. We have the tools at hand to lift the syndrome of stuttering from the realm of theories, mysteries, and riddles.

References

1. Abraham, K., "The first pregenital stage of the libido," in *Selected Papers*, London, Hogarth Press, 1927.
2. Abraham, K., "The process of introjection in melancholia," in *Selected Papers*, London, Hogarth Press, 1927.
3. Brill, A. A., "Speech disturbances in nervous and mental diseases," *Quarterly Journal of Speech Education*, IX, 1923.
4. Coriat, I. H., *Stammering: A Psychoanalytic Interpretation*, New York, Nervous and Mental Disease Monographs, 1927.
5. Coriat, I. H., "The dynamics of stammering," *Psychoanalytic Quarterly*, II, 1933.
6. Coriat, I. H., "The psychoanalytic concept of stammering," *The Nervous Child*, II, 1943.
7. Federn, P., personal communication (discussion transcription in A. A. Brill Library of the New York Psychoanalytic Society).
8. Federn, P., *Ego Psychology and the Psychoses*, New York, Basic Books, 1952.
9. Fenichel, O., "Early mental development: The archaic ego," ch. 4 in *The Psychoanalytic Theory of Neuroses*, New York, Norton, 1945.
10. Fenichel, O., "Pregenital conversions," ch. 15 in *The Psychoanalytic Theory of Neuroses*, New York, Norton, 1945.
11. Freud, S., "Analysis terminable and interminable," in *Collected Papers*, V, London, Hogarth Press, 1937.
12. Freud, S., discussion of paper by V. Tausk, "The origin of the 'influencing machine' in schizophrenia," *Psychoanalytic Quarterly*, II, 1933.

13. Freud, S., *The Ego and the Id*, London, Hogarth Press, 1935.
14. Freud, S., *Three Essays on the Theory of Sexuality*, Standard Ed., VII, London, Hogarth Press, 1905.
15. Freud, S., *The Interpretation of Dreams*, Standard Ed., IV and V, London, Hogarth Press, 1900.
16. Freud, S., *Moses and Monotheism*, New York, Knopf, 1939.
17. Freud, S., *Outline of Psychoanalysis*, New York, Norton, 1949.
18. Freud, S., *The Problem of Anxiety*, New York, Norton, 1936.
19. Freud, S., *The Psychopathology of Everyday Life*, New York, Macmillan, 1930.
20. Freud, S., and Breuer, J., *Studies on Hysteria*, Standard Ed., II, London, Hogarth Press, 1895.
21. Glauber, H. M., "The impact of a shift in the psychological constellation of the family on the treatment of a stuttering boy," *American Journal of Orthopsychiatry*, XXIII, 1953.
22. Glauber, I. P., "A deterrent in the study and practice of medicine," *Psychoanalytic Quarterly*, XXII, 1953.
23. Glauber, I. P., "Dynamic therapy for the stutterer," in *Specialized Techniques in Psychotherapy*, C. Bychowski and J. L. Despert (eds.), New York, Basic Books, 1952.
24. Glauber, I. P., "Ego development of the character of the stutterer," abstract, *Psychoanalytic Quarterly*, XVIII, 1949.
25. Glauber, I. P., "Freud's contributions on stuttering: Their relations to some current insights," *Journal of the American Psychoanalytic Association*, VI, 1958.
26. Glauber, I. P., "Observations on a primary form of anhedonia," *Psychoanalytic Quarterly*, XVIII, 1949.
27. Glauber, I. P., "On the meaning of agoraphilia," *Journal of the American Psychoanalytic Association*, VIII, 1954.
28. Glauber, I. P., "The mother in the etiology of stuttering," abstract, *Psychoanalytic Quarterly*, XX, 1951.
29. Glauber, I. P., "The rebirth motif in homosexuality and its teleological significance," *International Journal of Psychoanalysis*, XXXVII, 1956.
30. Glauber, I. P., "The use of projective tests in a private service for the treatment of the functional speech disorders," *Journal of the Hillside Hospital*, III, 1954.
31. Jones, Ernest, *The Life and Work of Sigmund Freud*, II, New York, Basic Books, 1955.
32. Laufer, M. W., Dinhoff, E., and Solomons, G., "Hyperkinetic impulse disorders in children's behavior problems," *Psychosomatic Medicine*, XIX, 1957.
33. Lewin, B. D., "The body as phallus," *Psychoanalytic Quarterly*, II, 1933.

CONFLICT THEORY OF STUTTERING

JOSEPH SHEEHAN, Ph.D.

Associate Professor of Psychology, University of California, Los Angeles; Consultant in Clinical Psychology, Veterans Administration Mental Hygiene Clinic, Los Angeles; Fellow of the American Speech and Hearing Association and the American Psychological Association; Diplomate in Clinical Psychology, American Board of Examiners in Professional Psychology; Associate Editor, Journal of Speech and Hearing Disorders.

Conflict Theory of Stuttering

Research and Theory

CONFLICT in some form is a basic element in every human problem. Most of us can conceal our fears and conflicts a good part of the time, as we are taught to do. Though our speech may reveal our inner selves to some extent, we learn where necessary to mask our voices as we mask our faces. The stutterer is robbed of this dignity. He wears his conflict, if not on his sleeve, in his voice and when he tries to speak reveals all too clearly the turmoil within.

Even so, what the stutterer shows when he struggles with words is not the major portion of the iceberg which goes to make up his handicap.[1] Far larger and more destructive is the portion which lies underneath the surface. The more he tries to spare his listener by covering up, the larger this unseen handicap becomes. He goes through anguished rehearsal of many a speaking crisis that never comes. Because he never knows with certainty just what the next situation will bring, he becomes a gambler with his self-esteem as the stake. He may be racked with self-doubt and anxiety even during apparently fluent moments. Even the listener seldom experiences the relief that the occasional fluent moments might bring, because he also knows that at any time the awkward blockings may return.

The listener, as well as the stutterer, is caught in a conflict. What should he do when the stutterer is struggling? Should he acknowledge in his behavior that the speaker is having trouble, or help him pretend it isn't there? Should he watch the stutterer, or avert his gaze? Should he help

[1] A stutterer may be defined as a person who shows, to a degree that sets him off from the rest of the population, any one or more of the following groups of symptoms: (1) blockings, stickings, grimaces, forcings, repetitions, prolongations, or other rhythm breaks or interruptions in the forward flow of speech; (2) fear or anticipation of blockings, fear of inability to speak, or related symptoms prior to words or to speaking situations; (3) a self-concept which includes a picture of himself as a stutterer, a stammerer, speech blocker, or a person lacking normal speech fluency.

the stutterer with a word which has become painfully obvious, or let him flounder? Not knowing much about the disorder, he gets his cue from the stutterer himself. And as a result, through a vicious circle of stutterer-listener interaction, he usually concludes it is something very shameful.

Compared to other speech disorders, a vast amount of research effort has been expended on the problem of stuttering. Prodigious effort has gone into the pursuit of pathways—perhaps necessary to the exploration of the maze—which have ended up in blind alleys. Probably the most famous such *umweg* is the cerebral-dominance-neurological-dysphemia theory developed by Travis during the 1930's and still echoing among us as the elusive predisposition concept.

Yet, from the mountain of effort there have come a number of good molehills of fact. Now there is much that is known, much that is partially known, still more that is strongly suspected, as well as a vast unknown area in the exploration of stuttering. It has become possible in recent years, not only from advances in speech pathology but from even more striking advances in clinical psychology and learning theory, to formulate in far more systematic terms a comprehensive theory of stuttering and to recommend treatment procedures stemming from this approach.

Observations of various kinds of conflicts operating on the stutterer have been made by various authorities, all the way back to the German writer Wyneken (52), who considered the stutterer a *sprachzweifler,* a "speech-doubter." The stutterer was like one seized with uncertainty at the moment of attempting a leap, therefore unable to make the leap with necessary aplomb.

Johnson and Knott described stuttering in terms of a configuration which involved a conflict between the communicative impulse and the impulse to inhibit expected stuttering (21). Related observations on conflict have been reviewed by the author as part of earlier publications of the approach-avoidance conflict theory of stuttering (32, 36, 38).

Wide divergence has appeared among various writers as to the nature of the conflict and its relation to the stuttering. For some it has been a conflict over gratification of instincts, for others a conscious interference with an automatic process, for still others a rivalry between cortical hemispheres.

Few who have ever observed a stutterer closely will dispute the essential accuracy of Wyneken's observation. Yet until recently very little systematic attention had been given to the role of conflict in stuttering, and no one seemed ready to build a theory based solidly on conflict as an essential explanation for the disorder or to relate treatment to such a theory. The six main theories of stuttering historically listed by Van Riper under the headings educational, imagery, inhibitory, neurotic, psychoanalytic, and neurological (45) give little attention to conflict theory.

The present writing concerns largely an expansion and revision of a theory of stuttering as an approach-avoidance conflict, in terms of conflicting urges to speak and to hold back from speaking.

Because the stutterer's conflict can be seen to operate at many levels, the theory as stated here represents a blend of several approaches—of psychoanalytic and learning theories with modern personality theory. As stated here, the approach-avoidance conflict theory of stuttering involves primarily its own levels of analysis; it is not designed to refute other theories with which it may be compatible or to deny the validity of other approaches to the complex problem of stuttering.

The theory does seek to integrate advances in clinical psychology and learning theory into a systematic theory of stuttering and to relate treatment procedures logically to a systematic theory.

Stuttering as an Approach-Avoidance Conflict: Basic Statement

In terms of its simplest aspects, what we have to account for in stuttering is a *momentary blocking*. In speaking the stutterer is stuck for a time, but not for all time; to be adequate, a theory must be able to account for the release from blocking as well as for the blocking itself.

Two propositions have been stated to account for these basic features of stuttering behavior:

1. The Conflict Hypothesis. The stutterer stops whenever conflicting approach and avoidance tendencies reach an equilibrium.
2. The Fear-Reduction Hypothesis. The occurrence of stuttering reduces the fear which elicited it, so that *during* the block there is sufficient reduction in fear-motivated avoidance to resolve the conflict, permitting release of the blocked word.

In his "Experimental Studies of Conflict" (25) Miller listed four basic kinds: (1) approach-approach conflict; (2) avoidance-approach conflict; (3) simple approach-avoidance conflict; (4) double approach-avoidance conflict. Of the four, by far the most significant in human problems is double approach-avoidance conflict. We have all been confronted with two alternatives, each of which contained both positive and negative features. Going ahead on any course of action is difficult, for once the decision is reached, the alternative course becomes more attractive.

Double approach-avoidance conflict is at the heart of the stuttering problem. This kind of conflict includes both avoidance-avoidance and simple approach-avoidance conflict. For a stutterer both speech and silence have positive and negative features.

The Fear of Silence

The conflict in stuttering is not simply between speaking versus inhibiting expected stuttering (19). In the double approach-avoidance conflict situation, there is both a conflict between speaking and not speaking and between being silent or not being silent. The avoidance does not come primarily from the fear of stuttering as such but from the competition between the alternative possibilities of speech and silence, with the stuttering a resultant of this conflict.

Guilt can become attached to speaking, to silence, and to stuttering. Caught as he is in double approach-avoidance conflict, the stutterer is caught between two choices, each of which threatens the bitter along with the sweet. He can speak, thus achieving his aim of communication, but at a cost of the shame and guilt he has learned to attach to his stuttering. Or he can remain silent, abandon communication, and suffer the frustration and guilt that such a retreat carries with it. These choices are depicted in Figure 1, showing stuttering as a double approach-avoidance conflict.

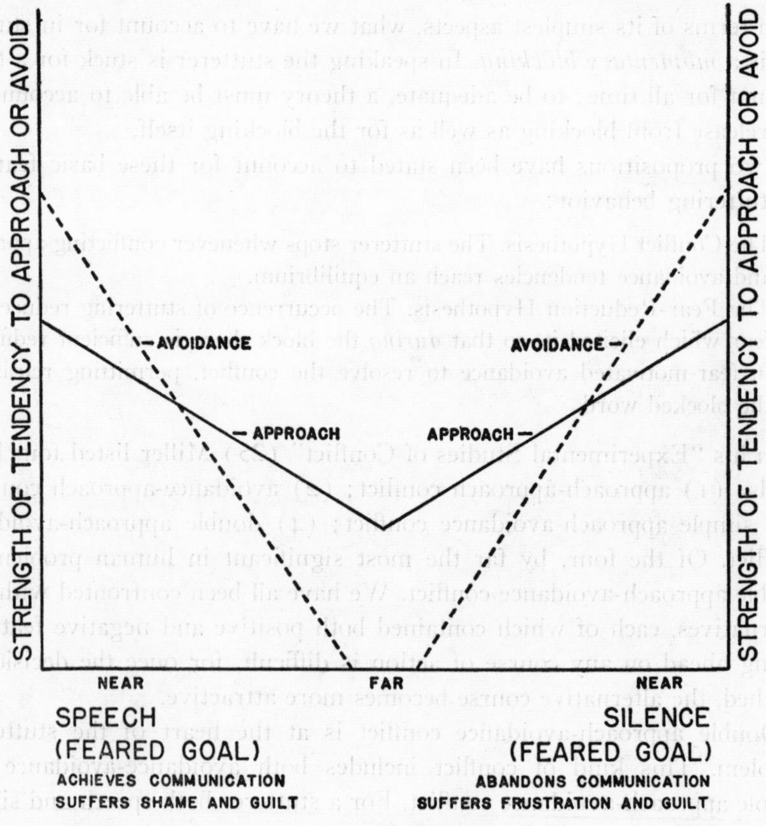

Figure 1. Stuttering as a Double Approach-Avoidance Conflict.

So the stutterer has a choice between shame or frustration. And guilt has become attached to either choice.

Speaking holds the promise of communication but the threat of stuttering; silence eliminates temporarily the threat involved in speaking, but at a cost of abandonment of communication and consequent frustration. Many stutterers show a *fear of silence,* and filibuster furiously in their speech to keep any pause from becoming dangerously long. Since most stuttering occurs initially, then silence plus initiation of speech becomes a conditioned cue for the painful experiences of anxiety and stuttering.

Why should silence come to be feared? In terms of conditioning theory, there is a very good reason for this. As studies by Brown (8) have shown, and as nearly all stutterers have found from experience, most stuttering occurs on initial sounds and more stuttering occurs on the first word of the sentence. Silences seem to freeze the stutterer, and he has trouble breaking the ice.

Since moments of silence precede moments of stuttering with the regularity of Pavlov's bell, it is not surprising that silence as such becomes a cue for arousal of anxiety in the stutterer. Many stutterers show such a dread of silence that they adopt filibustering symptoms into their stuttering patterns.

There is yet another reason, on a different level of analysis, why the stutterer should fear displaying silence. To be mute, in dreams, is a symbol of death; the dead are often represented this way in bereavement dreams. The use of silence for hostility, in those who dare not express it more openly, has been experienced, at least on the receiving end, by all of us. Catatonics are said to be rigid because they are holding their destructive impulses in check, and mute because they have turned their death wishes, originally felt toward others, toward themselves. Periods of silence may arouse guilt in the stutterer because of the hostility implied in the act. Fluent speech itself, as well as stuttering, may equally imply hostility and correspondingly produce guilt.

What of the conflict and fear-reduction hypotheses? The conflict hypothesis stated that when the stutterer reached a point of equilibrium or near equilibrium, he would either stop or oscillate in the zone where the gradients cross. But the forces apparently don't stay in equilibrium. If stuttering results from a conflict, how is the conflict resolved? Either the approach tendency must become stronger or the avoidance tendency must be reduced; the second possibility appears more likely. As the stutterer goes from point A, the beginning of the block, to point B, the ending of it, he stops momentarily, and then somehow the forces change so that he can go ahead again. How does he get from A to B? What happens? Most conspicuously, the stuttering itself happens. Apparently, the occurrence of stuttering has an effect on the fear and on the avoidance. To explain how stuttering may come to have the property of reducing the fear which elicited it, three hypotheses may be stated: (1) A major portion of the stutterer's fear stems from efforts to hide the difficulty. Once the stuttering has begun to occur, the thing the person has tried to avoid has now occurred. Therefore the occurrence of the block forces the stutterer to face it to a certain extent. (2) As the stutterer gets closer to the actual moment of stuttering, he gets more and more of a proprioceptive feedback from rehearsal. And, as he receives more information about the block, his sense of helplessness and his fear of the unknown are both reduced (27). (3) If we accept for a moment Fenichel's hypothesis that stuttering is an act of aggression against the listener (14), then the occurrence of the aggressive act, that is, stuttering, would reduce the need for aggression.

That the occurrence of stuttering seems to have the property of reducing the fear that elicited the stuttering is a paradoxical feature of the disorder. In clinics, it is commonly observed that stuttering goes in waves; part of the reason may be that the fluency produces the stuttering and the stuttering produces the fluency.

When a stutterer has had a fluent period, he frequently builds up tremendous tension. He wonders when he's going to stutter again. The unaccountable fluency may be strongly alien to the stutterer's self-image. Because the fluency seems strange, the stutterer feels guilt. He feels, "I shouldn't be talking this well." And when the blocks do come back, he experiences almost a relief. He is "himself" again.

Expressive Aspects of Stuttering

The conflict hypothesis refers to competing approach and avoidance tendencies to the act of speaking. The stutterer has a goal, that of communication, but also a fear, arising from several possible sources or levels of conflict. The stutterer then has a "feared goal." Since, as Miller's studies on conflict have shown (9, 25), the avoidance gradient is steeper than the approach gradient, what any organism does when caught in approach-avoidance conflict is to go part way and then stop. Repetition and prolongation, as the usual initiating symptoms in child stutterers and as the chief symptoms common to all stutterers, probably represent the oscillations and fixations found in approach-avoidance conflict. It is in this manner that the approach-avoidance conflict theory of stuttering has sought to account for the primary symptoms (36, 38).

The secondary symptoms of stuttering are equally accountable in terms of the conflict and fear-reduction hypotheses stated above. Because the conflict in stuttering is neatly externalized in observable behavior, and because different stutterers handle their moments of conflict in markedly different ways, stuttering behavior has an expressive aspect. New light can be thrown on what the stutterer does during his struggles when the secondary symptoms are viewed as expressive behavior, projective of the person behind the symptom, like other expressive behaviors. Since stuttering is such a stressful event for the stutterer, the manner in which he handles this stress becomes highly revealing.

There are just as many ways of handling the conflict moments in stuttering as there are individual personality patterns among stutterers, and for the same reason. If stuttering is the expression of a defense, surely the symptoms currently called secondary, which make up the main body of what the listener receives, reflect the nature of the defense. Some stutterers struggle furiously and grimace painfully when they stutter; some pretend to give up or wait for the listener to help them; others splutter and choke in a cultural caricature of inexpressible aggression.

If the primary symptoms of stuttering may be viewed as basic reactions to approach-avoidance conflict, then the secondary symptoms are either compensatory efforts to overcome the avoidance or behavior symbolizing unconsciously the stutterer's attitude toward his listeners or toward life itself. In any case, the choice of compensatory reactions is highly significant insofar as the dynamics of the chooser is concerned. To the experience of conflict the stutterer may respond either aggressively or in a more passive manner. In his efforts to overcome avoidance, the stutterer has the opportunity of choosing means which are openly or covertly aggressive, or more acquiescent techniques which strive to please the listener or conceal the stutterer's shame.

Are stuttering symptoms conversions,[2] symbolized aggressions, or merely learned acts? From the fear-reduction hypothesis and its corollaries, the fear will be satisfied principally through *visible* stuttering. For a given amount of fear the equation would be: visible abnormality $=$ form $\times$ duration. The stutterer may use a grimace to shorten the block, or he may use a postponement to prevent the grimace. When he has displayed enough abnormality, and thereby made the stuttering open for that word, he will be able to say it. The stutterer can use various means to satisfy

[2] In developing a "conversion" the individual expresses an emotional conflict through a physical symptom, often in a way which unconsciously relieves or provides a partial solution to the original problem. Viewed in this sense, conversions are, in effect, attempted physical solutions to psychological problems. Coriat believed that stuttering symptoms showed primarily a direct oral gratification, while Fenichel (**14**) thought stuttering to be a type of conversion symptom.

the fear through stuttering, and many tricks to avoid the difficulty. Those he does learn to employ habitually are not merely chance products of random instrumental learning, but necessarily reflect the dynamics of the stutterer and the pattern of interpersonal relation from which they emerged. The stuttering pattern is not a superficial symptom but a significant and revealing part of the stutterer's personality.

To what extent can you judge inner dynamics from overt symptoms? The clinically sensitive person can get at least a clue. After all, every time the stutterer has a block he is reliving one of the most important experiences of his life—that of finding his main channel of expression blocked. The way a stutterer responds to the experience of a block mirrors his self-concept, toleration for error, willingness to be himself without shame, persistence in the face of an obstacle, amount of drive toward success, and many other significant things about him.

Dynamic Significance of Speech, Silence, and Stuttering

Since stuttering may be termed a compromise between speech and silence, we should consider the symbolic significance of all three in analyzing what is expressed toward the listener. Depending upon our initial reference points, we may get widely differing results: (1) stuttering may be considered an act of aggression against the listener; fluency then would be nonaggressive or friendly behavior; (2) speech may be considered an aggressive, competitive, phallic act; silence here is presumably neutral; (3) silence in itself may be viewed as hostile. To be mute, in dreams, is a symbol of death. Symbolically, stuttering may be like partial mutism resulting from a turning inward against the stutterer's own ego of hostile urges originally directed against the listener. Perhaps it should be concluded simply that either stuttering or speech or silence can be used to express hostility or more positive feelings at various times, but that no constant or universal meaning can be offered. Whatever the behavior through which the feeling is expressed, the occurrence of stuttering will in part be determined by degree of conflict in the interpersonal relationship.

If stuttering may be viewed as a conflict between speech and silence, then what is the cumulative effect of not speaking, or remaining silent? If the person is silent for a time, then more conflict may ensue when speech attempts are resumed. The person may become so accustomed to silence that stuttering, or speech itself, becomes more ego-alien and grows more so when successfully avoided. Then when the blocks do return the punishments are experienced more vividly.

The Conflict Hypothesis: Evidence and Implications

If stuttering is a form of conflict, a resultant of competing urges to approach and avoid, then it should vary systematically as follows: Stuttering should be increased by (1) a heightening of the avoidance drive through an increase in the penalty upon which fear and avoidance are based; (2) a lowering of the approach drive. Stuttering should be decreased by (1) a reduction in the avoidance drive (fear, penalty); (2) an increase in the approach drive.

Let us look at the findings which bear on these predictions. The effect of penalty upon stuttering was shown in a study by Van Riper (44), who found that frequency of stuttering is increased by expectation of electric shock as a penalty for stuttering.

These results have been substantiated by Frick as part of his more comprehensive investigation of the relationship between punishment and stuttering (16). As part of his experiment, Frick administered shock for each stuttered word, in one condition at the end of the passage and in another immediately after the block. In each condition the added penalty resulted in greater frequency of stuttering. Porter found that the frequency of stuttering is increased by greater social penalty, as measured by the number of persons in the audience (28). On the other hand, Eisenson and Horowitz found that frequency of stuttering is decreased by a reduction in the meaningfulness of the material (11), while Eisenson and Wells obtained a similar result for degree of communicative responsibility (12).

Since less penalty is attached to not being able to utter relatively meaningless material, and less penalty and pressure is put on the speaker when he does not bear so much communicative responsibility, both findings in the Eisenson studies involve in part a decrease in stuttering stemming from a reduction in penalty and need for avoidance.

Bloodstein has suggested that the adaptation effect[3] may be explained on the basis of reduced propositionality (7). As in the Eisenson studies, this involves a reduction in penalty. When there is less meaning to convey, there is less penalty attached to the inability to convey it effectively. Bardrick and Sheehan (4, 5) found that a passage containing only numbers evoked less penalty than a neutral propositional passage, while emotionally

[3] With repeated reading of the same passage or speaking of the same material there is a reduction in stuttering which Johnson (20) has designated the adaptation effect. This effect has been extensively investigated in research studies summarized by Johnson (19).

loaded material produced the greatest amount of stuttering. These findings bear out predictions from approach-avoidance conflict theory.

So much for penalty, and increases or decreases in the avoidance drive. What about the approach drive? The evidence on this is sparse. That which we do have, mostly clinical observation, comes out as approach-avoidance theory would predict. Stutterers, like people generally, show markedly more hesitancy when dealing with material they are reluctant to reveal. Literature is full of descriptions of small boys stammering their excuses and of the hesitant speech of marriage proposals. Stuttering has been known to start from a parental demand of an oral confession of guilt. The reduction of communicatory drive in such a situation is fairly obvious. On the other hand, increases in the approach drive brought about through hypnosis, suggestion, or speaking under strong or unusual stimulation brings increased fluency (7). Stutterers sometimes surprise themselves and their associates by speaking normally in a crisis situation. Anger or sudden stress may produce a spectacular fluency. Such events point to the effect of a temporary increase in approach drive.

The Fear-Reduction Hypothesis: Evidence and Implications

What evidence is there that the occurrence of stuttering reduces the fear which elicited the stuttering?

Most important evidence is the existence of the adaptation effect in stuttering, as shown by Johnson and Knott (21), Van Riper and Hull (51). Johnson and Inness (20), Shulman (43), and in many other studies covered in Johnson's review of 30 years' research at the University of Iowa (19). The stuttering which occurs during the first reading decreases fear sufficiently to permit less stuttering on the second; that which occurs during the second reading reduces fear further so that there would be less stuttering on the third, etc.

As additional support for the fear-reduction hypothesis, three studies by the author may be cited. First, in a study of reinforcement in stuttering, it was found possible to have stutterers repeat stuttered words over and over again to a criterion of fluency. Simply saying the words over, stuttering on them, and thereby reducing fear led to fluency (33).

Second, in a phonetic analysis of stuttering patterns, it was found that stutterers tended to stutter with succeedingly larger samples of the word (35). Fear-reduction from the first attempt to say the word reduced fear and avoidance sufficiently so that succeeding points of stoppage occurred closer to the goal, i.e., nearer to the speaking of the word.

Third, in a study specifically designed to test the fear-reduction hypothesis, electromyographic measurements were taken from the masseter muscles of stutterers during the moment of stuttering. From the nature of approach-avoidance conflict, it was predicted that there would be an increase in fear elicited as the stutterer moved through the block, hence closer to the feared goal of speaking. Paradoxically, this increase in manifest tension resulted from the fear reduction which must occur during the moment of stuttering in order for release to take place. The results supported the fear-reduction hypothesis. Sheehan and Voas found that the maximum tension occurs late in the block, near the release, just as would be expected from the concept of stuttering as an approach-avoidance conflict (41).

The concept of stuttering as a fear reducer clarifies a number of relationships. When the stutterer is able to avoid stuttering he does not dissipate the anxiety, the tension builds up, and even though he may continue to be fluent he is building up future trouble through the avoidance. On the other hand, when he stutters or pretends to stutter, he is reducing his fears and building toward greater fluency later on. Hence we have a paradoxical relation—the stuttering produces the fluency and the fluency produces the stuttering. This is a possible explanation of something frequently observed, namely, that stuttering tends to occur in waves.

We could thus view stuttering as having a function similar to that of tics, asthma, and many neurotic symptoms, that it "binds" the anxiety and has the property of reducing it. We would have a parallel here to compulsive acts. When the person cannot stutter or successfully does not, the fear builds up. Stuttering may be thus viewed as an expression of accumulated anxiety. When the behavior occurs, the anxiety erupts and is let out. This concept may go a long way toward explaining the apparently paradoxical fact that we can build up a stutterer's tension by asking him to be fluent and we can reduce his fear by encouraging him to engage freely in the expression of the symptom.

On the concept of anxiety binding, Freud gives as one view: ". . . all symptom formation would be brought about solely to avoid anxiety. The symptoms bind the psychic energy which would otherwise be discharged as anxiety . . . if a compulsion neurotic is prevented from washing his hands after touching something, he becomes a prey to almost insupportable anxiety" (15).

It is as though each stutterer carries around with him a *reservoir of fear* which is tapped from time to time by the occurrence of stuttering. Such a concept, while more figurative than real, may help us understand the seemingly neurotic stutterer who suffers agonies in anticipation of stuttering that never quite happens. It is precisely because the individual never stutters that he never obtains relief. In a psychological sense he is much worse off than the individual who can express his conflict, and reduce his fear, through outward stuttering behavior. Such a concept suggests potentialities for *symptom expression*, or perhaps *symptom exploration*, as a psychotherapeutic technique with any problem based on fear.

A paradoxical effect of fear reduction during the block may be inferred from the nature of approach-avoidance conflict. By the lowering of the avoidance gradient, the stutterer is brought closer to the feared goal and hence may experience a paradoxical increase in "fear elicited." Thus, a reduction in fear shifts the equilibrium of the forces in conflict and brings the stutterer closer to the speaking of the word, but simultaneously he is experiencing more fear as he nears the goal.

It is important to distinguish between the fear reduction *during* the block which permits release and that which occurs after the release because the goal of speaking the word is reached. The fear reduction which determines the release from the block may be obscured somewhat by a simultaneous increase in fear, conflict, and avoidance strength with the nearing of the feared goal of speaking.

During a particular moment of stuttering, two shifts may be occurring at once. For a given amount of fear and avoidance tendency, the point at which the stutterer initially stops is determined in part by the strength of the approach drive, which is in turn a function of his need to communicate and ability to tolerate anxiety. When he reaches the point of stoppage the stuttering begins to occur, reducing the fear which elicited it and lowering the avoidance gradient so that he moves closer to the goal. Thus the amount of fear subjectively experienced may remain relatively constant throughout the block. If the stutterer does not complete the block but leaves the field or engages in some instrumental escape response, or if by using a device or trick he successfully reaches the goal in a roundabout manner, he does not "satisfy the fear" present and may continue to experience tension after the block. The unsatisfied fear may transfer over to a subsequent word and be dissipated on that word. When the opposite happens and there is rehearsal or subvocal satisfying of the fear first, there may be a stuttering on the word preceding the word originally feared (38). Since fear reduction reinforces the instrumental acts which bring it about and reinforced responses tend to move up in the response sequence, stuttering tends to become anticipatory. In a study of thoracic breathing, Van Riper noted that the actual form of the block is sometimes rehearsed in breathing patterns prior to speech attempt (47). From our theory, such rehearsal behavior will be fear reducing through secondary reinforcement. Proprioceptive feedback from rehearsal behavior is probably what enables the stutterer to anticipate his blocks, even to predict their duration with some accuracy (38).

Guilt as a Source of Conflict in Stuttering

Though the role of anxiety has been stressed by many writers, relatively little systematic consideration has been given to the probable source of much of the stutterer's fear and conflict—the factor of guilt. Both primary and secondary guilt in the stutterer may be distinguished, and the secondary guilt is far more significant than its name might imply.

Primary guilt would refer to the constellation of feelings which was behind the original appearance of the stuttering, which the symptom formation has the function of handling. Secondary guilt refers to the feelings the stutterer develops as a result of his inevitable knowledge that his blocks are distressing to others, more so at times than to himself.

Preliminary results of a research study on the role of guilt in stuttering undertaken by the author at the University of California, Los Angeles, indicate that stuttering is increased by the stutterer's knowledge that the symptom is painful to others. In one condition, one of the experimenters was a former professional actor who winced each time the stutterer had a block; in a second experimental condition, the stutterer was told that a neutral observer—innocent bystander—would receive an electric shock for each block the stutterer had in a 200-word passage. In a second investigation, stutterers responded to a sentence-completion test item in this fashion: "I have often fooled people about my stuttering" (common response in stutterers) or "myself." On another item, "I feel guilty about my stuttering" (31, 34).

Since guilt conspicuously produces blocking in the speech of young children and guilt is an important dynamic in the advanced stutterer, it is likely that guilt feelings lie heavily in the background of the onset of stuttering.

In the young secondary stutterer as in the adult, a rich source of guilt seems to arise from the artificial role playing to which nearly every stutterer falls victim. Because an almost endless variety of stage mannerisms, e.g., a Dixie accent or a British dialect, will produce a temporary fluency, the stutterer becomes in time a ham actor. Some assume a confident nonchalance; others pretend to be searching for the right word; still others keep not only a stiff upper lip but an entire poker face; while some greet each block with a feigned astonishment, as though this was something that had never happened to them before.

On the assumption that we feel guilty by not being honest with others, by not being what we seem to be or what we feel we should be, it is easy to see how guilty the stutterer feels over his counterfeited roles, despite whatever temporary fluency he achieves. When such devices are used frequently enough, guilt attaches itself through conditioning to the fluency itself, as well as to the spurious human relationships which preceded fluency and made it possible.

In later stages of treatment the equation of fluency and guilt in the stutterer often emerges very clearly; the stutterer may have feasted on false fluency so long that he comes to feel deeply that all fluency must be false and that he is undeserving of honest fluency. Adjustment to fluency is difficult not only because of ideal self-concept changes, but because of the guilt fluency engenders. All of these events highlight the fundamental importance of guilt in the psychology of the stutterer and in his treatment.

Levels of Conflict

Stuttering is an approach-avoidance conflict at several different levels, which may be specified according to the source of the avoidance drive at each level. Five distinct conflict levels appear: (1) word-level conflict; (2) situation-level conflict; (3) conflict due to emotional loading of speech; (4) relationship-level conflict, especially that involving authority relations; (5) ego-protective conflict, involving the defensive function of the stuttering.

At the *word level,* stuttering is a conflict between the urge to speak and the urge not to speak a particular word, through past conditioning on that particular word. Usually such conditioning is based on phonetic cues. The stutterer may avoid "hello" on the telephone, because of past experience with this and other *h* words. If he does go ahead, he has to force himself to do so.

At the *situation level,* there is a parallel conflict between entering and not entering a feared situation. The stutterer's behavior toward using the telephone, reciting in classes, or introducing himself to strangers illustrates this conflict. Many situations which demand speech hold enough threat to produce a competing drive to hold back.

Conflict may arise from the *emotional content* of the utterance, apart from its phonetic properties. All of us may hesitate in speech more when under the stress of expressing emotionally loaded material. Guilt, especially, produces both silence and stuttering speech. Anger appears to have a dual effect on stuttering. Up to a certain point, blocking increases, owing to build-up of inhibitory strength, a damming up. When pressure behind the dam becomes sufficient the dam seems to burst and the stutterer may express his rage with an eloquent profanity or at least a highly spectacular fluency. Not all stutterers, of course, follow this pattern. A few never seem to release feelings in large chunks, and with others the inhibitory dam is always too strong for breakthrough of fluency.

Relationship conflict in stuttering may be observed readily from the fact that most stutterers can speak with relative fluency when alone or when speaking to animals or to subordinates. Not only do adult stutterers stutter markedly more when speaking to authority figures, but it is worth noting that stuttering typically begins at an age when the child is conspicuously in the grip of large authority figures (30). In Freudian terms, stuttering begins during the oedipal period, at a time when conflict with adult authority, and threat from that authority, is especially intense. Oedipal conflict is more intense in boys because, unlike girls, they do not have to shift love objects, but rather experience an intensification of feeling toward what is the original love object of each, namely, the mother. Since four times as many boys stutter as girls, there are relationships and possibilities here that deserve further exploration.

Some stutterers experience no fear when they play a dominant role. One may give a fluent public address but stutter to individuals in the audience before and afterward. A child may block severely before one parent but speak easily to the other. An Army enlisted man could never say "sergeant" until he became one. The fact that many stutterers can act in plays seems to show the effect of changed role. Several of the conditions listed by Bloodstein (7) as involving the behavior of the listener may equally be interpreted in terms of relationship. Pointing out that the stutterer can usually talk well when alone, Adler concluded, ". . . I can only interpret his stammer as the expression of his attitude toward others" (1).

At the *ego-protective level* of conflict, stuttering can serve unconsciously as a means for keeping the individual out of competitive endeavors which would pose threat of failure or threat of success. The stutterer can adjust his aspirations so as to keep within zones of safety. This, rather than repression of forbidden impulses in the traditional Freudian sense, is probably the chief defensive function of stuttering. Experimental support for the concept of stuttering as an ego-protective type of conflict has been provided in a study of the aspiration levels of stutterers. Compared to normal speakers, stutterers stayed more in the success-area of goal setting, predicted more modest performances, and showed in general a lower level of aspiration. The differences were held to result from the stutterer's greater defensiveness and efforts to avert possibility of failure (42).

Research on Conflict Levels

For several years a research program has been under way at the University of California, Los Angeles, to test various parts of the approach-avoidance conflict theory of stuttering, particularly in relation to the five hypothesized levels of conflict just discussed.

Word level and *situation level* conflict have been investigated in connection with a study of reinforcement in stuttering reported in detail elsewhere (36), and in a study of the effect on stuttering frequency of therapy techniques involving approach and avoidance (38).

Emotional content as a level of conflict in stuttering has been verified by the results of Bardrick's dissertation (4), directed by the author. Data drawn from this study are presented more fully below.

Interpersonal or *relationship level* of conflict has been under investigation in three studies, still ongoing: (1) sex-relation study—effect of the sex of the experimenter on frequency of stuttering (39); (2) guilt study—effect on stuttering frequency of knowledge that stuttering will result in punishment of the audience; (3) authority-relation study—whether it is true, as hypothesized, that the stutterer is more likely to stutter in the presence of an authority figure.

Conflict at the *ego-protective* or ego-defensive level of conflict has been approached by two means: (1) Level of aspiration in stutterers, in a study by Sheehan and Zelen, was found to be significantly lower than that in non-stutterers, owing to their greater defensiveness and desire to avoid risk of failure (42). (2) A specially constructed sentence-completion test, reported at the 1956 meetings of the American Speech and Hearing Association in Chicago, has been administered to both child and adult stutterers. Items which bear on the defensive aspects of stuttering, as well as on the other conflict levels, include: "If my stuttering suddenly disappeared, I would ________"; "One good thing about being a stutterer ________"; and "If I had not stuttered, I would be different because ________." While the data are still undergoing analysis, it can be reported that for many stutterers the handicap seems to be chiefly a source of frustration, while in certain stutterers it does appear to serve a defensive function (34).

As an example of research which provided clear-cut evidence as to the validity of one conflict level in stuttering, the study of the effect of emotional loading on stuttering, reported by Bardrick and Sheehan at the 1956 meetings of the American Psychological Association (5), are presented below in some detail.

To what extent can stuttering be traced to conflict arising out of the emotionality of the material to be expressed? To answer this question 32 stutterers ranging in age from 16 to 45 read one emotionally laden experimental passage and three control passages.

The experimental passage, Passage *A*, consisted of derogatory statements about stutterers taken from psychoanalytic writings, e.g., "Stutterers are notoriously immature, narcissistic, weak individuals who ____

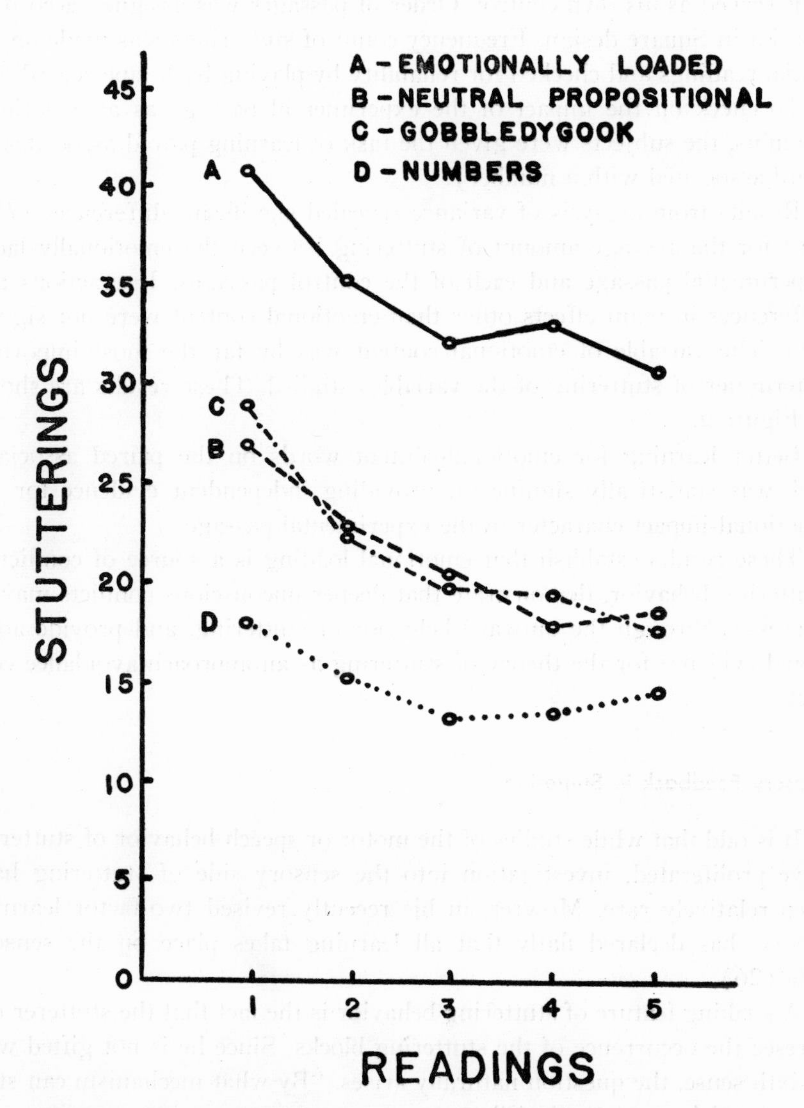

Figure 2. Emotional Loadings as a Source of Conflict in Stuttering. (From Bardrick and Sheehan, 5.)

__________." The stated assumption was that this passage would arouse ambivalent feelings in the stutterer because of threat to his self-esteem.

Control Passage *B*, neutral propositional, consisted of ordinary material taken from a popularization of archaeology. Control Passage *C* was made up of gobbledygook or neutral nonpropositional material. For Control Passage *D*, numbers were used.

Each subject read each of the four passages five consecutive times and thus served as his own control. Order of passages was assigned according to a Latin Square design. Frequency count of stutterings was made on the initial readings and checked for reliability by playing back tape recordings.

To check on the impact of the experimental passage as an emotional stimulus, the subjects were given the task of learning paired associates (a word associated with a number).

Results from analysis of variance revealed significant differences ($P = .01$) for the average amount of stuttering between the emotionally laden experimental passage and each of the control passages. Interactions and differences in main effects other than emotional content were not significant. The variable of emotional content was by far the most important determiner of stuttering of the variables studied. These results are shown in Figure 2.

Better learning for emotional-content words on the paired associates task was statistically significant, providing independent evidence for the emotional-impact character of the experimental passage.

These results establish that emotional loading is a source of conflict in stuttering behavior, demonstrate that deeper unconscious conflicts may be expressed through the outward behavior of stuttering, and provide additional evidence for the theory of stuttering as an approach-avoidance conflict.

Sensory Feedback in Stuttering

It is odd that while studies of the motor or speech behavior of stutterers have proliferated, investigation into the sensory side of stuttering have been relatively rare. Mowrer, in his recently revised two-factor learning theory, has declared flatly that all learning takes place on the sensory side (26).

A striking feature of stuttering behavior is the fact that the stutterer can foresee the occurrence of the stuttering blocks. Since he is not gifted with a sixth sense, the question naturally arises, "By what mechanism can stutterers anticipate stuttering?"

Apparently, proprioceptive feedback from rehearsal behavior enables the stutterer to anticipate his blocks, even to predict their duration accurately.

The behavior of the stutterer as approaching a feared goal, going part way and then stopping, can be understood somewhat more fully in terms of the sensory feedback occurring during approach-avoidance conflict. As he approaches the act of speaking, he is receiving both positive and negative kinds of feedback. If we may extend the Miller formulation on the intersecting gradients in approach-avoidance conflict, in combination with Mowrer's revised two-factor theory (26), we may hypothesize as follows:

As the stutterer approaches the feared word the feedback stimuli, bombarding him as he moves closer to the feared goal of speaking, become in the case of punishment learned avoidance responses, progressively and relatively much stronger than their analogues on the approach side. These stimuli may be visual, auditory, or proprioceptive. In other words, as the stutterer approaches the act of speaking, he is able to go ahead because of a predominance of positive feedback in the early stage, and he stops part way because the negative feedback which has been relatively weak far from the goal builds up more sharply as the goal is neared.

The manner in which feedback operates in the stutterer is probably very complex and deserves much further exploration. The intriguing work of F. Matthias Alexander in his book *The Use of the Self* (2), in which he devoted a chapter to the stutterer in terms of what he called "wrong habitual use" serves to point up the proprioceptive aspect of stuttering. It was Alexander's thesis that the stutterer was like a golfer who took his eye off the ball, under the delusion that because he was able to do what he "willed to do" in acts that are voluntary and therefore involve sensory experiences that are unfamiliar, he should be equally able to do what he "wills to do" in acts that are involuntary and therefore involve sensory acts that are familiar.

We come to adjust to whatever habit patterns we have developed so that they feel "right" to us, whereas unfamiliar acts which may be objectively more correct will have a wrong sensory feel. Much of Alexander's work, which he applied with some ingenuity to stuttering, including a set of therapeutic recommendations for the stutterer's approach to the feared word, is illuminated by, and in turn throws interesting light on, the application of feedback theory to stuttering behavior.

A second application in terms of the effects of proprioceptive feedback on stuttering behavior may be mentioned. Dollard and Miller (9) discuss maladaptive anticipatory behavior in terms of fractional anticipatory goal responses and proprioceptive feedback. They cite the example of the hunter and the gun. When the hunter first presses the trigger he does so very easily, with no avoidance mechanisms. Immediately the instrumental act of pressing the trigger leads to the firing of the gun, which is followed in turn by a startle response of the whole body. In successive pressings of the trigger the startle response tends to become anticipatory, that is, to occur before the explosion and the cessation of the noxious stimulus of the explosion. The hunter thus tenses on the trigger before he actually comes to press it, and he may spoil his marksmanship by jerking prior to the actual time to pull the trigger.

The parallel to stuttering behavior here is quite striking, in that stutterers tend to approach their explosion-laden feared words with the same trepidation, to tense in anticipation of the word and to jerk on the actual speech attempt. In the case of the therapeutic recommendations, the parallel becomes even more striking. The treatment for the hunter is to squeeze the trigger more slowly, so that the proprioceptive feedback which mediates the startle response leading to the maladaptive behavior does not occur with predictable regularity. Similarly, the stutterer may be asked to squeeze the trigger slowly, with such techniques as the "slide" or "smooth pattern" (40). It is likely that the old school of slowing down the stutterer had some of this same effect. Psychological barriers and delayed-reaction assignments probably help the stutterer on the same basis.

Visual feedback is of basic importance in any interpersonal-relationship difficulty, such as stuttering, because visual feedback is the main channel through which reactions of others are perceived. The stutterer responds not only to the visual feedback he constantly gets from his listener, but he gets another feedback from the way he perceives feared words. From a phonetic analysis of stuttering patterns, Sheehan (35) noted that stutterers frequently continue to attempt to say, and to visualize themselves as attempting to say, sounds which they actually were saying at that moment—that is, they were trying to say sounds they had already said successfully. For example, one stutterer whose last name began with *S* visualized *s* as his big hurdle while successfully saying the *s* sound to the exclusion of the remainder of the word. Another was so much the victim of his visual perceptions that in trying to answer the telephone he was actually found saying the name of the letter *h*, "aitch, hello," rather than the sound of *h*, because he perceived a giant *H* as his chief hurdle. So long as the stutterer perceives the first sound rather than the whole word as his major obstacle, he is likely to persevere in his attempt to say that first sound. Somehow, with this set he does not seem to be able to profit from the proprioceptive feedback that he has already uttered that initial sound successfully.

Another intriguing area in terms of feedback is the role of auditory factors in stuttering. On one hand, we have the effect of masking noise in reducing stuttering (29) and, on the other, the effect of delayed speech feedback in producing a kind of stuttering in normal speakers (6, 13, 22, 23). In other words, by varying the auditory input, it seems possible to produce stuttering in normal speakers and to produce relatively normal speech in stutterers. Taken together these findings suggest support for the concept of speech as a servomechanism (13) and further suggest that the occurrence of stuttering is mediated in part by cues relating to auditory feedback.

Thus, on the perceptual side, or at least on the sensory side, it appears that we have at least three kinds of feedback which are important in producing or modifying stuttering behavior—proprioceptive, visual, and auditory. In dealing with the stutterer it is important to remain aware of the complexity of these processes.

Time Pressure as a Factor in Stuttering

A basic feature of stuttering behavior is that the stutterer is under time pressure to a great extent. He comes to learn to dread pauses, and the room settles around him with awful stillness when he begins to speak. The stutterer's block always seems longer than it really is, both to the stutterer and to his listeners. An experiment in which stutterers estimated the length of blocks against the actual blocks showed that they estimated significantly longer times (37). This finding is in a process of verification as part of a program of research into the effects of time pressures on stuttering.

It is suggested that time pressure is a basic variable in stuttering, that it is through time pressure that the effect of interpersonal relations in stuttering is mediated. It is also through time pressure that anxiety and guilt and conflicts of all kinds come to play a part. When the stutterer feels in a subordinate or inferior role, or when speaking to an authority figure, he is likely to feel he isn't really worthy of taking the other person's time. Many stutterers feel apologetic and guilty about their stuttering because of this seeming imposition. Many of the devices of stutterers are adopted to speed up the speech attempt and to shorten the block; these conspicuously have a self-defeating purpose. For a stutterer "haste makes waste" is all too true. Unsystematic awareness of the role of time factors in stuttering has been shown by the older school of speech therapists, and even by neighbors and friends who are always urging the stutterer to slow down, to take it easy, to take his time. However ineffective these are as therapeutic measures, they do reflect probably accurate perception of the stutterer as a person who is hurrying himself to an abnormal extent. Stutterers learn to overtrigger the speech attempt, to startle, to become gun-shy of the speech itself. Implicit awareness of the effect of time pressure has been evidenced by such speech therapists as Van Riper with his "delayed response" (45, 46) or Wendell Johnson with his "delayed semantic reaction" (18). Either of these devices may appear mechanical or short-term, yet is occasionally effective in teaching the stutterer to take more time.

Many stutterers show a *fear of silence*, and any momentary pause or cessation of sound of their own speech brings on reactions approaching panic. Perhaps because most stuttering occurs on initial syllables and the stutterer has more trouble when he starts, he learns to dread the necessity for starting. He learns to dread any period of silence in his own speech, to fear it, and to become quite intolerant of it. For a stutterer, silence is followed with the regularity of Pavlov's bell by a punishment—the experience of stuttering. In this way the stutterer becomes conditioned to avoid silence in his speech. A great many of the stutterer's symptoms can be understood as filibustering, as measures taken to prevent the occurrence of silence. The stutterer is under such extreme time pressure because he has learned that silence is dangerous. Stuttering itself is a compromise between speech and silence, a result of conflicting urges to speak and not to speak. Any organisms in double approach-avoidance conflict are characteristically pulled one way and then the other and are likely to attempt response to competing cues. Similarly, many stutterers try to respond simultaneously to every cue in the situation.

The stutterer feels far more guilty over delaying his listener than the realities of the situation require. It is a common experience among speech pathologists to have stutterers report being unable to carry out speech assignments because they didn't want to take the person's time. Now, most stuttering blocks are not over two or three seconds' duration (35). The actual time the listener is made to wait is really very small, yet with a dominant or important figure or with more people in the room, guilt and resultant time pressure multiply. The more total time, in blocking-seconds, the stutterer piles up on people, the guiltier he feels about his stuttering.

How can we deal with this pressure therapeutically? Time pressure is so basic in stuttering that enumeration of nearly every therapist's goal would be required to deal with this problem. But reduction of the stutterer's guilt generally, especially that over taking other people's time, is certainly of basic importance in the process.

Time pressure, then, is an important variable in stuttering and perhaps in all interpersonal interaction. As such, it is worthy of systematic investigation. Yet previous research has left this important area virtually untouched. Here are some basic research questions relating to time pressure:

1. What is the relationship between anxiety and time pressure?
2. What is the relationship between the interpersonal factor and time pressure?

3. What is the relationship between guilt and time pressure?
4. What is the pattern of breakdown in terms of time pressure?
5. How can the stutterer learn to deal more effectively with time pressure?
6. How can he learn to deal with people who are impatient?
7. Can we slow down the stutterer without being part of the old relax-and-take-a-deep-breath school of speech therapy?
8. How can the stutterer's self-esteem be built up so that he feels less gap between his own worth and that of his listener?

Speech Inhibition and Symptom Formation

Inhibition of the speech function can take several forms. Its most complete form is found in the silent negativism of the catatonic, or in other forms of mutism. The mutism of the catatonic is believed to be part of the rigidity resulting from holding in check murderous or destructive impulses. Then there is phantom speech, sometimes incorrectly lumped with mutism, involving a movement of the lips without breath. Next is hysterical aphonia, involving a strained whisper, often with accessory hoarse phonation or false vocal-cord activity. The aphonic is never stuck on words but neither does he typically experience the periods of normal speech stutterers usually have. Cluttering, like stuttering, a disorder of the rhythm of speech, is symptomatic of tremendous pressure toward communication. In the stutterer, for reasons that are still a mystery, a different kind of symptom formation appears to have taken place.

The problem of symptom choice in stuttering resolves itself down to two questions: (1) Given an anxiety, why does it express itself through speech? (2) Given a focus on speech, why does it take the form of stuttering? Oddly, in view of the multitude of studies on other fronts, research has left these questions virtually untouched. The questions are stated here as fundamental issues for future research.

Some light is thrown on the first question by Dollard and Miller, who point out that fear readily inhibits vocal behavior (9).

The Relationship Between Speech Symptom and Personality Dynamics

What is the precise nature of the relationship between stuttering as an outward symptom and the personality dynamics which presumably underly this conflict? Several points should be noted in the future investigation of this relationship. If indeed it is true that stuttering is the outward expression of an inner conflict, then there are very puzzling things about the nature of the conflict. (1) The inner dynamics of stutterers, as reflected in projective test performance, such as the Rorschach, the TAT, and the Rosenzweig Picture-Frustration test, do not differ significantly from normal-speaking control subjects. (2) There is no common set of dynamics in the stutterer, as measured by the same methods, which can be related to the presumably "outward" symptom. (3) Once fully developed into the secondary phase, the symptom is remarkably stable. Stuttering behavior may remain virtually untouched throughout the course of a full-blown psychosis, or despite psychotherapy that is terminated by mutual feelings of success and completion, or long after disappearance of the apparent originating factors.

The writer has worked with a psychotic stutterer who stuttered with all the elaborate secondary pattern not only before and after a psychotic break but also *during* it. In this state, he was described in hospital records as "grossly psychotic." He was running about in a manicky, uncontrolled fashion, not stopping to eat, urinating and defecating freely as the urge arose, displaying inappropriate affects, not observing even the most elementary social inhibitions, and engaging in various other peculiar behaviors including bizarre verbalizations. Throughout this whole grossly psychotic episode, this patient continued to stutter with his characteristic secondary pattern.

Aside from many interesting research questions posed, this case appears to provide strong support for learned behavior interpretations of stuttering, especially for the conception that stuttering may become a closed system, functionally autonomous, a vicious circle continuing to operate long after the extinction of the forces which originally set it in motion.

Here are a few of the theoretical puzzles raised by such cases. If stuttering is an anxiety symptom, and if anxiety is partially a response to external reality, it is puzzling to find such a symptom remain intact when the individual is fundamentally out of contact. When stuttering behavior is sensitive enough to vary significantly with the emotional loading and communicative value of the utterance (4, 5, 11, 12), and when it is quite sensitive to changes in the speaker-listener relationship, and to externally imposed penalties (30, 16, 44), we would expect stuttering to be affected more by a departure from reality adjustment.

The discrepancy may be reconciled in part by two considerations: (1) Stuttering behavior is complex behavior arising out of several levels of conflict, and any single factor such as emotional loading, or speaker-listener relationship, contributes only a portion of the variance.[4] (2) Psychosis is

[4] Many of the statistically significant factors have been derived from group studies of the adaptation effect. Any experimenter who has worked with the adaptation model is well aware that there are always some subjects who contribute little or nothing to the main effect. Some reverse the effect, while quite a few are quite resistant to any diminution of stuttering below a certain level. Even for those who show emotional loading and interpersonal effects, there are many whose stuttering tends to become asymptotic at, for example, the level of 4% or 8% frequency on the reading passages.

not always, contrary to popular belief, a complete departure from reality adjustment, nor are anxiety and conversion symptoms by any means unknown in psychotics. Anyone who has worked with psychotics is aware that they do respond to external stimuli a good deal of the time, even though the mode of response may appear bizarre or meaningless to outsiders. Possibly our patient's fears relating to his speech were so deep-seated that he continued to respond to these fears long after a psychosis had solved most of his other anxieties. Possibly the learned pattern of his stuttering had become so thoroughly entwined with the learned pattern of his speech that his stuttering did indeed continue on a functionally autonomous basis. We do not know. But we do know that we need to discover more such cases, and that we need to explore more thoroughly the impact upon stuttering of severe personality breakdown.

Treatment

Goals: The Relationship of Speech Therapy to Psychotherapy

When stuttering is viewed as approach-avoidance conflict, operating at different levels, the fundamental goal of treatment becomes very clear: to eliminate all tendency to avoidance, whatever the source. Word fears and situation fears involving the more superficial levels of conflict are attacked most directly through speech therapy. Feelings, relationships, and defenses are reached through psychotherapy. In each case the basic goal is the same: to reduce the avoidance and its sources, permitting the stutterer to attack each communicative act as freely as possible. Treatment thus follows in broad outline the five levels of approach-avoidance conflict in stuttering (32, 36, 38).

In treating stutterers, two specific values of the approach-avoidance formulation should be mentioned: (1) Approach-avoidance theory relates fear, avoidance and conflict to stuttering, and theory to treatment in a systematic way. The paramount importance of reducing fears and avoidances becomes clearly apparent from the theory itself. (2) The analysis of levels of conflict and distinction between learned avoidances and unconscious motives for avoidance provides for an integration of psychotherapy and speech therapy not always apparent in the writings of psychologists and speech pathologists.

The relative utilization of speech therapy and psychotherapy in present-day clinical work offers many contrasts. On one hand, a few still use a purely symptomatic treatment which tries to ignore fears, prevent blocks, and build fluency directly through "confidence" measures. These people neglect all psychotherapy and, in a modern sense, speech therapy as well. At the opposite pole are many clinicians, often psychoanalytically oriented, who insist that we must "ignore the symptom" and work toward the original cause, presumably something in the stutterer's past. For these people the speech pathologist could offer the stutterer nothing except in terms of whatever general psychotherapeutic abilities he might possess.

However, when stuttering is treated as a form of conflict, speech therapy and psychotherapy are not in competition but have a common goal: the reduction of all tendencies to avoidance and of the fears which motivate them.

Although the stutterer's need for psychotherapy is now widely accepted, many of those who see this need most clearly continue to ask, "Why work on the speech at all?" To answer this question, and to defend the role that speech pathologists have come to assume in helping stutterers, we list the following points:

1. *The therapist can work with the externalization of the conflict.* If we are really justified in viewing stuttering as an externalized conflict, should we not avail ourselves of this ready avenue to other levels? Conflict at the relationship level, for example, is mediated through situation and word fear; why then not begin where the stuttering occurs and work back to the stutterer's relationships? The fact that stuttering does vary in accordance with the emotional content of the moment, and with shifts in interpersonal relationship, can be utilized by the therapist to point out how the stutterer is affected by certain kinds of feelings or certain kinds of people, including especially the therapist himself. The stutterer's blocks and his reactions to them mirror his self-concept, attitudes toward others, mechanisms for handling conflicts, and many other aspects of his personality. Each time the stutterer has a block he is reliving in a small way one of the most significant experiences of his life.

2. *The therapist can create an attitude of extreme permissiveness toward the stuttering.* Many speech clinics have been able to create an atmosphere such that there is status value to being a stutterer—the student clinicians find them interesting, they are in a most exclusive fraternity along with Charles Lamb, George VI, etc. To stutter openly is to display the badge of courage, and the blocks themselves are no longer occasions for shame but interesting items for analysis. Fear and avoidance are thereby greatly reduced.

3. *The therapist can share and reduce a portion of the guilt.* When the therapist encourages the individual to stutter freely, even assigning him to stutter deliberately, he thereby accepts responsibility for what happens to the stutterer's audience. Most stutterers probably would be more open

about it, if not haunted by their awareness of the distress their speech is constantly causing others. If the act of stuttering can be viewed as an act of aggression against the listener, then much of speech therapy is made up of systematic exercises in the expression of aggression, with the therapist assuming the major portion of the guilt. Eventually psychotherapy should help the stutterer reach a point where he feels neither need to act out aggressions on his audience nor guilt at the stuttering which may still occur.

4. *Many positive personality changes can result from speech therapy.* When a stutterer learns how to handle his fears and his blocks, develops healthier attitudes toward his handicap, toward himself, and toward others, he changes fundamentally in his personality. It is a common experience in speech clinics that the patient's change in feelings, attitudes, and personality far surpass those in overt speech characteristics. That such changes occur indicates how truly psychotherapeutic speech therapy can be.

5. *Many stutterers are tired of running away, and welcome the therapist's support in facing the problem.* This is especially likely to be true of the selected sample of cases who come for therapy, for the same forces which brought them into therapy gain strength from the therapist's support in abandoning the daily masquerade practiced by most stutterers. Stutterers, like people generally, find it a deeply moving experience to master situations from which they have always retreated.

6. *Unless the stutterer alters his pattern, he will be helpless to deal with the old blocks whenever they return.* Conventional psychotherapy alone, by leaving the self-maintaining, learned behavior system intact, would leave the stutterer helpless to deal with the cues which characteristically elicit the behavior.

7. *Through speech therapy the stutterer can learn how to handle his problem even during periods of emotional upset.* If the stutterer does not have this capacity, he will be the victim of every mood swing and future upheaval in his life. So long as emotional upsets are reflected inevitably in his speech, he will be in the precarious position of having his social and vocational handicap return at any time in full force. But through speech therapy it appears to be possible to teach stutterers more adequate modes of response to pressure situations, to teach them how to accept fears and blocks when they do occur.

8. *When the stutterer faces his stuttering, he removes the reinforcement derived from its ego-protective function.* An important secondary gain of stuttering is the protection it affords from competitive callings. When the stutterer can no longer use the symptom to escape from society or avert threat of failure, the stuttering loses its primary function.

Goals: The Relationship of Psychotherapy to Speech Therapy

The treatment of any stutterer is basically a process of psychotherapy. Considering the many who have regarded stuttering as a psychological problem, surprisingly few have attempted to work out a truly psychological therapy. Typically, the reference to psychotherapy is an afterthought, or confounded with such clinically dubious phrases as "appropriate personality assignment" or "calm, unemotional attitude."

Conspicuously, speech therapy is aimed at secondary effects, at the reactions to the stuttering, the stutterer's adjustment to it, rather than the origins of the problem. It is a therapy which aims at effects rather than causes.

Moreover, the language of speech therapy is generally alien to psychotherapists. Such terms as "symptomatic," "desensitization therapy," and the constant preoccupation with symptom analysis, "assets and liabilities," and "negative practice" are the hallmark of superficial therapy rather than a deeper therapy. One stutterer, undergoing intensive psychotherapy following a speech recovery in one of the best-known of these speech clinics, described it as the "symptom mill."

Yet it should not be inferred that speech therapy for the stutterer is to be abandoned, or that straight psychotherapy necessarily will meet the stutterer's problem squarely. Though he needs treatment in a psychotherapeutic context, experiences in simply referring the stutterer to the psychiatrist or analyst have not been impressively rewarding. Too many of us in speech therapy encounter (and treat successfully) numerous stutterers who have invested time and money in analysis without relief. The most positive comment usually is, "The therapy helped me generally, but not in my speech."

Many psychotherapists have become discouraged with the stutterer. They describe him as singularly resistant, or difficult to treat. Fenichel (14) ascribed to the stutterer all the difficulties that would be encountered with any obsessive-compulsive patient. Though he viewed the analysis of a stutterer as a dubious venture, lesser Freudians still enthusiastically hold up analysis for the stutterer as though it were some kind of ultimate.

A fact frequently overlooked in considering Freudian interpretation of stuttering is this: though he practiced extensively and wrote prolifically for over 40 years, Freud's specific writings on the subject of stuttering are remarkably meager. During his years of practice, Freud must have come into contact with a large number of stutterers, yet though he wrote on a wide range of subjects, and formulated in quite specific terms the dynamics of many other disorders, he did not come to any comparable systematic declaration of his views on the dynamics and treatment of the stutterer. Just why this is so is not clear. Various indirect sources have attributed to Freud viewpoints that are contradictory, so that the hearsay evidence is bewildering.

Esti Freud, in a personal communication to Henry Freund, quoted Sigmund Freud as saying: "Psychoanalysts don't understand the mechanism of stuttering and so far psychoanalytic techniques have been valueless in cases of stuttering."[5] Froeschels has quoted Freud in a somewhat similar vein.[6]

One of the five patients who made up Freud's classical *Studies on Hysteria* was, among other things, a stutterer, and Freud included here, says Glauber, "more about dynamics of stuttering than in any other one or all of the references he had ever made to this subject."[7] The patient, Frau Emmy von N., showed symptoms of "hysterical delirium," facial and neck tics, and a "group of speech disturbances. These consisted of a stutter, a tic-like clacking sound, and an involuntary utterance of her own name which was the same as that of one of her daughters." At times Freud referred to both the stutter and the clacking sound as tics.

The stuttering was unusual in that it began in an adult woman with no history of childhood stuttering. Glauber states, "I have also noticed that stutterers in general have a tendency similar to that of the group of hysterics referred to by Freud in this case history," emphasizing "instinctual phobias" and "traumatic events." The bulk of the article is made up of Glauber's own formulations on stuttering, interrupted occasionally by Freud's comments on the hysterical character, conversion, and Frau Emmy, and bolstered by references to such psychoanalytic writers as Coriat, Fenichel, and Federn. Freud ascribed the incompleteness of Frau Emmy's speech recovery to habit maintenance.

A careful reëxamination of Freud's comments on the case of Frau Emmy[8] has left this writer quite unconvinced that Freud had any intention of fostering generalizations upon the dynamics of the stutterer from this single rather atypical case. Considering his highly detailed account of her other features, Freud's references to Frau Emmy's speech were quite scanty, and his coverage of the possible dynamics of the speech symptom were even scantier. Freud believed that at least some of the symptoms of this patient, e.g., her "neck cramps," which produced among other com-

[5] Freud, Esti, Personal communication to Henry Freund.

[6] Froeschels, Emil, quoted in C. Van Riper, *Speech Therapy: A Book of Readings,* New York, Prentice-Hall, 1953.

[7] Glauber, I. P., "Freud's contributions on stuttering," *J. Amer. Psychoanalytic Association,* *6,* 1958, 326–347.

[8] Breuer, Josef, and Freud, Sigmund, "Studies on Hysteria," in *The Complete Works of Sigmund Freud, Vol. II* (*1893–95*), pp. 48–105.

plaints a six-to-twelve-hour incapacity to speak, were organic in origin, "similar to migraine." Moreover, since this case was reported relatively early in Freud's career, long before his more important formulations on the nature of anxiety (15), it seems clear that Freud never brought his most developed and mature thinking to bear on the problem of stuttering; in fact, he never dealt systematically with stuttering *per se*.

Compared to the extreme meagerness of Freud's references to stuttering, there is a fairly abundant proliferation of formulations on stuttering from followers of Freud. The disciples have not hesitated to rush in where the master seemed reluctant to tread. Nor have they always agreed. Coriat has argued that the stutterer is primarily oral, while Fenichel argued that he is primarily anal, a discrepancy suggesting that these two may have been trying to peer into their subject from opposite ends.

Lest the majestic authority of Freud be invoked too readily to bolster what may actually be a current analytic view, it might be well to recall Freud's own apt disclaimer: "As for me, I am not a Freudian."[9]

With the assumption that the treatment of the adult stutterer must be basically a psychotherapy, let us examine what has been developed in the way of speech therapy for the stutterer and see how it can be fitted into that context.

Because we need speech for getting almost everything we want, and because stuttering begins so early, virtually every consequential event in the life of a stutterer will have been affected to some degree by the fact of the stuttering. The secondary effects of stuttering are probably more pervasive than those of any other disorder. So important are the secondary developments that it has been argued that once started, stuttering tends to keep itself going and continues on a self-maintaining basis long after the original causes have disappeared (10, 48). The view of stuttering as a functionally autonomous symptom has had great influence on treatment, at least implicitly, for a great many techniques of speech therapy appear to have been developed to help the stutterer break out of the "vicious circle."

Therapy is above all a personal relationship. Whatever the roles of insight and interpretation, the relationship and the personality of the therapist who supplies this relationship is primary in the process.

The techniques of speech therapy can be powerfully psychotherapeutic, but they are not therapeutic unless fitted into a certain context. Group feeling, morale, *esprit de corps*—these are essential in the milieu of successful speech therapy. Perhaps because the stutterer suffers from a social handicap, he must be treated through socially structured methods. No one

[9] Quoted by Theodor Reik in *Listening With the Third Ear,* New York, Farrar, Straus, 1948.

ever overcame stuttering in a closet or on a couch. Too many stutterers have left an impression on psychiatrists' couches and their own pocketbooks, without any visible effect on the speaking handicap which set off the therapy.

The plight of one stutterer who spent three years getting a Beverly Hills psychoanalysis may illustrate this point. Asked by his friends upon his return to his Middle Western home to speak to them, he could only utter his usual blocks. They asked him: "What, you spent all this time and money on psychoanalysis, and you still stutter?" With a smile, he replied, "Yes—but now I know *why!*" Knowledge is not always power to the stutterer, and insight does not automatically assure free speech.

People are maladjusted to the extent that they lack good interpersonal relationships. In undoing maladjustment, the therapist has as one of his chief functions the supplying of the relationships which have been lacking. Hence the therapist becomes not only a parent figure but at times a sibling figure, friend, and the like. Since stuttering varies so conspicuously with the relationship between the stutterer and his listener, some psychotherapy is necessarily indicated for every stutterer. The speech therapist who can at the same time be a psychotherapist, or the psychotherapist who equally understands modern stuttering therapy, is best fitted to offer therapy to a stutterer.

Diagnosis and Prognosis

Since the level of therapy is dependent upon the level of conflict, thorough exploration of possible sources of conflict should be incorporated into whatever diagnostic procedure is undertaken. If the intake procedures —interview, case history, autobiography, psychological testing—indicate reasonably well-functioning defenses and good ego strength, speech therapy may be offered the stutterer first. For the precariously adjusted, speech therapy which challenges the stutterer to face his problems probably should not be offered, not because it has ever proved dangerous, but because the person will almost certainly collect another defeat.

Since the stutterer's reaction to speech therapy reveals the nature and extent of his resistances, speech therapy in itself can be considered a diagnostic procedure, though too expensive and time-consuming to be part of intake.

Actually, little samples of speech therapy can be used as part of examination procedures. The stutterer's reaction to trial speech therapy can be an important indication of his ego strength and therapeutic potential.

In the diagnostic examination of stutterers, far too much emphasis has been placed in the past upon the elaborate classification of secondary symptoms and other superficial aspects of the occurrence or nonoccurrence of the blocks, and not enough on the person behind the symptom. Projective techniques have become an important short cut to the stutterer's dynamics, and their usefulness is such that personality questionnaires and psychometrics, unless indicated by some special feature of the case, are falling into discard.

A much neglected and important aspect of diagnosis is consideration of what the diagnostic procedure does to the therapeutic relationship, both initially and ultimately. Certainly there are many patients who arrive in such a state that diagnostic procedures should be dispensed with, at least during the initial stages of therapy. With anyone who shows acute anxiety symptoms, depression, traumatic neurosis, or a great urgency to talk about the problem or to get started in treatment, therapy should begin formally with the initial interview.

The system of expectations of each stutterer should be explored at intake. Does he believe a magic wand will give him effortless eloquence by next Tuesday? Or have previous abortive efforts at therapy left him fundamentally discouraged that he can ever be helped? Have parents or friends propelled him into treatment, or has he on his own reached a point in his life where he felt something must be done? What conception does he have of psychotherapy and the processes by which he can improve?

Speech Therapy for Stutterers

Speech therapy with stutterers is a specialized form of psychotherapy and functions best when operated in conjunction with group psychotherapy. Therapy involving overcoming the avoidances of the stutterer seems to require group support and group morale for the challenging venture of attacking the old fears and seeking out new ones.

Thirty years ago, speech therapy for the stutterer aimed chiefly at the avoidance of the occurrence of the stuttering block. The assumption was that the proper treatment for the stutterer was somehow to prevent the stuttering from ever occurring again. Suggestion, faith, hypnosis, drills, distraction, relaxation formulas, breathing exercises, and many other curious rituals were employed to prevent blocks. In modern clinics and school systems, these methods have largely disappeared.

Only hypnosis survives in any significant clinical use, but not just for symptom prevention. Newer approaches are exploring the use of hypnosis for attitude changes and for support in going ahead in the face of guilt and shame, or of reducing these feelings long enough to enable the stutterer to experience success in going ahead.

Modern speech therapy has largely rejected direct efforts to produce fluency in the stutterer as being superficial and symptomatic, and sets as its goal the weakening of the stutterer's avoidance gradient.

Here are some of the methods, at the more immediate levels of conflict, by which the stutterer can be helped through a dynamically oriented speech therapy.

1. *Rediscover the stuttering.* Help the stutterer rediscover his stuttering. This involves an uncovering of the repression with which he has concealed the symptoms from himself. The stutterer covers up his stuttering not only from others but also from himself, most of all. He, too, needs to see the concealed portion of the iceberg, if it is to be melted away in the open daylight. Sometimes the stutterer represses his symptoms from himself so thoroughly that he actually has very little conception of what his stuttering is like. A first step in the self-acceptance, self-confrontation, and facing of the problem which therapy necessitates is for the stutterer to discover again what his stuttering is really like. Because stuttering is an unpleasant experience for him, he has learned not to look at it. The stutterer conceals his difficulty from many people, but most of all from himself.

2. *Rediscover listener reactions.* Early listener reactions probably punished the stutterer enough so that he avoids watching his listeners. In this phase of therapy the stutterer is asked to rediscover how his listeners really feel about his stuttering. Most stutterers feel far more guilt than they need to, because they project upon present listeners the punishments imposed by past listeners. Three simple methods by which the stutterer can rediscover listener reactions are (a) eye contact with listeners, particularly during the moment of stuttering; (b) observing the listeners' actual movements and expressions; and (c) conducting informal interviews to discover what the attitudes of his listeners really are. In Gallup-poll fashion he may include such questions as: "What do you think causes stuttering? What do you think should be done about it? Have you ever known someone who stuttered? How do you feel when you see that I am having trouble speaking to you?"

3. *Reduce anxiety and avoidance.* It is important to reduce the avoidance tendencies of the stutterer both in terms of word and situation avoidances. The tragedy of the stutterer's avoidance is not that it always fails, but that it sometimes succeeds. He is then encouraged to continue rituals or acts which go to make up so much of his visible handicap. So long as he continues in the avoidance of words and situations, he will never be freed from the handicap. It should be pointed out to him that successful avoidance is probably his worst enemy, because it lures him insidiously on

to a path which offers only transitory relief at a cost of long-term aggravation of the avoidance tendencies which are responsible for his conflict.

4. *Break up the relationship between anxiety and stuttering.* It is possible to stutter without anxiety, and it is possible to experience anxiety without having it followed inevitably by the old stuttering. In the process of rediscovering his stuttering, in the first phase of therapy, the stutterer may learn that if he lets himself stutter freely, it is possible to go through the experience of stuttering without the old accompaniment of the anxiety, shame, and hatred. It is likewise possible for a stutterer to learn how to handle himself so that in response to low moods or periods of anxiety he may respond discriminatingly, without the old struggle and frustration stemming from the avoidance. If he does not break up the relationship between his stuttering and his anxiety, then whenever he hits a low mood or a period of upset this is going to be reflected inevitably in his speech, bringing back his vocational and social handicap in full force. On the other hand, if he learns how to stutter without fear and to respond to old fears without the old struggle, then he will be largely freed from his handicap. Many stutterers have learned modes of handling their fears and blocks which may be relatively independent of their mood level or the way they feel at the moment. Unless the stutterer can develop this capacity, and can reduce the old ratio of fear to stuttering, he will be the victim of every change in mood and every upset in his life.

5. *Break up the relationship between guilt and stuttering.* Just as the stutterer can learn that it is possible to stutter without anxiety, so he can learn to stutter without guilt. He can learn techniques for making his audience feel more at ease and himself less guilty. Open stuttering is one important method of achieving this separation of guilt and stuttering. As the stutterer accepts himself and his own feelings more, there will be less guilt and therefore less stuttering arising out of the emotionality of the utterance.

6. *Break up the relationship between guilt and silence.* Silence, it is said, is the friend of the accused. There does seem to be, moreover, a relationship between silence and guilt. As a response to threat in a new situation or from unknown forces, silence is a natural defensive reaction which is found all the way up and down the phylogenetic scale. Yet in a situation which calls for speech, the stutterer may come to feel quite guilty over his silences. Take, for example, the familiar case of the boy who knows the answers in school but who remains silent rather than risk reciting. All guilt stems in a sense from a feeling of not measuring up, not being the person you should be. In such a situation the young stutterer will develop guilt quite readily. Many stutterers, even the most severe, show almost a compulsion to keep talking, and seem willing to do almost anything to

prevent the occurrence of silence. For these reasons it is important in therapy to help the stutterer free himself from the tyranny of silence. He needs to learn to feel comfortable during silence, to feel free to tolerate silence without the old fear and guilt which has so pressingly accompanied his silences in the past.

7. *Break up the relationship between guilt and fluency.* In the double approach-avoidance conflict, there is guilt over fluent speech as well as guilt over stuttering. Fluent speech can become so alien to the stutterer's concept of himself that when he does hit a wave of fluency in his speech, he often feels strange and apprehensive, as though it is better speaking than he deserves. Because of this factor, and because in many situations fluent speech is a highly aggressive act, many stutterers appear to suffer an unconscious guilt from fluency, as well as from stuttering. In therapy it is always wise to inquire into the real meaning of fluency to the stutterer and to interpret guilt feelings where they appear. Possibly one reason for the ability of many stutterers to speak better under temporarily strong positive suggestion is that the hypnotist or other suggester in effect reassures the stutterer: "It will be all right for you to speak fluently to these people. I say you can do it, so it is my responsibility, not yours."

8. *Build secure authority relationships.* The stutterer needs to become more comfortable in interpersonal relationships, especially authority figures. Some techniques of speech therapy, by "desensitizing" the stutterer or building up schizoidlike "psychological barriers," appear to go exactly counter to the basic principle of psychotherapy, which aims at bringing the stutterer into closer relationships with other people so that he will feel less disturbance in their presence. Psychological barriers, and all "public-be-damned" type of techniques which the older authorities in speech correction have advocated, are essentially repressively symptomatic; they are antithetical to good psychotherapy and sound interpersonal relationships. The aim of therapy should be to make the person less, not more, alone with others.

9. *Integration of role.* The stutterer needs to integrate himself in a new role. For some, probably a minority, a way out seems to be in a new role as a normal speaker. For others, and more commonly, the new role must be as a thoroughly integrated and self-accepting stutterer. Again, there is a division in our practice. Should we make the stutterer feel less like other people or more like other people? Possibly, the persistent efforts by naive stutterers to make themselves feel like normal speakers reveals a basically sound striving toward a path out of the maze.

10. *Adjustment to fluency.* When a stutterer accepts himself and gives up efforts at role playing, he no longer has need for the defensive functions of the symptom. He foregoes the neurotic gratification of being a "giant

in chains," and instead must reconcile himself to being an ordinary mortal with ordinary weaknesses. This step involves the terminal phases of therapy and involves adjustment to fluency, to the sensations of strangeness and guilt that fluency so often brings to the stutterer. The therapist must help the stutterer adjust to his new smoother speech, just as earlier in therapy he helped the stutterer adjust to his broken speech. A systematic preparation for recovery is usually indicated, as well as a continuation of therapy well beyond the point of the first attainment of fluency. Usually, this phase includes a thorough joint exploration of the stutterer's life goals and attitudes and is probably the most crucial step in the entire treatment process. The stutterer must be willing to relinquish the secondary gains of the symptom, a step already facilitated by some of the earlier phases. For example, when the stutterer faces his stuttering and is open about it, he necessarily loses much of the reinforcement derived from the ego-protective functions of the symptom. He no longer can use the stuttering to escape from society or to avoid threat of failure, so that the stuttering loses any real protective function it may have had.

Child Therapy

The younger the stutterer, the less important relatively are the secondary factors and the more important the primary factors. In the adult, it has become possible to deal effectively, in a large proportion of cases, with a therapy that is aimed primarily at secondary features, e.g., shame, struggle reaction, concealment, situation avoidance, rather than original causes. In part this approach is based on the assumption that stuttering becomes a vicious circle, a self-maintaining behavior system that continues long after the original causes have ceased to operate (**10, 48**). With a child no such assumption is possible. The stuttering child is still caught up in the matrix of the forces which surrounded the initial appearance of the symptom. His own parents are still the main authority figures with which he must deal. The therapist is also an authority figure, and because of his bigness may pose to the stutterer the threat of being changed by one bigger and more powerful than himself. The child is far less aware of the potential handicap of his stuttering. Usually, he is drafted or dragged into therapy in the first place. He has far less readiness to cope with the somewhat intellectualized verbal systems of current speech therapy.

Because of these differences, the child stutterer without a well-developed awareness and secondary pattern is best treated in terms of the general methods of child psychotherapy. He may be helped indirectly through the parents, through activity therapy or play therapy, or some form of release therapy (**24**). Whether the techniques described in this chapter can be modified to fit into the process of psychotherapy for the child stutterer depends upon a number of individual factors. Among the more important of these are his awareness of his stuttering, his self-concept, how much he evinces of struggle, how much he uses tricks, how much of a secondary stuttering pattern he shows, and especially to what extent causal factors, in terms of parental relationship, are still operative. Most of the discussion in this section deals with the treatment of the advanced young secondary stutterer or with the adult. Among child psychotherapies which seem especially effective with child stutterers are the "relationship therapy" of Frederick Allen (3) and the "release therapy" of David Levy (24). These therapies happen to deal directly with two of the deeper levels of conflict in approach-avoidance conflict theory—emotional content and relationship-conflict (38).

Psychotherapy: Expression of Feelings

Every psychotherapy is based to some extent upon the release of feeling, but it is rare that the speech of a patient can point so sensitively to the areas in which expression is especially needed. Most stutterers reveal emotionally loaded areas in which they are likely to experience more blocking, even within the context of the same interpersonal relationship. The study by Bardrick and Sheehan (4, 5) demonstrated that verbal content which involved a threat to the stutterer's self-esteem, or lowering of his status in the listener's eyes, is likely to produce more stuttering.

Conflict at the feeling level in stuttering intrudes conspicuously into the therapeutic situation. The feeling of guilt, which has an inhibiting effect upon speech even in normal speakers, conspicuously produces blocking in the stutterer, just as it does in the small boy trying to make excuses. Although there are factors other than emotional loading which help to determine the stuttering occurring in the therapeutic situation, the discriminating therapist who is able to exercise some clinical judgment is usually on fairly safe ground in exploring the feelings behind any sudden surges of severe blocking, or raising interpretive questions as the source of such blockings.

The special speech therapy which has been developed for adult stutterers, largely by Van Riper, Johnson, Bryngelson, and a few others, has tended to provide, in addition to the rationale originally given by these therapists, a form of emotional release, a series of more or less systematic exercises in the expression of aggression toward the stutterer's audience. Unlike the customary expression of aggression through speech which might make the stutterer feel highly guilty and aggravate his speech conflicts, in the context of this therapy the assumption by the therapist of the guilt, due to what the stutterer does to his audience, enables the stutterer to take a more aggressive role without the inhibitions he would usually apply to himself. He is enabled to be himself without the necessity of holding back in terms of his usual tendencies to incorporate guilt from situations in which the stuttering makes some listener uncomfortable. Though there is a certain element of acting out in such therapy, in the initial phases, at least, the benefits in supporting the stutterer in the venture of undertaking new and more outgoing roles seem to outweigh the disadvantages. Such acting out of aggressive roles seems helpful to some stutterers, though it is neither a sufficient therapy, nor for many, a necessary one.

With a combined program of psychotherapy and speech therapy based on the reduction of the avoidance tendencies, the stutterer may be enabled to progress beyond this supported acting out of aggressions to a grasp of the speaker-listener relationship to a degreee which renders acting out of aggressions no longer necessary. He can accept his needs without the necessity for acting out on them. When that stage is reached, the stutterer will be much further along the road to a permanent recovery.

Feelings of guilt frequently crop up during the therapy in relation to the progress the stutterer feels he should make. Stuttering therapy differs from other therapies in that the stuttering itself provides such a ready index of apparent progress. Perhaps no other type of patient reflects so faithfully momentary shifts in the relationship to the therapist and to the outside world.

Initially, the stutterer often feels that he must put on a good front for the therapist or that he must impress the therapist with his motivation and effort. By reassuring the therapist that continual progress is being made, he attempts to reassure himself. Unless the therapist takes some active position in identifying such role-playing, the stutterer begins to respond artificially and falsely to the therapist, just as he does to other listeners. So the stutterer comes to feel just as guilty toward the therapist as he does toward outside society. With such an eventuality, all effective therapy grinds to a halt. Such dangers are prone to arise from two sources: (1) the inherent challenge to the stutterer in the reduction of avoidance; (2) the structuring of the therapeutic course, as "it's up to you" without sufficient qualification, or sometimes even with it.

In terms of the feelings of the stutterer, the special technique of stuttering therapy involves another problem in which there is perhaps a basic unresolved conflict between this therapy and other psychotherapies. With conventional psychotherapy, there is a maximum permissiveness on the superego dimension, that is, on the dimension of what the patient *should* or *should not* do. The therapist, it is said, is on the side of the id. He is not interested in the day-to-day behavioral outcomes of the patient, except as the patient may feel that he has problems deriving from his day-to-day behavior. The conventional psychotherapist has the luxury of being able to remain fairly detached and noncommittal on any issue of whether the patient has done something wrong. He can respond with, "How do you feel about it?" and accept whatever verbalization the patient next gives him. The speech therapist, who knows how reinforcement of avoidance can make the stutterer worse or retard his recovery, may find it difficult to be this neutral about the outcome.

The speech therapist working with the stutterer has often an initial task of teaching a certain philosophy, and teaching certain relationships between avoidance, conflict, fear, and speech-blocking. He cannot sit passively while the stutterer flounders through his repertoire of sporadically successful tricks. Because of the learned behavior aspect and the reinforcement aspect of stuttering, the speech therapist has to impress a certain amount of *should* and *should not* upon the stutterer. This poses a great many problems for therapy. Among these is this very important problem: Later on in therapy the stutterer may come to a conflict area in which he needs a highly permissive kind of psychotherapeutic relationship. The "stuttering therapist" may already have cast himself in a superego role to such an extent that he cannot deal effectively with the problem, or in some instances the stutterer may be unable to bring up the problem at all.

We know of no magic or all-wise solutions to the foregoing dilemma, but we have observed and experienced it, and we have tried some clinical variations to meet the problem of the therapist's changing roles. We have tried offering speech therapy from one clinician, and a client-centered-type psychotherapy in conjunction with individual speech therapy. We have also tried, for individuals who seemed suited in terms of the picture presented at intake, or from practical limitations, speech therapy without formal psychotherapy for some individuals and straight psychotherapy without any work on the stuttering for others. The results seem to hinge, more than any other one factor, on the personality of the individual or group therapist and the strength and nature of the relationship the therapist is able to develop. We also have the impression, partly bolstered by a study of prognostic potential using the Rorschach, that the initial motivational and ego structure of the patient is a far greater determining force in the outcome than the formal arrangements.

The important message for the "stuttering therapist" in these considerations lies in this: The therapist must expect and plan to handle difficulties in the expression of feelings from the stutterer if he is informational, didactic, challenging, or otherwise active in the initial stages of treatment, as many speech therapists tend to be.

At different stages in therapy, the therapist for the stutterer must restructure his role, perhaps openly to the stutterer, as being somewhat different with respect to the expression of feeling. In the early stages of therapy, the therapist is interested in the stutterer's feelings, and he may be highly sympathetic to the stutterer's urge to substitute, run away, or otherwise avoid. But the therapist cannot remain entirely neutral with respect to what the stutterer *does* about these feelings. That is, the speech therapist can be permissive on the feeling level but cannot be completely permissive on the doing level, unless he is willing to work for an indefinite period in an entirely supportive (and dubiously supportive) role.

If the therapist is sensitive to some of the problems detailed in the foregoing, then he will structure the therapy and restructure the relationship at times as the stutterer passes through some of the phases of the treatment process. In any case, all these processes will be facilitated considerably by the outward expression of the stutterer's approach-avoidance conflict at the level of feelings, the level of emotional loading of verbal content. Usually it is wiser to work therapeutically with word fears and situations first, and then with feelings, including providing opportunity for maximally free expression of feelings, before very much can be done in a direct way about relationships and ego defenses. Not every case follows a rigid sequence, of course. Rather, the conflict level can be used as a rough guide of what is frequently the procession through conflict areas in the treatment of stuttering.

Psychotherapy: The Building of New Relationships

Psychotherapy may be defined as the undoing or reversal of the process of maladjustment. Maladjustment, in turn, involves essentially unsatisfactory relationships with other human beings, which have stemmed largely from unsatisfactory relationships in the individual's past, especially parental relationships. The process of psychotherapy requires a new parental figure, the therapist, who supplies affection or support which has theoretically been lacking in parental contact.

The importance of interpersonal factors in stuttering is highlighted by the observation that the stutterer does not have trouble when alone, save perhaps for a few who seem to project an audience for themselves. He stutters more or less according to the number of people in the room and conspicuously has more trouble talking to authority figures. Approach-avoidance conflict arising out of the interpersonal factor is a fundamental level of conflict in stuttering.

Since interpersonal relations and the respective roles of speaker and listener so strikingly affect stuttering behavior, the working through by the stutterer of feelings and conflicts revolving around certain crucial relationships becomes essential to success. Perhaps this is why group therapy, at least as part of the program, is so often employed in the treatment of the adult stutterer.

Stuttering appears to be aggravated in the presence of authority figures. Since the therapist is usually an "authority," one of the more important functions of the therapy is to provide the stutterer experience in relating to an authority who is more permissive and more giving of love than were perhaps some earlier authority figures in the stutterer's life.

Psychotherapy: Integration in a New Role

In our culture the male is pushed toward competition and achievement more than the female, and the prevalence of male over female stutterers may not be unrelated to this circumstance. Through its defensive function of keeping the stutterer out of dangerous competition, the disorder may lead to a feeling, probably furthered by the Demosthenes legend, that if only he did not stutter there could be no limit to his accomplishments.

When he finally achieves a fair degree of fluency, the stutterer seems to experience reactions in two stages. First is a feeling of strangeness that he should be talking so well, a feeling almost of guilt over fluency, possibly a recathexis of some of the old guilt attached to stuttering. Unless measures are taken through psychotherapy to deal with these feelings, relapse may occur at this point, just when the stutterer appears to have found relief at last.

A second stage in the stutterer's adjustment to his fluency may involve, surprisingly, reactions of disappointment. Some painful adjustments in self-concept take place. No longer can the stutterer maintain his rationalizations of the tremendous strides he would make if only the stuttering did not hold him back.

Once he has attained fluency, the stutterer and his new-found free speech do not automatically live happily ever after, and clinical experience shows that many problems can result from fluency. Two of our cases illustrated this point. One was the cure that almost produced a divorce: a previously meek accountant used his new gift of tongue to lash back at his dominating wife, and the storms that followed almost broke up their marriage. The other was a 15-year-old whose parents were shocked by the by-products of his sudden improvement. He went through a period of being a thoroughly revolting adolescent, and not until they were willing to accept him in a new role did the behavior problem diminish.

Because such events are not rare, continuation of therapy well beyond the first attainment of fluency is usually advisable. When fluency is reached, therapy should not terminate but merely enter a new final phase. Only after he has adjusted to his fluency, and to the problems resulting from his own improvement, is the stutterer ready to handle a more normal role in society.

References

1. Adler, A., *Problems of Neurosis*, London, Kegan Paul, Trench, Trubner, 1929.
2. Alexander, F. M., *The Use of the Self*, New York, Dutton, 1932.
3. Allen, F. H., *Psychotherapy with Children*, New York, Norton, 1942.
4. Bardrick, R. A., "Emotional content as a factor in stuttering behavior," Ph. D. dissertation, University of California at Los Angeles, 1956.
5. Bardrick, R. A., and Sheehan, J. G., "Emotional loading as a source of conflict in stuttering," *American Psychologist*, XI, 1956.
6. Black, J. W., "The effect of delayed side-tone upon vocal rate and intensity," *Journal of Speech and Hearing Disorders*, XVI, 1951.
7. Bloodstein, O., "Conditions under which stuttering is reduced or absent: A review of literature," *Journal of Speech Disorders*, XIV, 1949.
8. Brown, S. F., "The loci of stutterings in the speech sequence," *Journal of Speech Disorders*, X, 1945.
9. Dollard, J., and Miller, N. E., *Personality and Psychotherapy*, New York, McGraw-Hill, 1950.
10. Dunlap, K., *Habits: Their Making and Unmaking*, New York, Liveright, 1932.
11. Eisenson, J., and Horowitz, E., "The influence of propositionality on stuttering," *Journal of Speech Disorders*, X, 1945.
12. Eisenson, J., and Wells, C., "A study of the influence of communicative responsibility in a choral speech situation for stutterers," *Journal of Speech Disorders*, VII, 1942.
13. Fairbanks, G., "Systematic research in experimental phonetics: I. A theory of the speech mechanism as a servosystem," *Journal of Speech and Hearing Disorders*, XIX, 1954.
14. Fenichel, O., *The Psychoanalytic Theory of Neurosis*, New York, Norton, 1945, pp. 311–317.
15. Freud, S., *The Problem of Anxiety*, New York, Norton, 1936.
16. Frick, J. V., "An exploratory study of the effect of punishment (electric shock) upon stuttering behavior," Ph. D. dissertation, State University of Iowa, 1951.
17. Herzberg, A., *Active Psychotherapy*, New York, Grune and Stratton, 1945.
18. Johnson, W., *People in Quandaries: The Semantics of Personal Adjustment*, New York, Harper, 1946.

19. Johnson, W., ed., assisted by Leutenegger, R. R., *Stuttering in Children and Adults: Thirty Years of Research at the University of Iowa,* Minneapolis, University of Minnesota Press, 1955.
20. Johnson, W., and Inness, M., "Studies in the psychology of stuttering: Statistical analysis of the adaptation and consistency effects in relation to stuttering," *Journal of Speech Disorders,* IV, 1939.
21. Johnson, W., and Knott, J. R., "The moment of stuttering," *Journal of Genetic Psychology,* XLVIII, 1936, 475–480.
22. Lee, B. S., "Artificial stutter," *Journal of Speech and Hearing Disorders,* XVI, 1951.
23. Lee, B. S., "Effects of delayed speech feedback," *Journal of the Accoustical Society of America,* XXII, 1950.
24. Levy, D., "Release therapy," in *Contemporary Psychopathology,* S. S. Tomkins (ed.), Cambridge, Cambridge University, 1947.
25. Miller, N. E., "Experimental studies of conflict," in *Personality and the Behavior Disorders,* J. McV. Hunt (ed.), New York, Ronald Press, 1944.
26. Mowrer, O. H., "Two-factor learning theory reconsidered, with special reference to secondary reinforcement and the concept of habit," *Psychological Review,* LXIII, 1956.
27. Mowrer, O. H., and Viek, P., "An experimental analogue of fear from a sense of helplessness," *Journal of Abnormal and Social Psychology,* XLIII, 1948.
28. Porter, H. V. K., "Studies in the psychology of stuttering: Stuttering phenomena related to size and personnel of audience," *Journal of Speech Disorders,* IV, 1939.
29. Shane, M. L. S., "Effect on stuttering of alteration in auditory feedback," in *Stuttering in Children and Adults,* W. Johnson (ed.), Minneapolis, University of Minnesota Press, 1955.
30. Sheehan, J. G., "Authority relation as an interpersonal factor in stuttering," unpublished manuscript, Speech Clinic, University of California at Los Angeles, 1955.
31. Sheehan, J. G., "Guilt as a source of conflict in stuttering," paper read before meetings of American Speech and Hearing Association, Cincinnati, 1957.
32. Sheehan, J. G., "An integration of psychotherapy and speech therapy through a conflict theory of stuttering," *Journal of Speech and Hearing Disorders,* XIX, 1954.
33. Sheehan, J. G., "The modification of stuttering through nonreinforcement," *Journal of Abnormal and Social Psychology,* XLVI, 1951.
34. Sheehan, J. G., "A sentence completion test for stutterers," paper read before meetings of American Speech and Hearing Association, Chicago, 1956.
35. Sheehan, J. G., "A study of the phenomena of stuttering," M.A. thesis, University of Michigan, 1946.

36. Sheehan, J. G., "Stuttering in terms of conflict and reinforcement," in *Stuttering: Significant Theories and Therapies*, E. Hahn (ed.), 2nd ed., Stanford, Stanford University Press, 1956.
37. Sheehan, J. G., "Time pressure as an interpersonal factor in stuttering," unpublished manuscript, Speech Clinic, University of California at Los Angeles, 1957.
38. Sheehan, J. G., "Theory and treatment of stuttering as an approach-avoidance conflict," *Journal of Psychology,* XXXVI, 1953.
39. Sheehan, J. G., and Bardrick, R. A., "Sex of the listener as an interpersonal factor in stuttering," unpublished manuscript, Speech Clinic, University of California at Los Angeles, 1955.
40. Sheehan, J. G., and Voas, R. B., "Stuttering as conflict: I. Comparison of therapy techniques involving approach and avoidance," *Journal of Speech and Hearing Disorders,* in press.
41. Sheehan, J. G., and Voas, R. B., "Tension patterns during stuttering in relation to conflict, fear-reduction, and reinforcement," *Speech Monographs,* XXI, 1954.
42. Sheehan, J. G., and Zelen, S., "Level of aspiration in stutterers and non-stutterers," *Journal of Abnormal and Social Psychology,* LI, 1955.
43. Shulman, E., "Factors influencing the variability of stuttering," in *Stuttering in Children and Adults,* W. Johnson (ed.), Minneapolis, University of Minnesota Press, 1955.
44. Van Riper, C., "The effects of penalty upon frequency of stuttering spasms," *Journal of General Psychology,* L, 1937.
45. Van Riper, C., *Speech Correction: Principles and Methods,* 2nd ed., New York, Prentice-Hall, 1947.
46. Van Riper, C., *Speech Correction: Principles and Methods,* 3rd ed., New York, Prentice-Hall, 1954.
47. Van Riper, C., "A study of the thoracic breathing of stutterers during expectancy and occurrence of stuttering spasms," *Journal of Speech Disorders,* I, 1936.
48. Van Riper, C., in *Stuttering: Significant Theories and Therapies,* E. Hahn (ed.), 2nd ed., Stanford, Stanford University Press, 1956.
49. Van Riper, C., "Symptomatic therapy for stuttering," in *Handbook of Speech Pathology,* L. E. Travis (ed.), New York, Appleton-Century-Crofts, 1957.
50. Van Riper, C., "To the stutterer as he begins his speech therapy," *Journal of Speech and Hearing Disorders,* XIV, 1949.
51. Van Riper, C., and Hull, C. J., "The quantitative measurement of the effect of certain situations on stuttering," in *Stuttering in Children and Adults,* W. Johnson (ed.), Minneapolis, University of Minneapolis Press, 1955.
52. Wyneken, C., "Ueber das stottern und dessen heilung [Concerning stuttering and its cure]," *Zeitschrift für Rationelle Medizin,* XXXI, 1868.

AN AGNOSTIC'S SPECULATIONS ABOUT STUTTERING

ROBERT WEST, Ph.D.

Professor of Speech and Director of the Speech and Hearing Center, Brooklyn College; Clinical Professor in the Department of Physical Medicine and Rehabilitation, New York Medical College; formerly, Professor of Speech and Director of the Speech and Hearing Clinic, University of Wisconsin; Fellow and first President of the American Speech and Hearing Association and Editor (1955–1958) of the American Speech and Hearing Association; coauthor of Phonetics *(with Claude E. Kantner) and of* The Rehabilitation of Speech *(with Merle Ansberry and Anna Carr); contributor to many professional journals including the* Quarterly Journal of Speech *and the* Journal of Speech and Hearing Disorders.

An Agnostic's Speculations About Stuttering

I. INTRODUCTION

Agnosticism as to Stuttering Theory

It is interesting to me that in the 30 years my name has been on the rolls of the American Speech and Hearing Association the percentage of the membership who profess to know the precise etiology of stuttering has steadily fallen. This in spite of the vast amount of research that has gone into the study of stuttering. Conversely, the percentage of agnostics has, of course, increased. I frankly rank myself as one of these, and I join battle only with those who, in the light of presently known facts, claim to know the basic etiology of this most enigmatic syndrome.

I have a yardstick by which I measure and appraise every theory that comes to my attention—a meter that I have consciously, or unconsciously, developed from long years in the practice of diagnosis. When one is concerned with the problem of whether a given patient fails to talk because of disease X or because of disease Y, the diagnostician must protocol the known facts: those that support either diagnosis, those that support only X, those that support only Y, and those that support neither. That habit of studying the particular I am prone to follow in studying the general. Before I can accept as a demonstrated proposition any theory of the etiology of stuttering, I submit that theory to investigation as to whether it gives a plausible explanation of the known facts about stuttering. Listed below are the principal data that constitute my yardstick. These are not statements of the steps or aspects of the etiological theory of stuttering. When we have formulated these factual aspects of knowledge about stuttering we still will not have arrived anywhere in stating an etiological principle, but we will have a schema for analyzing theories that may be proposed by ourselves and others.

The Ten-Fact Yardstick

1. *Stuttering is a phenomenon of childhood.* Some diseases are phenomena of the precocious involution of specific organs of the body; they are classed as degenerative disorders. Some are phenomena of the tardy development of certain organs or the lack of such development; they may be called, by analogy, agenerative. Clearly stuttering is not *de*generative, though it may be *a*generative.

2. *Stuttering is more prevalent among males than among females.* Though it usually begins at that period of life when there is difference in body patterns between males and females, stuttering appears to be at least partially sex-limited. Those sex differences with which stuttering is associated seem not to be those directly dependent upon the mechanism of procreation, because no marked increase in stuttering appears at the onset of puberty, and because some procreating females stutter. The sex differences involved here are also distinguishable from masculo-feminine differences, since the few girls and women who stutter are not as a class more masculine than their sisters; and the boys who stutter are not as a class deviant in masculinity from the average of their sex. We must, therefore, consider these sexual differences more basic than those concerned with the provision of nature's economy as to which sex bears the offspring.

3. *Stuttering, or the tendency to stutter, runs in families,* whether or not it is inherited à la Mendel.[1]

4. *Stuttering more often appears in families in which left-handedness occurs than in families characterized by uniform right-handedness.* It appears to be associated with the late acquisition of a basic preference for, or a greater skill of, one hand over the other.

5. *Stuttering appears more frequently in families in which multiple births occur than in families in which the children come one by one.*

6. *Stuttering is associated with the late acquisition of speech and with the perseveration into the second decade of the child's life of phonetic lapses that are normally found only in the first.* Stutterers also often show clumsy articulation.

7. *Stuttering rarely begins with an acute episode in the child's life, but*

[1] Mendelian traits are transmitted by the germ plasm at conception. Social and cultural heredity often resembles the germinal.

usually is insidious in its onset. The child is discovered to be a "stutterer," but rarely is he seen to begin stuttering. In the stutterer's life the beginning of stuttering is as hard to date as the beginning of puberty, of adulthood, or of senility.

8. *Stuttering is a convulsive phenomenon.* The breaks in speech do not involve momentary failures of muscular tonus, but sudden spasms. In addition, the stutterer demonstrates generally heightened tonus of the striate musculature. His vocal inflections are less labile. Diadochocinesis[2] of the muscles of articulation is slower generally than that of the nonstutterer, in some cases approaching that of the spastic paretic.

9. *Stuttering is reflexive psychosocially.* The fear that the patient may stutter in a given situation increases the tendency to stutter in that situation. This feared situation is usually one in which it is important—at least the patient thinks so—that he does not stutter. Examples are situations in which he talks to teacher, policeman, judge, or other special authority figures; talks before a class or group of persons; is expected to convey some specific information, such as an address, telephone number, his age, his father's name, for which there are no substitute verbal forms.

10. *Stuttering is manifest in persons who exhibit differences from the nonstutterer in certain basic physiological reactions.* Though these differences are within normal limits they appear significant, viz.: the heart rhythm of the stuttering child does not regularize itself as early as does that of the nonstutterer; stutterers as a group are more allergic than nonstutterers; they show higher blood-sugar ratings than do nonstutterers.[3]

These are the stubborn facts that must be explained by the theorist who would advance a working hypothesis as to the cause of stuttering. These facts, and others yet to be discovered, are part of the jigsaw puzzle that someday may be assembled to furnish the answer to our enigma. None of the current published theories of the etiology of stuttering furnishes a frame in which the pieces of this puzzle may be precisely and completely assembled.

From the above statements one may infer that I am describing the usual, common, garden variety of stuttering. I am not trying to explain all varieties. Particularly do I rule out the case of a person whose stuttering did not appear in childhood but began suddenly with some traumatic

[2] See p. 182 for a more detailed discussion of this aspect of stuttering.
[3] Kopp, G. A., "Metabolic studies of stutterers," *Speech Monographs,* I, 1934.

episode in his adult life. I would judge that all such cases of stuttering belong in another syndrome—say hysteria—since they usually lack many or all of the identifying characteristics I have described above. In separating them from the usual variety of stuttering, we should, of course, be aware of the tendency of persons to forget unpleasant experiences of their youth or to conceal the defects of their children or of their families. We should be especially suspicious that childhood stuttering has been forgotten or concealed if any or all of the following facts appear in the history of the individual in question:

1. He is left-handed or comes from a family in which one or more left-handed members are found.
2. He is a twin or comes from a "twinning" family.
3. His speech began late and exhibits, or at one time exhibited, articulatory defects other than, or in addition to, the stuttering.

If the reader has in mind some unusual adult stutterer whose symptoms are not mere exacerbations of childhood defects, I exclude such a case from any generalizations about stuttering that may be included in this monograph. The only characteristics such a case has in common with the patients I am attempting to describe are the present overt speech symptoms. There are also sporadic cases of stuttering in adulthood in which the speech symptom is the prodromal sign or forerunner, of brain disease or deterioration. Then, of course, what seems to be stuttering may accompany motor aphasias. I am not discussing these and similar symptom pictures.

The Agnostic Answers Certain Basic Questions

When one says that he is an agnostic he must mean, of course, that he doubts that answers are available to certain fundamental questions. Two agnostics need not necessarily agree on which questions to answer *"non scio."* What are these fundamental questions?

1. Is stuttering a real independent syndrome, a definite entity in the catalogue of symptom complexes?
2. Is it a semantic creation produced by giving a name to an aspect of the child's normal development?
3. Is it basically psychogenic, psychosocially caused?
4. Is it basically physiogenic, organically caused?
5. Does it have one cause?
6. Does it have many causes?

7. Is there a distinction to be drawn between the basic etiology of stuttering and its precipitating factors?
8. What is the cause, or causes, of the syndrome called stuttering?
9. What are the factors precipitating it?

Let me now define my agnosticism in terms of the questions above.

1. *Is stuttering a real etiologic entity?* Yes. The very fact that we can definitely generalize about its phenomenology bespeaks its reality. The *Journal of Speech and Hearing Disorders* is heavily larded with statistical studies showing the characteristics distinguishing stutterers from nonstutterers. Stuttering is a reality that parents, teachers, and physicians all recognize with a high order of agreement or reliability.

2. *Is stuttering "semantic"?* The term "semantic" here refers to the establishment of a definitely recognizable functional syndrome by assigning a pejorative designation to phenomena not essentially symptomatic of a disorder. The semantogenic theory as an explanation of stuttering, which is discussed in this volume by another contributor, implies that it is the reaction of the child to a stigmatizing label. According to this theory stuttering is the result of an attempt on the part of the child to disclaim and avoid the penalizing designation "stutterer."

Is stuttering thus semantic? No. Since many of the differences between stutterer and nonstutterer are in traits that have no connection with the mere label "stuttering," it seems obvious to me that the essence of the syndrome is in the condition rather than the name. One might accept the semantic theory if stuttering did not embrace reactions and conditions of the child, many of them antedating the stuttering, about which the child and his parents are quite ignorant and which, therefore, cannot enter into the process of labeling. If one refused to use the term "mumps" in the presence of a child suffering from parotitis, the child would still have a swollen jaw. The concept of the semantogenesis, or diagnosogenesis, of stuttering is readily accepted by the stutterer himself. In it he finds some comfort, some ego support. Such morale building may have a beneficial effect upon his stuttering, even though the basis for his morale may be faulty introspection and an overpersonalized insight. To me, a nonstutterer, who can view the syndrome from a perspective distance, the concept of its semantogenesis seems invalid.

3. *Is stuttering basically psychogenic?* Probably not. In the confirmed stutterer the factors that trigger or precipitate the blockings of speech appear to be psychic, and it may be that stuttering therapy must be directed at these precipitating factors; but the underlying, original cause, immedicable though it may be, probably does not lie in the psychosocial environment of the child.

4. *Is stuttering basically physiogenic?* Yes, probably. Too many signposts point in this direction for one to deny the organicity of stuttering. It is true that some of the signs are ambiguous; but even if we misinterpret a few of them the conclusion to be drawn from their general agreement is highly presumptive of a physiogenic explanation. It should be recalled that we are trying to explain something that appears at a definite time of life, predominantly in one sex, and reappears in succeeding generations in association with other basic biologic traits. To say that the explanation is probably in some organic factor is only a modest assumption from these premises.

5. *Does stuttering have one cause?* I do not know, but its uniformity of manifestations from person to person would suggest a uniformity of etiology. The difference of stuttering phenomena from case to case may be explained as individual variations due to physical, cultural, physiological, or even pathological deviations—factors independent of the syndrome of stuttering.

6. *Does stuttering have many causes?* Stuttering probably has only a single cause, but many precipitators.

7. *Can we distinguish between basic and precipitating factors of causation?* Yes, probably. Our literature is replete with articles distinguishing between primary and secondary stuttering. It is quite likely that those who make this distinction are talking about the difference that takes place in the child when the precipitating factors conspire with, or replace, the basic causes of stuttering.

8. *What is the cause of stuttering?* I do not know.

9. *What are the factors precipitating the speech manifestations of stuttering?* So far, research has provided many clear descriptions of these factors. I shall allude to many of these findings later in this monograph. Let us not, however, mistake these factors for basic causes.

In summary of the credo: Stuttering *probably* has one organic cause, so far not identified, and many precipitating factors.

II. THE "ORGANICITY" OF STUTTERING

Speculations and Comparisons

I wish now to engage in a bit of speculation about one possible organic cause—speculation that may both explain the credo and suggest the direction of our search for this cause. We shall begin with the nature of the chief symptom of stuttering, its clonic spasms. We must test the postulate that stuttering belongs to the great group of convulsive disorders. We must consider the possibility that in the family of speech disorders stuttering may be only a stepchild and that if a specialist in convulsive disorders, without any previous experience with or knowledge of stuttering, came upon a stutterer, he might at once label the disorder a seizure. Such a specialist would compare stuttering with the spasms that sweep through the muscles of the head, neck, and upper extremities when the athetotic person attempts to speak, or with the seizure mechanisms of the mildly epileptic. Let us pursue for a few pages the speculation that stuttering is a form of seizure and, more particularly, that it is epileptiform.

One of the stutterer's basic phenomena is general hypertonicity in musculature. Obviously it is in such a setting that epilepsy appears. One of the characteristics of the stutterer's voice is its tonic lack of lability of inflection. It is a byword of the medical clinic that the epileptic shows a "plateau voice," a spastic monotone.

Stuttering, a Relative of Epilepsy

I realize that convulsions do not always stem from what is properly called *epilepsy*. There is epilepsy proper, called *idiopathic epilepsy;* there are the related disorders, the *epilepsies;* and there are *epileptiform seizures.* Some convulsive disorders bear only a superficial resemblance to idiopathic epilepsy. Some are due to focal lesions in the brain, some to special, and often temporary, acid-base imbalances; some are symptoms of specific intoxicating diseases. The significant connecting element in all of these disorders is that the convulsions come and go with very slight changes of causative factors. Normalcy appears to hang on a very slender thread. With such a disorder any fear, excitement, or emotional tension may be sufficient to break that thread. In physiological terms, the patient never deviates far from his convulsive threshold. When one asks the mother, "Did John ever have convulsions?" she is likely to reply, "No, except the time when he had the indigestion." Other children with the same indigestion escape the convulsions, but John's threshold is so low that the indigestion appears to be the "cause" of the seizure. Thus epilepsy seems to be "triggered," i.e., the reaction appears to be all out of proportion to the apparent cause. It is said, therefore, that there are basic *causes* and precipitating *factors.* It is this tendency of epilepsy to respond to the trigger that often involves it in functional psychosocial tie-ups. Hence in some cases it may be partly a primitive unconscious malingering; or the disease may appear to be wholly hysterical in persons whose threshold of convulsion, though within normal limits, is low.

In our parallel between stuttering and epilepsy let us consider epilepsy proper and those convulsive disorders that have similar causes, omitting disorders that are similar only in symptoms. Besides being convulsive, both stuttering and epilepsy are more common in childhood than after puberty. Both are more frequent in males than in females. Idiopathic epilepsy is, like stuttering, familial. Both epilepsy and stuttering are reflexive, i.e., just as the anticipation of stuttering spasms will aggravate the condition, so the fear of a convulsion may precipitate one. The most intriguing parallel, however, between stuttering and epilepsy is in the area of the physiological reactions, particularly with respect to sugar metabolism. The aspect of epilepsy to which attention is here drawn is, of course, its manifestation of convulsions—clonic twitching, tonic postural distortion, and squirming.[4]

The Role of Blood Sugar in Stuttering

Here our speculations lead us to consider two antithetical disorders, epilepsy and diabetes mellitus, the former characterized by a drop in blood sugar and the latter by its rise. One of the connecting links between epilepsy and diabetes is insulin. If the patient has too little insulin in his blood, his sugar rises; in extreme insulin debt he becomes comatose. Put too much insulin into the blood stream and he becomes virtually a temporary epileptic. A dose of sugar, however, ends the convulsions.

This comparison becomes impressive when we note that rarely, if ever, is stuttering found among diabetics[5] while it is often found in association with epilepsy. We speculate, therefore, whether the high sugar ratings

[4] The epileptiform nature of stuttering is suggested and supported by the findings of Harrison, H. S., "A study of the speech of sixty institutionalized epileptics," M.A. thesis, Louisiana State University, 1946 (Abstract of thesis, *Speech Monographs,* XIV, 1947). Harrison found that an inordinately large number of these epileptics were stutterers.

[5] The documentation of this assertion is difficult, largely because of its negative nature. The author had the good fortune to have access to the records of the diabetics in one of the hospitals in which the original experimentation with insulinization of diabetics was checked and verified. Of the volumes of diabetic case records not one was found in which stuttering was mentioned. The author is aware that the interns and residents who wrote the histories might have neglected to investigate the speech symptoms of their patients and possibly might have failed to mention stuttering even if they observed it. On the other hand, one physician who read every history, saw every case, and interviewed every patient at length said he was "positive" that he found no stutterers among them. Since that time the author has seen countless stutterers and has drawn up their histories without finding a single diabetic. Since diabetes mellitus is by no means a rare disease and is year by year becoming more frequently recognized, the simultaneous occurrence of diabetes and stuttering should by chance have often taken place. The fact that such occurrence has not taken place (or has not been reported) seems indicative of the incompatibility of these two disorders.

of the stutterer may not be evidence of a failing attempt on the part of the system to arrest the factors of ictogenesis[6] that trigger the stuttering. If epileptics had an automatic secretion of animal sugar into the blood whenever the aura of a seizure appeared, the convulsion might be aborted and the term "epilepsy" might never have been applied to this illness. One of the devices recommended to epileptic patients to abort or prevent the convulsion is, at the appearance of the aura, to grasp one hand with the other and, tensing all the muscles of the body in an isometric[7] contraction, hold on until the aura disappears—in short, to substitute a voluntary, controlled "spasm" for the involuntary and uncontrolled seizure. Doubtless one of the side effects of this preventive device is the secretion into the blood of quantities of glycogen, animal sugar, immediately available to the tissues. It is interesting to note that one of the commonly used techniques for learning to control involuntary stuttering is the production of vigorous voluntary stuttering. It is possible that the rationale usually offered for this therapy should be extended to include what is intended in the prevention of overt convulsions of epilepsy.

May we postulate, then, that the function of the high blood sugar of the stutterer is to arrest convulsions, and that without the sugar the stutterer would exhibit much severer spasms. Without the glycogen his spasms might be frankly epileptiform. Viewed thus, the stutterer is a person with a low spasm threshold, but with a compensatory device for raising the threshold to prevent out-and-out convulsions when placed under psychosocial pressure. The spasms that do occur would seem under this light to be partially aborted convulsions. The stutterer may be seen, then, as a variety of epileptic who has an automatic control of those factors that arrest convulsions whenever they start. He has a cybernetically balanced sugar metabolism that acts like the automatic sprinkler system for fire protection of flammable buildings.

This "ictostat" of the stutterer, however, does not completely inhibit convulsions. It arrests the *grand mal* but allows minor spasms to occur. The convulsions that do occur take place in muscles that are under control of those centers of the brain stem in which are stored the patterns for the automatic emotional behavior of the cerebrospinal system. Those parts of the striped musculature that are involved in laughing, smiling, crying, weeping, and in reactions of fear are the parts of the stutterer's musculature that go into convulsions in spite of the cybernetic checks upon them. Other muscles of his body do not participate in these spasms except as they

[6] "Ictogenesis" is a frankly contrived word, assembled from the Latin part *ictus* ("stroke") and the Greek element *genesis* ("beginning," or "causing"). It is generally employed to cover those factors that predispose to convulsions.

[7] "Isometric": *iso* ("equal") and *meter* ("measure"); thus, here, a contraction without a change of muscle length.

are drawn into the reaction pattern when secondary psychoneurotic tics are superimposed upon the original, primary stuttering.

In venturing to suggest that stuttering may be a relative of epilepsy we do not assume as great a burden of proof as at first appears. If a chance acquaintance is observed to go into a short series of clonic contractions of the muscles of the face and neck when he essays to drink a glass of water, we are likely to wonder if he is a sufferer from *petit mal* epilepsy. If, however, the same person, in attempting to speak his name, goes into similar spasms of the articulators, we say he is a stutterer. Why not consider these two clonic interferences with purposive acts as being homologous? Why one name for clonic spasms of speech and another for similar spasms in other than speech behavior?

Pyknolepsy as a Disorder of Speech

Medical chapters on epilepsy contain a section on pyknoepilepsy, or pyknolepsy. This interesting convulsive disorder no student of stuttering should fail to investigate. In brief, pyknolepsy is chiefly confined to those very muscles that are first involved in childhood stuttering; its onset is between the ages of 4 and 10; convulsions occur often, sometimes as many as 100 per day; they are of such momentary duration that apparently they are not accompanied by loss of consciousness or preceded by aurae; the symptoms usually disappear in a few years, leaving the intelligence unimpaired. One of the identifying phenomena of pyknolepsy most significant for the student of stuttering is that during the convulsion speech is arrested. When we read the clinical description of pyknolepsy, or see some patient labeled as pyknoleptic demonstrated in the clinic, we wonder how many times before we may have seen such a patient and mislabeled him a *severe stutterer*. Or perhaps the mistake was made in the other direction: a severe stutterer was picked up by the specialist in convulsive disorders and diagnosed as pyknoleptic. Or—and we speculate here—it may be that Johnson[8] is partly right; it is largely a matter of semantics. We may be looking at the same entity in two different contextual relationships, and severe stuttering is pyknolepsy and vice versa. And it may be that what Johnson calls childhood "nonfluency" (more about that later) is but subclinical pyknolepsy, severe nonfluency being pyknolepsy proper.[9]

Thus as we grade convulsive epileptiform disorders in severity from *grand mal* to pyknolepsy we approach closer and closer to convulsions that

[8] Johnson, W., *et al.* "A study of the onset and development of stuttering," *Journal of Speech Disorders,* VII, 1942.

[9] "Pykno" is from the Greek word *pyknos,* meaning "dense" or "concentrated." In this connection, therefore, it designates clusters of many separate convulsions.

parallel stuttering. Hence we may well wonder if stuttering is not a form of partially compensated pyknolepsy. Perhaps we could give it a name indicative of how it appears from this point of view, viz., "phemolepsy," a telescoping of "epilepsy" with *pheme* ("speech").

Sex Distribution of Stuttering

Let us now return to the basic fact about stuttering—that it is more common in boys than in girls. So is epilepsy. What in maleness is related to this ictogenic factor common to the two syndromes? It is obvious that the etiology does not lie in the male organs of sex, since some girls appear as both stutterers and epileptics. In answering the question as to where the etiology may lie, or attempting to do so, we again resort to the technique of reviewing the facts. What is known about the sexual differences between boys and girls?

In the first place, girls mature faster than boys, physically, intellectually, and emotionally. We might assume that emotional acceleration is an effect of difference in social treatment accorded girls, were it not correlated with acceleration in intelligence, which is less affected by such treatment, and with physical acceleration, which is independent of factors of social milieu.

In the second place, both morbidity and mortality rates are higher in male children. Practically all diseases of childhood, even infectious ones, afflict boys oftener than girls. The course of childhood is fraught with more obstacles of disease for boys. It is less of a hazard to be born a girl.

In the third place, more spontaneous abortions, stillbirths, and premature deliveries of male than of female embryos and fetuses take place, though the number of live males born is greater than that of live females. This fact becomes more significant when we consider its corollary, viz., that in order to maintain this difference there must be conceived a larger number of males than of females. We are here contemplating, then, two groups, male and female, who begin existence under fundamentally different conditions. Male embryos are produced to run the gamut of a selective weeding-out process in which the destroyer of the weakest individuals is a factor above and beyond that of diseases and accidents of the mother, to which both males and females are equally exposed.

Basic Congenital Retardation of the Male

Now to return to our speculation. We may take the position that the difference in the rate of maturation of the sexes is inherent—that females pass through a different pattern of ontogeny and this pattern is innate. Such an assumption, however, makes it difficult to explain those apparently normal females who mature at rates slower than that of the average male, or the occasional males who mature faster than the average female. The other assumption, that the difference in the rate of maturation is an acquired one, seems more compatible with both the rule of sex difference and its exceptions. The assumption is that, at least until puberty, all children would develop at the same rate (though not necessarily to the same degree), but that certain factors retard many of them. Few probably develop without some braking effect of these factors. Of retarded children the greater proportion by far are males, and of unretarded the greater proportion are females.

These retarding factors are, of course, diseases, to which, as we have observed, males are more prone. (I refer here to diseases suffered by the children, not by their mothers.) The assumption, however, goes one step farther: the proneness to disease begins before birth. Failure of the male embryo to develop as well as the female is not due to prejudicial conditions of physical environment, nor to special exposure of the male to infections, but rather to catalytic differences. As the female embryo develops, it grows more and more in the biochemical likeness of its environment. The hormones of its body gradually begin to match, in proportions, if not in concentrations, the hormones of the mother. The male embryo, however, as it develops encounters an ever-increasing incompatibility, from which it can escape only by separation from the mother. (Incidentally, the mother also suffers effects of this incompatibility, which doubtless accounts for the larger proportion of aborted males.) This incompatibility results in a primary retardation and a proneness to disease which in turn further retard the child's growth and development, his increment and his metamorphosis. Most males suffer effects of these primary and secondary retardations until puberty affords a rebalancing of the endocrine system.

We have, then, two groups of children, one containing those who are relatively undamaged by the process of gestation and the struggle of birth, and the other made up of those survivors whose conditions vary all the way from subclinical damage to obvious chronic pathology. In the second group, which contains more males than females, we find developmental retardation, perseveration of infantilism of speech, low resistance to disease, a low convulsive threshold, and *more stuttering.*

To summarize what I have said about the congenital deficiencies of the stutterer: I should like to try an experiment of so rearranging the economy of nature that only female offspring are brought into the world through the agency of the female parents, and all males are born of their fathers. I conjecture that such a division of labor would raise the health level of the boys. It might, of course, have the effect of canceling the principle of survival of the fittest as it operates to sort out strong males from weak. In the long run it might reduce both extremes in the variations among boys, the number of defectives being cut down[10] and also the number of "supermen." Males might lose both their class inferiority and their superiority. We might have fewer orators, but my guess is that we would also have fewer stutterers.

Effects of Retardation

Aside from the fundamental predisposition of males to convulsive disorders, of which stuttering is an evidence, there is a secondary complication that stems from this congenital retardation and tendency toward disease. This secondary complex may be outlined as follows:

1. Boys belong to the sex which, in maturity, has larger muscles and greater speed in their use. It is not mere culture that requires separate competitions for males and females in the Olympics.

2. Boys belong to the sex which bears the sword and wears the armor, not only in international war, but in the war for family support and survival. Even in families where the mother "goes to business" every morning, the boy is being psychically prepared to be the defender of the family that he will someday "head" (as the income-tax collector would quaintly put it), while the girl is being prepared to be the homemaker, her mother's example being ignored or regarded as a temporary expediency.

3. Before puberty, boys, as we have seen, are the more vulnerable sex; age for age they are inferior to their sisters. Yet even in this period of inferiority they are expected to play the roles of strong-muscled, agile defenders of the family. Tradition and culture have given them parts in the play for which they are not as well equipped as their sisters.

4. Boys are compared, usually to their disadvantage, with girls of their own age. As far as intersexual social contacts are arranged for boys, they are matched—or mismatched—with girls of their own ages. They are

[10] My convictions about the damage suffered by males *in utero* were developed through the course of many discussions about stuttering with Dr. Mildred Freeburg Berry. A summary of these discussions is found in the Berry article on the medical history of stuttering children, cited in the bibliography of this monograph. For those who wish to delve deeper into the theory of congenital damage suffered by the male embryo, Dr. Berry's article provides its own bibliographic suggestions: Berry, M. F., "A study of the medical history of stuttering children," *Speech Monographs,* V, 1938.

expected to assume someday the role of leadership; but they are trained in "followship."

5. Boys suffer, specifically, from one inferiority that is especially significant in the development of speech, viz., age for age, they are slower than girls in the rate of diadochocinesis. This "tapping rate" is a fundamental measure that increases with the maturation of the central nervous system. It is basic and limiting in the speed of voluntary serial behavior patterns such as running, writing, skipping, and speaking. Though boys are slower, age for age, in diadochocinesis, they eventually overtake their sisters; and the average adult male is faster than the female—hence their superiority in the use of musical instruments that involve rapid movements of fingers or tongue. Children who are slow in basic diadochocinesis have difficulty in articulation. Many words and phrases, uttered at the normal rate attained by adults, are negotiated practically at the rate of diadochocinesis of the muscles involved. "Mississippi," "Methodist," "Episcopal Church," "dedicated to the proposition," etc., are tongue-taxing utterances. Such words or phrases the child must take slowly, more slowly than his adult exemplars. Many children refuse to be driven beyond their basic diadochocinetic speed. They appear to drawl or even to whine. We notice this difference in basic rate of speech in a program of children's recitations. The evening begins with "pieces" by preschool children; after they have gone home to bed it continues with recitations by older children and then closes with high-school boys and girls. The rate advances by grade, the last selections being like LP records played at 78 r.p.m.

The preschool child often cannot resist the atmosphere of speed with which he is surrounded. Several factors spur him on to rates beyond his limits: his intense desire to express himself; the impatience of his elders and their unwillingness to give him more than a moment's listening time; intense competition for the center of attention by other members of the family, who will take the audience away from him if he does not speak fast; and the feeling or notion on his part that the tempo of a word or phrase is as essential a part of the utterance as loudness or the quality of phonetic elements. If he yields to this pressure and attempts a speed beyond his limit he will distort his words and phrases and will surely stumble. This behavior we may well call "cluttering." If, however, he is possessed of a tendency to convulsions, cluttering gives way to stuttering. The individuals who are thus handicapped in imitating normal cadences of speech are those whose central nervous systems are either damaged or immature. Children, therefore, are in this group, and boys, for reasons mentioned above, are more frequently to be included than girls.

6. Boys are generally later than girls in starting to speak and slower

in speech development. One of the principal reasons for slow development of speech in boys can best be explained in terms of the onset of speech. *When* speech begins depends upon *how* it begins.

A close observation of the onset of speech in the child will show two types of beginning, the word type and the sentence type. With the first, the child develops utterances that consist of single words, usually quite intelligible in the contexts in which he uses them. The first words are monosyllabic, and the child is likely to make a monosyllable out of any word he wants to use, by dropping all but the stressed syllable. After he gets a few words perfected, he essays the task of combining syllables in longer words, phrases, or short sentences. Up to this period the learning of speech is largely "imitative," i.e., there is much random activity of the speech organs with occasional vocables that are close enough to the code of speech to be accepted by the child's associates as words. When these successes are repeated they not only become less random, more consistent from occasion to occasion, and more like the vocables used by the child's exemplars, but they also become automatic, i.e., the need for specific communication triggers specifically appropriate words. The routes of association through the brain become shortened and simplified. These routes may be called the "engrams" of oral speech. The readiness for the establishment of these neurograms in the cerebrum is one of the determiners of the time of speech onset. This is the period at which the child is beginning to think in words. He is beginning to store up automatic patterns for the expression of basic ideas, needs, relationships, qualities, and acts.

The sentence[11] type of speech onset begins with the utterance of whole phrases or sentences. At first, however, there are no well-formed separate words. The sentence is tonal imitation of what the child's elders may say to him in a given setting. He imitates vocal inflections and occasional vowel qualities. His language is expressive of a relationship to his acquaintances rather than of definite concepts. After he has the framework of the sentence well established, he adds the particular verbal symbols.

These two types of speech onset approach each other in quality as children increase in age. The finished speech process is like a string of beads: the first child starts with the beads and finds the string to assemble them; the second starts with the string and finds the beads to put on it. With

[11] The word "sentence" is here used, not in the grammatical sense indicating a propositional statement or question, but in the sense of mere continuity of utterance which results in an expression that resembles in acoustic pattern the polysyllabic sentences of his adult associates. A one-syllable utterance may well be a sentence, grammatically speaking; but the kind of sentence referred to here is that in which many syllables are joined in one utterance.

both children the assembly of vocables into words of more than one syllable, or into phrases or sentences, depends upon the development of the memory span for sounds. Mistakes of speech due to shortness of this span are omission of syllables, transposition of syllables, or distortion of syllables by substituting the consonant of one syllable for that of the next. It is interesting that children do not begin to stutter until they reach this age of syllable assembly. One-word speakers do not stutter, nor do children who murmur their sentences without any discrete words. Stuttering begins, if it does, at some time during the months that follow, as the child is learning and storing up words, parts of words, phrases, short sentences, and parts of sentences, that will make up the repertoire he will later use in an almost infinite variety of combinations for automatic use in communication. Stuttering is a failure of these first-stored neurograms to function automatically. The failure is apparently due to minor muscular spasms that are tripped off simultaneously with the "playing" of the neurograms. The neural impulse that starts the word also releases the spasm. Hence, most primary stuttering spasms start with the beginning of the syllable, which should be automatic, and which actually is automatic when the stutterer is not under pressure. So long as the child is in the one-syllable, one-word stage of speech development, each utterance is a separate and special voluntary act, with little automatization; but when he learns to "string the beads" he builds automatisms. In this stage of learning these mechanical patterns, the former voluntary method of utterance often persists to interfere with the automatic utterance, particularly at the beginning of a word or phrase. At this point the child has not learned the technique of shifting from voluntary to automatic control—from conscious to cybernetic ordering of his speech behavior. His beginning stuttering, therefore, may be seen as an ambivalence of control. At this age the "cure" of stuttering is the development of the technique of smooth shifting from voluntary to automatic control as the needs of communication require.

When the stutterer learns to fear the spasms that occur when this shifting fails to take place smoothly, he attempts to prevent the stutter by taking the utterance of the word out of the automatic mechanism and putting it under wholly conscious and voluntary control. It is like trying to walk a rail by conscious guidance of one's feet, step by step, rather than by leaving the walking to automatism. Thus stuttering is especially likely to occur in those children who fail to develop a memory span for speech sounds before they are projected into a psychosocial situation that compels the attempt at verbal expression. If the child's emotional pressures and mental experiences increase faster than his linguistic automatisms, he is a potential stutterer; and such a child will be a full-blown primary stutterer if his seizure threshold is low.

Like intelligence, emotional control, and diadochocinesis, this factor of memory span for sounds is developmental. Children who are physiologically advanced surpass, age for age, those who are physiologically retarded. Thus we identify another factor of the etiology of stuttering that is less prevalent among girls than among boys. Children who are shorter in memory span are later in perfecting the automatisms without which real speech does not take place. The memory span for sounds is developmental. Any factor that retards the child's general ontogeny delays the development of this faculty necessary to speech; and since, in general, the ontogeny of boys is slower than that of girls, the speech automatisms of boys are later to form.

We are now ready to assemble and interpret the overall meaning of these six facts. The boy reaches the age when it is imperative to him to express himself in speech. He listens to the speech of his elders and attempts to copy their code in quality and rate. He is frustrated, not only by his failures to adopt the code, but by the comparisons, drawn by him and others, between his speech and that of other children. He notes the place that his father and other adult males assume in the conversation of the family. Tremendous social anxiety develops which soon takes on the quality of morbid self-consciousness. In those boys, and some girls, in whom the spasm threshold is low, this self-consciousness is sufficient to trigger the stuttering. As soon as the stuttering has stubbornly fastened itself upon him, the child has added reason for this damaging self-consciousness. Any situation thereafter in which social anxiety develops starts this cycle of reflexive precipitation of stuttering—the more anxiety, the more stuttering; and the more stuttering the more anxiety.

Personality of the Stutterer

Let us now look at the confirmed stutterer. What are his traits? It is difficult, indeed, to generalize about stutterers. One has no sooner declared himself as to a trait possessed by "all stutterers," when around the corner comes a stutterer who lacks the given trait. Nevertheless I am bold enough to affirm that in my experience with stutterers there is one such trait common to most, if not all, stutterers. To name this trait would risk misleading the reader. Such a name would be like the designations or terms assigned to the special patterns of response to personality tests. The psychologist can isolate, identify, and objectify certain personality aspects without misinforming; but when he labels the traits "submissiveness," "aggressiveness," "neurosis," or what not, he makes an interpretation of the test that is valid only for those who have exactly the same meanings for these words as he does. For all others the test does not measure "submissiveness," but tests only what the test tests, and that thing would best be unnamed. Let us at first, therefore, not name this uniform trait of stutterers, but rather describe it as it appears clinically.

The confirmed stutterer refuses to make compromises with his moral standards. With him the principle of ethics is vastly inclusive. It encompasses standards of physical, sexual, intellectual, spiritual, social, civic, financial, religious, and legal behavior. He is possessed of what has been described as the New England conscience—i.e., though it may not prevent one's sinning, "it sure as Tarnation takes all the fun out of it." The stutterer differs from many others in that he does not departmentalize his moral life. He is a perfectionist who feels delinquent morally no matter when he falls short of his standards. He cannot fail in deed, thought, or wish and "laugh it off." Many persons can rationalize their failures to live up to their standards by saying, "Honor is his who can afford that luxury"; not so the stutterer. He may break his own rules of conduct, but he cannot successfully rationalize the break. He is often quite unrealistic in his standards. Such a person may deem it a sin to look with pleasure upon a girl in a swimming suit; and when, in spite of himself, he watches her and is aware of the flood of imagination that she starts within his consciousness, he is filled with feelings of guilt. His unrealistic attitude thus leads to markedly ambivalent reactions to people around him. The same person could be to him both attractive and feared, loved and hated, intriguing and disgusting. This unrealistic ambivalence extends even to his attitude toward himself. His own standards may clash with one another; his social code may pull him this way, his religious code another. He is caught in a trap of his own setting. He is plagued by feelings of guilt no matter what decision he makes.

Now that we have described this trait of stutterers, we may be able to assign it a name without fear of being misunderstood. Let's call it "moral perfectionism."

Whence comes this trait? Is it an aspect of the basic physiology of the child who starts to stutter? I think it may well be a part of the underlying neuropathology of stuttering. Few diseases involving the nervous system are without their typical patterns of personality. The mongol is notoriously placid and free of jealousy; the multiple sclerotic often shows euphoria and optimism; so also do chorea, parkinsonism, and epilepsy write their signatures on the personality. These aspects of the disease are now regarded as being both primary and secondary, both a part of the disease itself and also a result of the disease. Indeed, the remark may be made in the clinic, "Joe has become a 'parkinson' case? Too bad, but he has had a parkinson rigidity of personality for a long time." This means that stuttering includes much more than the physical symptoms; that it begins before the physical symptoms appear; that in periods when there are no spasms the patient is still a stutterer; that many patients still are stutterers though they have shed their spasms, if they still have the personality picture of stuttering; and that many real stutterers may never outwardly show their spasms.

Another source of this moral perfectionism may well be a second effect of that plan of nature by which boys are born of women. The cutting of the psychic umbilical cord is difficult for mothers of children of either sex. If the dissection is imperfect, emotional problems may result for the girl as well as the boy. We are here referring, however, to the special problems growing out of the difference in sex between mother and child. We need not review here the psychoanalytic reasons for the intensity of this heterosexual attachment of mother and son; nor need we recount in detail the stages through which the mother passes in separating herself from her son. In the days after birth the boy is to her a sort of detached organ of her own body. Gradually week by week he becomes more and more an independent organism with a will of his own. Here begins the conflict between her desire for him to be, on the one hand, a strong, independent, self-reliant mother-protector and, on the other, to be hers, even as he was hers the day he was born, and to remain so. This conflict is unreasoning and unreasonable.

During the months and years in which the child remains under the tutelage of the mother, she exercises control over his moral development. In most so-called civilized cultures the intensity of this direction, the completeness of this control, and the effectiveness of this moral suasion surpass any other influences upon the character and pattern of the child's life. Mother's power, for good or for evil, is often lost sight of because of its ubiquity. She has, however, left her impressions in great profusion upon the character of the stutterer. She has built in him a moral foundation that no influence whatever will avail to eradicate. She has become for him the great lawgiver. She has succeeded, where often father has failed, to set so firm a law that her son will follow it when mother is not present to enforce it, or even after mother has gone. The time comes when the boy calls this influence by the name of conscience.

Let no one quote me as implying that in the United States of America the mother figure is not at least 99 percent wholesome. I am speaking about that last 1 percent—not the last 1 percent of the mothers, but the 1 percent of the influence. I am speaking, therefore, about typical mothers—more about some than about others, but in part about all. Because the mother is herself struggling, sometimes in a blind frenzy, with antagonistic purposes in the education of her son, she cannot give him a moral code that is balanced, realistic, and infallible. In those hours of heartsickness when she contemplates that someday her son will leave her and in that day she may need him most, she teaches him principles of loyalty to parents and particularly of mother loyalty. Filial obligations transcend all other debts. But in hours of strength and courage, when she contemplates the joy that may come to her when her son shall have gone out into the world and the effulgence of his fame shall light her face from the distance, she teaches him intellectual honesty, independent courage, and sexual morality. She does not realize that someday her second teaching may conflict with the first. Intellectual honesty may be a divisive influence between mother and son; independent courage may prompt him to marry without his mother's consent; and sexual morality may engender a loyalty to another woman, another lawgiver. She does not realize that she is building up not only a moral code, but the basis of inevitable guilt in the attempt to follow the code. No human placed in the situation in which the mother finds herself can ever be wise enough to inculcate in the child a completely rational moral code. No matter how intelligent she may be, she is still too personally involved in the relationship to use her intelligence effectively. The child must himself make the compromises necessary to implement the code his mother gave him. Most children negotiate this compromise without serious damage. Some make antisocial compromises. The stutterer makes few compromises of any kind. Though, or because, he is plagued with feelings of guilt he is seldom a criminal.[12] We search a long time in

[12] An impressive demonstration of this picture of the stutterer was made by Dr. Paul Schroeder, Medical Director of the Illinois Institute for Juvenile Research (Chicago), in a study of 5,000 children referred to the institute because of behavior difficulties. This study was reported under the title "Relationship of Personality and Behavior Difficulties to Disorders of Speech," at the Symposium on Stuttering (Stammering) in Chicago, December 1930. The speech is to be found on pp. 52–56 in the report of that meeting issued by the American Speech and Hearing Association (then styled the American Society for the Study of Disorders of Speech). After citing Alfred Adler and Franz Alexander as maintaining that crime and neuroses are antithetical and incompatible, Dr. Schroeder said, "It may be inferred, therefore, from these theories that stammering and criminality tend not to exist simultaneously. Our observation that stammering among prisoners is rarely observed tends to bear out these theories."

Dr. Schroeder found significantly less stuttering in children reported for the following behavior manifestations: heterosexual delinquency, leading others into bad conduct, rude behavior, exclusion or suspension from school, truancy from school, contrariness, indifference toward schoolwork, destructiveness or vandalism, and stealing.

He summarized his address: "The general conclusion from this survey of about a hundred personality and conduct traits is that stammering appears to be a characteristic of the shy, sensitive, inadequate, and neurotic sort of child rather than of the child with aggressive conduct traits."

If we assume that these traits are in any important part the effect of training, then the implication of the Schroeder study is that the proper goal of the training of the stuttering child is the development of socially acceptable behavior patterns that involve aggressiveness.

the prisons of the country to find a stutterer. Only crimes of passion and ignorance are committed by these mother-controlled boys.

It is futile to assess the responsibility of the mother in the establishment of a moral perfectionism in her stuttering son. "Blame" is a word that should not be used in this context. It is likely that the harmful effect of her discipline is more easily observable in hindsight than in foresight. It is only possible that what appears to have been unwise discipline for the stutterer would not have been harmful—nay, even wholesome—for a son whose basic constitution was that of the nonstutterer. The implication here, therefore, is that stutterers are those who manifest unfortunate "side effects" of the usually beneficial medicine of parental moralism. It is strong medicine, generally needed; but some children are hypersensitive to the normal dosage, and one of the signs of that sensitivity is stuttering. Such children require for their proper discipline something less than the amount that may be safely received by their brothers and, particularly, by their sisters.

There are, then, two influences that engender in the stutterer feelings of social anxiety, feelings that trigger his convulsions or blocks. Place him in a situation in which social pressures are reduced, and his stuttering abates. Get him so angry that he forgets to care what people think of him and even forgets his mother's code, and his tongue is loosed. Alcohol has a similar effect by deadening social consciousness. Let him talk to an animal, to a small baby, to God, or to himself, with no one else listening, and speech improves. These situations are not social. They are not conversational. Stuttering is triggered not by fear of speech but by fear of conversation and all it involves. It is the *conversatio*, the turning about, that frightens the stutterer.

There is more to the social triggering of stuttering, however, than fear of the conversational setup. If fears were the whole picture, the stutterer would talk very little. The child who is afraid of the water avoids going into it. But the stutterer does not avoid talking—far from it. He usually is as loquacious as the nonstutterer. It has been said that the difference between the stutterer and the "shy" person is that though both are timid in conversation the latter has discovered that he does not have to talk, while the former has not found it out. That aphorism omits one consideration, viz., that the stutterer really has to talk; speech is a compulsion with him. He is constantly trying to talk his guilt feelings out of existence. Speech is his way of squaring himself with others and with his own conscience. He is constantly seeking a more comfortable moral position. With him it seems as though just around the corner, with just one more sentence, he will have achieved a stable and defensible ethical platform or a pleasant social relationship. That he gets himself into pitfalls in the attempt to get out of others does not dissuade him from continuing to try to talk his way out. He is caught, therefore, in a stringent ambivalence: his fear of conversation and his compulsion to enter it. He is afraid of the water, but he feels that to save his life he has to swim. It is not enough merely to float.

In this section I have been discussing the part that mothers play in the precipitation of stuttering. I advised the reader that I was not necessarily making comparisons between mothers of stutterers and mothers of nonstutterers. Other influences than the mother's may engender social anxieties. I was really intending a comparison between mothers who are markedly ambivalent in their moral suasion and mothers who show relatively little ambivalence, the former group precipitating stuttering more frequently than the latter. Our comparison was on the patterns of moral suasion, not on its intensity. It is obvious that the closer the mother comes to establishing in the child a realistic conscience, the less will he be disturbed by morbid feelings of guilt. Another way to avoid the establishment of these feelings is to bring up the child without moral suasion, or at least without suasion that is centered in the parent.

So now we embark upon a discussion of another grouping of mothers, those who are directive and those who are permissive. The directive mothers engender in their children wholesome or unwholesome consciences, firmness of conscience being dependent not upon its wholesomeness, but upon the effectiveness of the mother's directive techniques. Nondirective, or permissive, mothers leave the building of conscience to the child's natural interaction with his associates. Of course no mothers are 100 percent directive or 100 percent permissive; but we can array them along a continuum from one extreme to the other.

The Semantogenic Theory

Johnson and others have called attention to the fact that in certain cultures there is very little stuttering, and that in the same cultures there are no words designating this particular speech defect. Naturally, if there were no stutterers in a tribe no name would be needed to describe them; but that is not Johnson's point. His theory is that there are no stutterers because it requires a name to produce a stutterer, and the lack of a name prevents the development of stuttering. It seems to me, however, that the lack of a name points to a lack of personal responsibility on the part of the parents. To me the Johnson findings about the Sioux Indians mean that cultures (for the Sioux may be compared with other similar cultures) that are permissive produce less stuttering than those that are directive. In such a culture the children before puberty live a life of unmoral irresponsibility. They are not shamed or punished for thumb-sucking, dirty ears, masturbation, nakedness, prolonged nursing at mother's breast, sexual play, or blocks in speech. If there is any difference between Johnson and me on this matter it is this: he claims that their relatively low incidence of stuttering is due to the fact that children are not shamed or punished by a stigmatizing label for blocks in speech; while I claim this low incidence rate is due to the fact that they are not shamed or punished, period. In these cultures the mothers are permissive, and what consciences the children acquire are realistic and practical. Little ambivalence obtains in the moral lives of these people, and little stuttering. In puritanical cultures, on the other hand, where it is a matter of family pride to have roses as pretty as the neighbors', or a car as good, or a TV aerial as tall, or a son who is toilet-trained as soon, or a son who speaks as early or as well, there are words for all the deficits as well as for all the assets. The roses, the car, and the TV do not suffer in this stern competition, but the son does. If, moreover, there were no name for stuttering, the directive parents would still make it known to the deficient son how grievously he had disappointed them, and in what way; and in the child predisposed to stutter under social anxiety enuresis would precipitate stuttering, if lapses of speech did not.

Stuttering as Inefficient Speech

Speech is efficient when it yields to the speaker a maximum of satisfaction per minute. (1) If the purpose of the speaker is to convey specific facts, anything that impedes the communication of these facts reduces the efficiency of the utterance. (2) If the purpose of the speaker is to ask for items of specific information, anything that interferes with the transmission of these items also reduces the efficiency of speech. (3) If the purpose is merely to produce a series of vocables of attention-capturing quality, or to produce a series of sensory-motor experiences for the sheer enjoyment of their production, the only thing that reduces the efficiency of speech is that which impedes utterance. Some speakers may be assigned high efficiency ratings and some low. If the purpose of speech be communication of facts or of items of interrogation, adults are generally more efficient in speech than are children, and nonstutterers than stutterers. If, however, the purpose be the third listed above, in which communication of ideas is not important, children show more efficiency than most adults, and some stutterers may be as efficient as nonstutterers.

Not all factors that lower the efficiency of speech can be labeled "stuttering." Certainly, considering speech as communication, cleft palate, spastic paralysis, aphonia, etc., reduce its efficiency; but insofar as these conditions are constant impediments of all attempts at speech, their effects are not labeled "stuttering." We reserve that term to describe cases of reduced efficiency of speech in which the factors of reduction of efficiency are intermittent. It is because of this intermittency that stuttering is often described as lacking fluency. The even flow of vocables, or of ideas, is now and then momentarily interrupted. Speech may be said to possess a low degree of fluency when momentary blocks reduce its efficiency. Unless one knows, however, what the speaker's purpose is, one cannot decide how efficient his utterance is and, consequently, how fluent is his speech. Repetitions and iterations may in one instance reduce efficiency and in another increase it, hence may sometimes lower and sometimes raise the level of fluency.

Although the term "fluency" has been used for generations in connection with speech, it remained for the present generation to invent, and apply to the subject of stuttering, the term "nonfluency." Johnson has sponsored the term and many persons credit and employ it. He asserts that stuttering results from the attaching of a label, "stuttering," to the normal "nonfluency" of the young child. Let us examine this apparently meaningful compound word. Obviously Johnson cannot have derived his word "nonfluency" from the "fluency" that was defined above as a quality of speech efficiency. Fluency of that kind is a relative thing, like temperature. One may describe a high, or a low, level of either of these conditions; but one cannot talk about nonfluency (of this kind) any more than one can speak of the nontempertaure of an autumn day. It may be, however, that Webster[13] can give us a more liberal definition of "fluency." He says it is the "quality of being fluent." "Fluent" is defined as "ready in the use of words; voluble; copious; as, a *fluent* speaker; hence, flowing; voluble; smooth; — said of language; as, *fluent* speech. . . . Ant. — Inarticulate, mute, stuttering, hesitant." Webster gives no listing of "nonfluent" or "nonfluency,"[14] except by implication of the definition of the word unit "non-."

Webster says about "non-": "generally less emphatic than *in-* or *un-*, being merely negative, while *in-* or *un-* are positive, often implying an opposite thing or quality. Cf. *non*religious, *ir*religious; *non*moral, *im*moral;

[13] *Webster's New International Dictionary,* 2nd ed., G. & C. Merriam, Springfield, Mass., 1939.

[14] The failure to list the word "nonfluency," however, should not be taken as evidence that the word is an improper one. It is unfortunate that it is not listed and defined, for definitions give solidity to discussion, but when so famous an author as Johnson employs a word we can only say that the dictionary that omits the word is, in that omission, definitely behind the time. May I hope that this discussion may help some future lexicographer to define the word *nonfluency,* when, as must be, it is listed.

*non*Christian, *un*christian." Hence, to be logical, consistent, and congruent with other "non-" words, "nonfluent" must not be stretched to cover the antonyms of "fluent," given above, one of which, ironically enough, is the word "stuttering." Strictly speaking, therefore, "nonfluency" means nothing positive. It does not designate what the child's speech is; it merely states what it is not. The fact is that General Semanticist Johnson had available to him accepted words given as antonyms of "fluent"—"inarticulate," "mute," "stuttering," "hesitant"—and chose, instead of using them, to coin one of his own. What did he mean? We must assume that he meant to describe by the word "nonfluency" something positive; for certainly parents cannot attach a name to something that is not. We must therefore assume also that what he meant to designate was something that possessed qualities that were at least different from, and probably opposite to, fluency.

Parents' Criteria as to Stuttering

Let us examine the speech of the young child, and more particularly the speech of the child who is beginning to stutter,[15] to see what it is that the parents discover in the speech of the child that Johnson labels as nonfluent and the parent calls stuttering. From long years of experience with such parents, I can list that behavior that brings the mother to see me with the whispered introduction "my boy is beginning to stutter."

1. The child may repeat words or syllables.
2. The child may vocalize without articulation either at the beginning of a word or phrase or between words or phrases, using some form of the neutral vowel.
3. The child may show obvious spasms, tonic or clonic, of the muscles of articulation or phonation.
4. The child may exhibit movement patterns in other muscles than the direct articulators and phonators—of the scalp, eyelids, face, neck, shoulders, arms, hands, and even of the legs and feet. These patterns of movement assume the nature of tics and are accompaniments of speech efforts.

[15] It is interesting to behold the mental squirmings in the presence of Wendell Johnson of those who, like the author of this monograph, believe that stuttering is not merely a diagnosogenic phenomenon, but a real entity. They forget that Johnson is able to understand their use of the word "stuttering," and they struggle to find a word in his vocabulary that expresses their meaning. Johnson blandly pretends that he cannot help them, since, he says, they are looking for a word for something that does not exist. Then he takes his tongue out of his cheek and begins to talk about "nonfluency." The parents, he says, label the *nonfluency* as "stuttering." It seems just as fair to say that Johnson labels incipient *stuttering* as "nonfluency." Is there no more to the argument than the change of labels on the can?

Let us analyze these aspects of what the parents call stuttering. Let us ask in each case, "Is this an absence of, or a break in, fluency? First, the iterations, the repetitions of words and phrases. Perhaps the most fluent of all vocables, in Webster's meaning of "flowing" or "smooth," are those that involve reduplications. We have some that are completely reduplicative, exactly repetitive, such as *mama, papa,* and *bye-bye.* Many such words occur in the so-called primitive languages spoken by peoples who are reared by permissive mothers—peoples who incidentally have little stuttering. In English these words are found chiefly in the speech of children; adults use them with apology. It may be *papa* in the home even until the child is grown, but outside the word chosen is a vocable that is less repetitive. Among the Polynesians perfect reduplicatives are as acceptable among adults as among children—*hula-hula, mahi-mahi, pago-pago,* etc. Apparently such expressions increase, rather than decrease, the fluency of the language. Then there are repetitive words and phrases in which the vowel changes, but the consonants are repeated—*ding-dong, crisscross, teeter-totter, tick-tack-toe,* etc. Again, these reduplicatives are found more frequently in the speech of children. Next there are reduplicatives in which the vowel remains the same and the consonants change—*pell-mell, turkey-lurkey, helter-skelter,* etc. Judging from the fact that many of the classical reduplicatives have been created out of phrases that are only roughly repetitive, such as *crisscross* from *Christ's Cross,* it is safe to say that ease and smoothness of utterance is one of the primary reasons for the development and persistence of these repetitions. We may conclude then, that when Johnson uses the term "nonfluency," he is not accurately describing the child's iterations.

The second aspect of the child's stuttering is the vocalization that the child interposes between words and phrases and employs at beginnings of utterances—the linguistically redundant neutral vowel. This type of utterance is frequently employed by the adult, particularly in public speaking in situations in which it is necessary for him to develop his ideas step by step as he stands before his hearers. In pauses of speaking in which he is determining the next step to be taken in the argument, explanation, or narrative, or the correct word or phrase to express his meaning, he continues vocalization as though to assure his auditor he is still "sending." This undoubtedly contributes to the fluency (in Webster's meaning of "flowing" or "smooth") of his speaking, since otherwise the speech would be interspersed with conspicuous pauses. The Polynesians, too, have discovered that redundant vowels lend fluency to the sentence. Words like *Kaaawa* are frequent in the language and certainly lend smoothness to its expression. In fine, it is hard to see how the term "nonfluency" could cover interstitial vocalization.

The third and fourth manifest behavior patterns of the child described by the parents as a stutterer are the spasms and tics. These are clearly lacking in smoothness. It is this behavior that, in all probability, was the reason for the selection of the term "nonfluent." In addition, however, to the exception that I have already taken to the use of this term, i.e., that it is purely negative and consequently empty of positive signification, I have two objections to its use to describe the speech of the incipient or potential stutterer: first, it implies that the speech of the child's exemplar—the normal speech of the adult—is notably fluent (that is, "flowing, voluble, smooth"); second, it covers, at best, only about half of the speech differences between the stutterer and the normal speaker.

To return to the first additional objection. If one listens analytically to oral speech of persons around him, one notices many rough spots, even when there are no mistakes of articulation, word choice, or idea that require recasting of the language. The correct, expected, normal utterance of the sentence I am writing at this moment is not smooth, far from it. It is irregular in rhythm; it is composed of a great variety of mechanical noises that possess no consistency of pattern. The noisiest of man-made wheel-driven machines is more fluent, or flowing, than the oral reading of this sentence; record it and play it backwards, so as to rob it of meaning, and it loses what little smoothness it seems to possess. The poet and the lyricist struggle to give speech some smoothness. Some languages are inherently more suited to poetry and song than others, but, at best, speech requires much ornamentation to give it fluency. I object, therefore, to saying that the young child's speech significantly lacks what normal speech does not markedly possess.

Now, the second additional objection is that, even if the term "non-fluency" could be understood to mean the opposite of "fluency," it would cover only the spasms and would omit the other significant manifestations of the speech of the child. An analysis of the child's behavior shows that he has more difficulty than does the adult with the purely functional and utilitarian combination of movements that make up speech. He finds speech very irregular and lacking in fluidity. He cannot negotiate it without endowing it with smoothness. Hence, some of the behavior of the child who is learning to speak is due to the inability of his neuromuscular system to handle adult speech, and some to his attempt so to modify speech as to make it negotiable by him. The more he employs reduplications and interstitial vocalizations, the fewer the spasms. In fact, if he makes his speech completely fluid, by intoning it as in song, the spasms disappear. Stuttering begins, therefore, with attempt on the part of the young child to imitate the series of irregular articulatory gymnastics involved in the speech of the adult and is evidenced, in large part, by the introduction of elements of *fluency* à la Webster. Children endowed with early speech readiness will have less difficulty than others in learning our lingual calisthenics; those with late speech readiness, particularly those with a low spasm threshold, will develop much compensatory fluidity. I deem it significant that, in those linguistic cultures in which reduplications and interstitial vocalizations are a part of the accepted pattern of speech, there is less stuttering. But which is cause and which is effect? Do these compensations prevent stuttering, or is it the permissiveness of early discipline that prevents it and, at the same time, permits fluid ornamentation of speech? I suspect both chains of effect are operating. Perhaps (1) the "Indians have no word" for stuttering because children are permitted to modify or reject all words upon which they might stutter; and (2) Johnson's Indians[16] are brought up with consciences that produce little social fear and, in particular, little anxiety and guilt about the compensations they employ in speech. To summarize my objections, it is because the term "nonfluency" leaves so much unsaid, says so little itself, and seems to say what is misleading, that I think the term should be discarded as a characterization of the young child's speech. If one insists on incorporating the fluency idea into the definition of stuttering, he should employ the idea positively. As it is now generally employed, stuttering is said to be an anticipatory avoidance of *nonfluency*. Would it not be truer to say it this way: stuttering *is the appearance* of spasms and the anticipatory development of *fluency* to override and mitigate them? The theory that stuttering is an attempt to avoid a break in fluency may seem tenable on first reading, but on the second it appears to be a generalization based upon a priori reasoning; it is as though the stutterer found the principle first and then attempted to make it fit the facts. A close observation of the behavior of the beginning stutterer,[17] followed by an analysis of what is seen and heard, throws considerable doubt upon the "nonfluency" concept of the etiology of stuttering.

Nonstuttering as a Status Achieved by the Able

If stutterers are made by a label, life for the child becomes a simple game of tag. A "touch" makes one "it." Some children are often "it" and some

[16] Lemert, though agreeing with Johnson that some Indians do not have a word for stuttering, calls attention to the fact that Indians of certain cultures not only have words for stuttering, but they have plenty of stuttering, and even have traditional "cures" for it. Lemert, E. M., "Some Indians who stutter," *Journal of Speech and Hearing Disorders,* XVIII, 1953.

[17] The idea that the child adopts fluidity, particularly in the form of iterations, to prevent his stuttering blocks came to my mind while listening to, and reading from, Eisenson. I am not sure that he would endorse my adaptation of his theories about stuttering as a manifestation of basic perseveration; but I hope that he, as editor, will at least allow me to make this use, or abuse, of his idea.

are seldom "it." Thus in time they divide themselves into two classes, "its" and "non-its"—stutterers and nonstutterers. But let us examine these two classes. True, a touch makes a child "it," but why is he touched? He is caught because (1) he is not a skillful dodger, or (2) he cannot run fast enough to escape the tag or to get rid of it. The "non-its," who are they? Simply those who have not been touched? Ah, no! Some children who are touched simply refuse to admit the validity of the tag and deny their "itness." There the game would stop, unless the others accepted the renege at face value. Most of the "non-its," however, are the fast, agile children, who generally escape getting touched, or who, if they are tagged, immediately pass "it" on. So the real difference between "its" and "non-its," between stutterers and nonstutterers, is not in the tags, but in how and why they got the tags; and when we find just what that difference is, we shall find the essential meanings of the tags—the essential nature of stuttering.

If stuttering is the effect of a label, then what is nonstuttering? Is it the negative afterimage of the stuttering label? It is true that we probably would not have a word for normalcy were it not for illness, which gives us a need to express a difference; but without illness the essential nature of the normal status would be the same. Nonstuttering is the absence of the status of stuttering in a person who is normal or, if he is not normal, whose diseases, deficiencies, or dysfunctions are not related to the condition called stuttering. Nonstuttering is based upon efficiencies and proficiencies that are just as real as the deficiencies and disorders that constitute the syndrome of stuttering. The child must grow in "stature and grace" to achieve the age of speech as a nonstutterer.

III. TEST OF THE THEORY OF STUTTERING

Statement of the Theory

Etiologically speaking, what is stuttering?

The hypothesis: Stuttering is primarily an epileptic disorder that manifests itself in dyssynergies of the neuromotor mechanism for oral language. Its spasms are precipitated by social anxieties involved in communication by oral language. These anxieties, engendered by any agency or agencies of moral training, are most effective as precipitants of stuttering when they assume the form of conscious feelings of guilt, and particularly of guilt about what the patient speaks and how he utters it.

Thus primary stuttering is a convulsive disorder that involves a certain circumscribed relationship to those around the patient. It cannot, or at least does not, appear outside the frame of this relationship, viz., communication or social intercourse. It is in this aspect different from *petit mal* epilepsy, which apparently is not encompassed in any special frame or situational context.

There is, however, an interesting parallel to be drawn between stuttering and a certain nonpathological convulsion that is aroused by what is called "tickling." Obviously the two conditions are of different genera. They are, however, characterized by convulsions and are situation-connected. Let us examine this tickle reaction. It obviously depends upon a low threshold of seizure, since some persons cannot be tickled, and since apparently as the child matures his response to the tickling diminishes. Like stuttering it has a large emotional involvement, and, as in stuttering, this emotional involvement is ambivalent; the person tickled shows the reaction of amusement, and yet he does not enjoy the experience and avoids a repetition of it. He seems to laugh; it sounds like laughter or giggling; but the expression on the face is that of anxiety or apprehension.[18] A child cannot produce the spasms in himself by poking his own ribs. Neither does contact between his ribs and some inanimate object produce the spasms, unless that object is directed by another human; even so, the child is not usually thrown into convulsions unless he believes the person who is holding the stimulating object is intending to "tickle" him. Further, if two tickle-sensitive children engage in a wrestling bout, their hands may contact each other's ribs without producing the spasms. Let one of them say, however, "I am going to tickle you," and immediately the spasms start; and the child who realizes he has thus thrown his opponent out of control is not himself "tickleable" by his antagonist, though he may be thrown into spasms by a third child. Children are more vulnerable to tickling by adults than by other children. The 14-year-old can easily "tickle" the 6-year-old, but not vice versa. I need not belabor the parallels here between these phenomena and those of stuttering, except to say that the principle involved is this: essential conditions producing convulsions may include not only specific physical conditions but also special social milieus.

In this connection one should recall the belief, frequently reflected in questions which mothers ask the speech correctionist, that stuttering is caused by tickling. A mother may declare that her boy stutters because the uncle used to tickle him when he was a baby. Clearly an old wives' notion; but there is at least good reason why the notion got acceptance.

[18] An acquaintance of the author told him once that if a person tickled her on the ankles or on the neck and if there were no other way to stop the tickling than to kill the tickler, she would be compelled to do it.

I realize that in some circles in which stuttering is discussed the terms *primary* and *secondary* are discarded; but in the concept that I have here outlined the terms are useful. I have defined above the primary aspect of stuttering. Let us continue, where my definition stopped, to generalize about the secondary aspect: The spasms of stuttering have two side effects upon the speech of the child: (1) the introduction of artificial fluency, and (2) the adoption by the patient of tics that accompany his attempts at speech.

I have discussed above the reason for, and mechanism of, the introduction of fluency. The term "tic" is usually restricted to a "memory spasm" —the stereotyping of a purposive act and its perseveration into situations in which its original purpose no longer obtains. Tics may be simple clonic movements such as eye blinks, or involved serial patterns such as spoken phrases. When the original purposive act becomes involuntary, the tic is full-blown. In stuttering these tics take the form of squinting, bobbing of the head, twisting of the neck or the body, clenching of the hands, sliding of the feet on the floor, utterance of such phrases as "I mean to say," "Well, that is," "So," "Now," etc. The stutterer can often remember the first time he employed a given tic. He discovered on that occasion that the act facilitated his speech. It helped him to override the spasm. It was efficacious just long enough to become stereotyped, after which time it became a part of the constellation of reactions that stigmatize the stutterer.

Most of these tics are convulsive in nature. They appear in the stutterer because his seizure threshold is critically low. Though their genesis is different from the primary spasms of the stuttering, they grow in the same kind of soil. The child with cleft palate has just as much reason to be embarrassed about his speech as the stutterer; but, because his seizure threshold is not, in the nature of his case, below average, he develops only those compensatory habit patterns that are consistently useful to him in speech. His compensations are not convulsive, but smoothly coordinated with the other movements of speech.

Aside from the fact that primary convulsions of stuttering are confined to the immediate musculature of phonation and articulation, while secondary spasms may involve quite disparate muscles, there are two other differences. (1) Primary convulsions are triggered by the *act* of communication, while the secondary convulsions, the tics, are precipitated by the *failure* of communication. The child does not develop the tic until he has had considerable experience with interruptions of his transmission system. The first tics to develop are those intended to thwart the primary seizure of stuttering; next to develop are those to arrest the secondary seizures. Thus, particularly in late childhood, stuttering tics are cumulative. (2) The second difference between primary and secondary spasms is that the former are largely beneath the level of consciousness, while the latter depend for their genesis upon a definite awareness of both the secondary patterns and the primary (or secondary) seizures they are originally intended to obviate.

If primary stuttering is, as I hypothesize, a close relative of pyknolepsy, it ceases at puberty or thereabouts. Hence we may assume that most, if not all, of the stuttering of adolescence and adulthood is secondary. If we could break the psychoneurotic chain that connects the stuttering boy of 18 with the beginning stutterer he was at the age of 4, we could solve his problem easily. But we cannot, and the psychoneurotic aspect is the more difficult to handle.

Application of the 10-Fact Yardstick

Let us now return to our yardstick by which we measure the validity of any theory of the etiology of stuttering. This measure is a listing of the basic facts about stuttering. How well does our theory match the facts?

1. *Stuttering is a phenomenon of childhood.* We have learned that epilepsies are primarily seen in children and the nearest possible relative of stuttering, pyknolepsy, is particularly associated with prepubescent life. Inasmuch as one of the anxieties precipitating stuttering is that involved with a feeling of guilt about one's speech behavior, the time of learning of speech is the period when stuttering is most likely to be triggered. Stuttering strikes in early childhood when both the rate of diadochocinesis and the span of memory for sounds—faculties necessary for establishing the automatisms of speech—are low.

2. *Stuttering is more prevalent among males than among females.* Epilepsy is also more prevalent among boys than among girls. Since boys achieve "speech readiness" later than girls, their social anxieties about speech are greater. This special retardation of development is due to the incompatible endocrine environment under which the male embryo and fetus is nurtured. The special tendency of boys to experience morbid feelings of guilt stems from maternal attachment, which is more possessive and directive for the boy than for the girl.

3. *Stuttering runs in families.* So does epilepsy. Further: concepts of morality are passed on from generation to generation, and criteria of normalcy about speech. Hence both the basic predisposition to stutter and the precipitating factors of stuttering may appear in successive generations.

4. *Stuttering is found in association with left-handedness.* The prefer-

ential use of one hand over the other, in the young child, increases with his age. The period of the establishment of this preference is in general that of speech learning. This period is also that of the onset of most stuttering. With most children the preference of hand use is for the right. Hence this period is called that of "dextralization," from the Latin *dextrus* ("right"). Delay in this phase of dextralization is often associated with a corresponding delay in the acquisition of skilled acts, including those involved in speech. Hence in many cases what appears to be left-handedness may be an effect or aspect of retardation.[19] Many students of the phenomena of stuttering have observed an association between it and what has been variously styled left-handedeness, ambidexterity, ambilevousness, or retarded dextralization. It seems clear that this condition, whatever its fundamental nature, is often, like stuttering, familial.

5. *Stuttering is found also in association with twinning.* Multiple birth involves a prenatal handicap to the embryo, and particularly to the fetus, that has retarding effects lasting throughout the childhood period.

6. *Stuttering is associated with late acquisition of speech and retention of baby talk.* This speech retardation is but one aspect of the general retardation that underlies spasmophemia, or phemolepsy. Secondarily, this speech slowness contribues to the feeling of moral inadequacy and thus serves as a factor precipitating stuttering. Speech defects other than stuttering that these patients exhibit often have the appearance and acoustic affect of the dysarthrias of brain deficit, again suggesting an organicity of etiology.

7. *Stuttering is rarely episodic.* It usually begins without any acute psychic or physical traumata. The same may be said of pyknolepsy. Both conditions develop so insidiously as to appear spontaneous. In stuttering the precipitating factors, as well as the basic causes, involve growth and the slow accumulation of familial and cultural effects.

8. *Stuttering is a convulsive phenomenon.* So is pyknolepsy.

9. *Stuttering is psychosocially reflexive.* So is pyknolepsy. Particularly when the patient has developed the secondary aspects of stuttering, the more he stutters, the more he stutters. Since the secondary stuttering is a futile stereotypy of a failing attempt to thwart convulsions, the more the

[19] The word "retardation" should not be thought of as indicating what is commonly meant by the phrase "mental retardation." It is often rather loosely employed to cover not only abnormal slowness of ontogeny, with no implications as to the final status of the child when development has stopped, but also that condition in which damage to the C.N.S. has arrested the development so that normal status is not to be expected at adulthood. In the context of paragraph 4, "retardation" indicates a slowing of metamorphosis without particularization as to what functions are retarded or as to whether the retardation may be compensated for by an extension of the time of the developmental process. We have seen that retardation is, at the least, one of the factors precipitating stuttering.

child is exposed to social situations in which it is disadvantageous for him to fail in communication, the more secondary stuttering appears, causing more failure in communication, etc.

10. The last item on the 10-fact yardstick is that *stutterers show basic physiological differences from nonstutterers.* Those listed in the introduction were (a) age of regularization of the heartbeat, (b) susceptibility to allergies, and (c) blood-sugar ratings. In none of these specific items is the parallel clear between stuttering and epilepsy. That is, nonstutterers do not clearly show the same physiological differences from stutterers that nonepileptics show when compared with epileptics. At least, the author has not seen scholarly findings to support this last item of his case for the epileptoid nature of stuttering. On the other hand, neither has he found clearly negative evidence. In fact, it is precisely and especially on this point that he hopes research will be done. Speculations on this matter and suggestions for future research are to be found in Section I.

This is the theory—the hypothesis—as to the etiology of stuttering. Much remains, of course, to be said and done before we can say Q.E.D. This thesis is humbly presented as a venture in speculation, in the hope that there are in the possession of my readers unpublished facts that may be forthcoming, which, if assembled, may support or contradict this hypothesis. I make no claim to the originality of this theory, though I do believe that at the time of this writing this is the most elaborate published blueprint of the thesis. It is hoped, also, that this monograph will stimulate research along lines suggested here—research that will either substantiate or refute the basic theory. To me the hypothesis seems possible, plausible, probable, but not proved. It seems, therefore, worthy of the expenditure of much study. I hope that many persons will be inspired to help solve this problem. For the time being, may we call it the ictocongenital hypothesis—the theory that stuttering is congenital and convulsive.

IV. THE THERAPY OF STUTTERING

Etiological Arguments Drawn from the Effects of Therapy

In the remaining pages of this monograph I shall develop the implications of this theory—the ictocongenital hypothesis—in the area of therapy. It may be argued that the therapy should be based upon the cause, and that, if it is so based and the therapy is effective, this is proof that we have discovered the cause. Such an argument is a cogent one for the repairers of watches, radios, and automobiles, but nowhere near as valid for the repairers of human beings. The watch cannot participate in the repair process; it is only acted upon; but the human being reacts voluntarily, though perhaps unconsciously, to the process of therapy, either to support or to hinder the work of the therapist. In some repairs this participation of the patient is relatively small in comparison with the work being done upon him—removal of an infected appendix, for example. In conditions like stuttering, however, in which the patient is so balanced upon a knife edge that slight pressures may cause his symptoms to appear or disappear, the participation of the patient may be the major quantum of the therapy. Thus we cannot say definitely that therapy based upon a theory of etiology proves or disproves the theory.

At the beginning of this monograph I referred to the large percentage of members of the American Speech and Hearing Association who formerly believed they knew the specific cause of stuttering. They were convinced by their own successes with stutterers that their theories were correct, blandly ignoring the fact that others with quite different theories had equal successes when they put their theories to the test of therapy—ignoring also the frequent failures in the application of their own theories. This means that what a therapist thinks he is doing and what he actually does may be two quite different things; that the theoretical rationale for his therapy and the actual therapeutic principle at work may not coincide.

The late John Fletcher of Tulane University used to say that it is unfortunate that stuttering yields to so many therapies. If there were only one effective therapy for the disorder, he maintained, we could deduce from that what caused the stuttering. A specific remedy for a specific disease is a principle that seems not to apply to stuttering. It may be, however, that there is one common factor in all the therapies—a factor that stimulates the patient's participation in the process of therapy. Some have used the word "suggestion" to designate this common thing in all therapies. This may be employing the term loosely, but the implication is that in cases in which stuttering therapy is effective, the patient has such faith in the therapist that, no matter what the therapist does, the patient will receive some benefit. Hence, benefit to the patient from etiologically based therapy is by no means a proof of the etiology.

Goals of Therapy

With these words of caution as to the implications of therapy, let us outline a rationale based upon our theory. Let us divide the therapy into that for beginning stutterers and that for confirmed stutterers. In any good therapeutic program one starts with a realistic goal. What should our goal be? With beginning stutterers our goal should be complete "cure." We should look forward to and strive to achieve a status of the patient in which he talks freely, effortlessly, with no need to guard himself against interfering blocks or spasms. With a few confirmed stutterers the same goal is realistic.

With another group, made up largely of confirmed stutterers, goal two may be set, i.e., a status in which the patient can talk without fear of blocks and without conscious regard for how he speaks, if he avoids certain emotionally surcharged situations. Many such "cured" stutterers are among us, about whom even their friends sometimes say, "You stutter? I certainly never would have guessed it."

Another group of confirmed stutterers require a less ambitious goal. For them the advice of Van Riper and others is pertinent: Teach them to stutter better. The status strived for is to be able to talk without blocks, or at least without discernible blocks, if the patient preserves a right attitude toward his listener and handles his speech with the right checks and safeguards. He can never lower his guard and leave his oral expression to pure automatic control, but at least he can talk without conspicuous stuttering. In one speech clinic (not at Kalamazoo, Michigan) this group is said to have been "vanriperized."

The last group of stutterers are those for whom we look forward to a time when, though the patient continues to stutter, he stutters less frequently and he learns to live with his stuttering without morbid feelings about it or about himself as a stutterer. He frees himself of resentment that he had to be a stutterer. He accepts it, and though he cannot ignore it, he learns to disregard it. This is a goal of considerable value, though strictly speaking it is not a "cure."

Recipes for Stuttering Therapy

Many texts in the field of speech correction give considerable space to specific devices, games, and exercises to be employed with stutterers. These texts on techniques should be used intelligently. If followed slavishly they may do more harm than good. Recipes are no substitute for resourcefulness. For the most part they should be thought of as suggestions on the sort of thing that might be employed rather than as formulae of cure. If used as described in the book, one must be sure that they are appropriate to (1) the goal of the therapy, (2) the personality of the therapist, and (3) the special needs and interests of the patient. The availability of numerous recipes should not hamper the inventiveness of the therapist. "Custom-tailored" devices are usually better than hand-me-downs. Ready-made helps are usually included in texts because the publisher insists upon them; and he insists upon them because he knows the book will sell better with these helps than without. The demand for the recipe comes from two sources: (1) therapists in the field whose "pitchers are running dry" and (2) teachers who need, or think they need, the support of the printed page to reinforce their suggestions to therapists in training. Then there are persons in this world who prefer to follow a prescription rather than to have to analyze and to plan. Were this not true the writers of popular books on bridge would have to turn to other fields. I shall have much to say here about therapy; but what I say will be about rationales to be followed, not about specific recipes. If the therapist understands the rationale and is resourceful, the devices can do no harm; but such a therapist scarcely needs the formulary. If he does not understand the rationale and is not resourceful, the formulary will avail him little and may even harm his patient.

Prophylaxis in Stuttering

Keep the Stutterer in Ignorance of His Stuttering. Let us now discuss the therapy for the beginner in stuttering. Assume that the stutterer is a child who has not yet become aware that he is a stutterer. (And, of course, if he has not become aware of it, that raises a semantic question which gets Dr. Johnson's tongue back into his cheek.) The first principle with such a child is to keep him unaware of his stuttering. No reference is to be made in his presence to any peculiarities or defects of his speech. He is not to be enjoined to "talk slow," "take a good breath before you speak," "think it out before you start," "relax," or "try to stop repeating." When he is stuttering in the presence of guests, the mother must not shut him off, or openly wince at his efforts, or apologize for the child to the company.

Give the Stutterer Practice with Good Speech. The second principle is to give him all possible experience with speech under conditions that facilitate it. If it cannot be arranged otherwise, let the mother or father plan an hour or two each day alone with the child. Let the parent put the child into a mood of relaxation by setting an example of relaxation. If, as frequently happens, mealtime becomes a time of frustration for the stutterer, because it gives him a need to express himself but gives him also a difficult speech situation, arrange it so that the mother and the stutterer eat their meal in a quiet session before or after the rest of the family. If the child comes rushing into the house to try to tell the parent something that he has seen on the street and he is stuttering badly in the telling of it, let the parent skillfully put the boy off on the excuse that some important task takes precedence for the moment. Let the parent tell the child that he or she is interested in what has happened and that the child should not go away, but wait. Then, when the parent sees that the child has relaxed and is becoming just a bit bored by the waiting, the parent sits, relaxes, and invites the child to tell his story.

The tempo of the parent's speech, when he is talking directly to the child, should be slow. It should match that of the child when he is relaxed, or when he feels that he is not limited as to the time he has at his disposal for conversation. It is quite impractical to advise that all conversation in the child's presence should be at his tempo; but at least one can admonish the parents of the beginning stutterer to slow their tempo when they address their remarks to him, and to choose simple words, preferably monosyllabic.

The parent should not expect sudden responses to his requests, questions, or admonitions. It takes time for the child to make decisions, and a stuttering child should not be rushed. Different approaches to the child are illustrated by the dialogues of two short scenes:

PARENT: What did you do down town today, Johnnie?
CHILD (playing on the floor with building blocks): What?
PARENT: Now, Johnnie, why do you say "what" all the time?
CHILD (mumbling): I don't know.
PARENT: Well, did you hear what I said?
CHILD: Yes.
PARENT: What did I say?
CHILD: You said, what did I do down town.
PARENT: Then why did you say "what," Johnnie?
CHILD: I don't know.

The child, in truth, does not know. But I can tell the parent the answer. "What" is really a way of saying, "Please, Daddy, give me more time. You are too abrupt. I can't react so suddenly." The child has his consciousness engrossed in a plan of building with his blocks. The parent speaks rapidly. The child does not even know he is being addressed until the end of the question, when he hears his name spoken. First he has to drop from his thought the plans about his building. Then he has to go back in his memory and reconstruct the sentence. This takes time. To show that he has heard and to temporize he says "What." This word, if repeated often, should be interpreted as a danger signal. The parent should ask, "Why does he say 'what'?"

Now the other scene, the dialogue that should take place between the child and the parent who wants to apply real prophylaxis:

PARENT: Johnnie (with gently falling inflection).
CHILD: What?
PARENT (slowly, and with rising inflection on the last word): What did you do down town today?
CHILD: We went for a ride on the ferry. And, Daddy, did you know that big boat took the cars [etc.]?

Note the difference in this dialogue. Here the parent gives the child an opportunity to "tune in" first before he challenges his attention. The child then uses his "what" and gets it over with. The following question is not a jarring disturbance, as it was in the first dialogue. The slowly spoken question sets the mood for the child's answer. The child now has a model to follow that is within the range of his ability.

Exercise Caution in Criticizing the Speech of the Stutterer. Nothing should be said to the child who does not know he is a stutterer that may be interpreted to mean that the parents are in the least displeased with, or anxious about, any aspect of the child's speech. He should not even be praised for a period of exceptionally good speech; for praise endows speech habits with moral values. This aspect must by all means be avoided. He may be helped with difficult sounds, words, or phrases, particularly if he asks for help; but help it must be, not commandment. One injunction is so important here that, if I put it in capitals which by their size indicated its importance, the publisher would have to use a folio format for this book: *The beginning stutterer should never be interrupted in the midst of a communication, for the purpose of correcting his speech.* A parent who frequently interrupts the child with expressions like "Don't talk so loud," "Isn't, not ain't," "Don't scream so," "Red dress, not wed dwess," "Stop! now, relax and start again," should have the child taken away from him. He should then buy himself a dog and learn how to train a living creature. These interruptions will aggravate, never mitigate, the stuttering. Help in the child's speech should be given after the child has finished expressing what he has to say.

Give the Stutterer Few Moral Injunctions. With the beginning stutterer, injunctions as to his behavior should be reduced to an absolute minimum. When in doubt about whether to say "don't" to the child, the parent should say it to himself. The parent should remember that the stutterer is a congenitally rigid personality—one who codifies his behavior into a stricter system than that of the average child. The parents' examples are sufficient, without their precepts, to give the child all the conscience he can carry safely.

It is, of course, essential that the home in which the stutterer is reared be as free of friction, discord, and quarrel as possible. The home that is ideal for the normal child is, for the stutterer, an essential. Anything that gives the child feelings of fear, anxiety, or insecurity must be eliminated. The home must be one in which he can relax. It must be a "city of refuge."

As Prophylaxis, Formal Relaxation Exercises Are Futile. We come now to the subject of a frequently used modality of therapy—relaxation. We are still discussing the beginning stutterer who is unaware of his stuttering. When he is brought to the speech correctionist, all too frequently he undergoes a regime of relaxation exercises. He is taught to make himself "limp," to play "rag doll," or to play "dead." Such devices, in themselves, can have no significant effect upon the child's stuttering. If he knew that they were supposed to cure his stuttering, they might have the force of suggestion, but he does not even know he stutters (that is, if, as should be, his visits to the speech correctionist have been disguised as to their purpose), so suggestion does not lessen his stuttering. The young child cannot carry over to the speaking situation an exercise that was learned in another situation, especially if he is unaware of when the relaxation is intended to be applied. A child can be as relaxed as a sleepy cat one moment and in the next as tense as a cat about to spring. The relaxation of the former state in no wise diminishes the tension of the latter. Relaxation exercises do nothing to effect a raising of the threshold of seizure in the young child except for the immediate time in which the child is relaxed. Relaxation may be adopted as a therapy for secondary aspects of stuttering, particularly in children old enough to have insight into the behavior of their bodies; but for the beginning stutterer it is feckless, except for possible hygienic benefits which could have only a very indirect effect upon his speech.

Most of the effective clinical work for the beginning stutterer is done with the parents, relatives, friends, and teachers of the child. There is inverse correlation between the amount of time spent upon clinic work with parents and the age of the patient. The best use of the clinic time for the beginning stutterer is to afford the child what he does not get enough of at home, viz., the opportunity to converse in a quiet situation with someone who has the time and patience to listen and who uses simple language at a tempo he can imitate. Here relaxation can be learned by imitation and can be learned in the situation in which it is to be applied. This kind of training in relaxation is useful and directly effective in reducing the stuttering. But the few hours per month that the child spends in such an environment are insignificant in his training if the situation in the home is incongruous with that in the clinic. Hence the need of much parental counseling. At best the clinic can be only supplementary to the home.

Therapy for the Secondary Stutterer

Stuttering Should Be Explained to the Stutterer. We come now to the rationale of therapy for the child who has become aware of his stuttering. He has as yet developed only a few secondary aspects of stuttering. Someone has called his stuttering to his attention, with or without a name; or he may have discovered his stuttering quite by his own self-analysis. Suddenly, therefore, the first principle of therapy, that of hiding it from him, is inapplicable. He cannot very well have a guilt feeling about something of which he is in ignorance, but as soon as he recognizes his difference from others, the fat is in the fire. Now the facts must be faced realistically. It will only do harm to deny what he has discovered, even though the denial is diplomatically couched in the explanation of "normal nonfluency." The child should be told the truth, or as nearly the truth as is expedient, expressed somewhat as follows: Every normal child passes through periods or phases of development. With some it is fingernail biting, with others bed-wetting or masturbation, or thumb-sucking, or nightmares, or stuttering. About one boy in four passes through the stuttering phase. Practically all of these phases are successfully outgrown. The stutterer can be grateful if he has to suffer through only one of these phases. He should be assured that, if he takes the matter calmly, the stuttering will pass; that it will be confirmed and fixed only if he fights it.

This antidote for the poison of self-consciousness about stuttering is effective only if the parent makes the child believe it. The trouble is that many parents cannot convince themselves of the truth of the doctrine they are preaching to their children; and the children read in their parents' attitude a story of disbelief, anxiety, and dread. The antidote is of no avail if administered under those conditions. If the parent is skeptical of this doctrine, he had better learn the art of acting what he does not feel. At this period of the child's life, apprehension about whether or not he is to grow up a stutterer is definitely *disastrous.*

This is the period, when physiologic reasons for stuttering are disappearing and psychologic reasons are developing, that primary stuttering wanes and secondary stuttering waxes. This is the last good opportunity for a real cure of stuttering—goal number one. If the child is allowed to carry his stuttering beyond this phase, therapy is more difficult and prognosis definitely less favorable. This is the end of the period when nature is on the side of the therapist, when the natural development of the child, accompanied by a raising of the seizure threshold, makes conditions favorable for a cure.

The Stutterer's Secondary Tics Should Be Attacked Directly. Secondary aspects of stuttering, once they appear, are rapidly cumulative. In this period of the stutterer's life the therapist must center his attention upon two points of attack, the tics and the stutterer's attitudes; and the earlier he gets at these problems, the better. The longer he delays, the greater the number of tics he has to deal with, and the more profound and fixed the morbid attitude of the patient. He need not approach the therapy by indirection, as with the beginning stutterer. He takes the patient into his confidence. The cure, if one is attained, is not in the hands of the parents and friends, as with the beginning stutterer, but in his own.

There is only one way—a hard one—to eliminate the tics, and that is by consciously stopping them. It is like stopping cigarette smoking (which, by the way, is for many persons a sort of tic); the best way to quit the habit is to stop lighting the cigarettes. Whole books have been written on breaking the tobacco habit. Much advice is given in these works about strengthening one's moral courage, rewarding oneself for partial victories, and excusing himself for temporary failures. What to do for a complete relapse, and how to secure the help of one's friends, are additional topics in such books. These chapters are not really helpful. They merely emphasize the difficulty of the task before anyone who vows to "lick a tic."

Any device that brings the tic into the focus of the stutterer's awareness is to be recommended: stuttering before a mirror; keeping a pocket notebook handy to score the number of tics in a given time; ringing a bell, or sounding a castanet, every time a tic is evident; voluntarily inducing artificial tics; studying the tics of other people and comparing them with one's own.

This fighting to eradicate the secondary spasms takes much attention. In fact, it may spoil many an otherwise good conversation. It is difficult, but by far the easiest part of the achievement of a realistic goal for the psychoneurotic stutterer. The hardest tasks are those in which the stutterer wrestles with his own soul in the development of attitudes of communication that will check the spasms at their origin. The attitudes that need attention are those concerning (1) the listener or conversational party, (2) himself as a party to the conversation, and (3) himself as a stutterer.

The Stutterer's Attitude Toward His Listener Must Be Changed. The basic concern of the stutterer is for his standing in the eyes of those around him. When he is engaged in conversation with a new acquaintance, his attention is focused upon his listener, not to discover who or what he is, but to search for any clues as to what his listener thinks of him. He is fearful of what goes on behind the brow of his listener, what evaluation is being made, what weaknesses discovered, and particularly whether the listener has discerned the stuttering. As long as he persists in this attitude he will continue to stutter. It should be pointed out to him that certain situations minimize the stuttering. Examples: When he is so angry with his listener that he is primarily concerned with what he, the speaker, feels about the listener, he forgets himself in his wrath and may not stutter at all. When he is talking to a small baby, with no one else listening, or to a dog, or to God, he stutters less than when he is talking to his father. When he is a little drunk, his tongue is freed. Illustration after illustration of this principle should be drawn for him from his own experiences, until he cannot escape their meaning. He must be convinced that if he were freed of his egocentric worry about what the listener thought of him, his speech would be, if not normal, at least greatly improved.

The Stutterer's Attitude Toward Himself Must Be Changed. In order to help him conquer this ingrained tendency to center his attention upon his psychic defenses an evaluation should be made of the stutterer's assets. He has some or many of the valuable qualities that he should hold in mind when he is talking to others, such as good looks, physical health, strength, good clothes, fine family, ample financial backing, athletic prowess, good mind, high academic record, cultural experiences, desirable friends, etc. He must be shown that the ability of a person to hold up his head without constantly considering the world's evaluation of him depends upon his possessing what the world values. Since he has many of these qualities,[20] he becomes self-centered if he continues to act as though he possessed none of them. As with the campaign to get him to see the meaning of his ability to talk to children without stuttering, the doctrine

[20] It must be admitted that this critical step in therapy is difficult for the "ill-favored" child, as he was referred to in the fairy tales. The presence of many valuable qualities makes the step easy and their absence makes it difficult, if not impossible.

has to be preached to him over and over again. He will tell the therapist one day that he grasps the point, and yet when the same point is made a week later it will apparently come as a new idea. Until he gets the thought so deeply implanted within him that he dreams it, it will not affect his stuttering.

Another step in the evolution of an aggressive, rather than a defensive, attitude toward his listener, is to get him deliberately and consciously to focus his attention upon his conversational partner, to see, not what the partner thinks of him, but what he thinks of the partner. He should be asked to report on conversations he has had with new acquaintances, giving a description of each in great detail, as to both physical and personal characteristics. Again he should be asked to study the effect upon his listener of faked stuttering, or he should be told to try the experiment of influencing the listener's attitude toward himself or toward some other listener. The experiment can be made plain in this fashion. S is the patient. A and B are two persons with whom he is in conversation. S wants A to feel comfortable, so he praises him for some real excellence. S watches both A and B to see the effect of his remarks. Perhaps the best way to get an aggressive attitude is for the stutterer to watch the tensions of his listeners and see what he can do to relieve them.[21] The approach to this subject can best be illustrated by quoting what the therapist might say to the stutterer:

All these years you have been centering your attention upon the cross of stuttering that you have had to bear. You have felt sorry for yourself, and you know that others have shared this pity. Remember that it is hard for pity and admiration to exist side by side in the same person at the same time. You want admiration, not pity, from your friends. One way you can get it is to try to relieve them of the suspense, tension, anxiety, and worry about whether, when you start to speak a sentence, you are going to make it. Keep your mind on your listener's cross, not on yours.

When you first started to stutter your mother watched and listened with infinite concern and compassion. At her knee you developed your present attitude of self-concern. You are forcing others to assume the role of your mother. Don't do it. It is not fair to them. Constantly watch them to keep them comfortable while you talk.

And always remember that, with those who know you are a stutterer, failures in conquering the stuttering will elicit pity from your friends and disgust from your enemies; but successes in your campaign will win admiration from both. Keep them in mind, if you want admiration.

[21] Suppose that, as part of the psychoneurosis of the stutterer, he enjoys watching his listener squirm; what should his modified attitude be? Answer: Such a person is a sadistic psychopath. He belongs in a different book. He is a psychoneurotic who happens to stutter and uses that tool convenient to his hand. The author's "suppose," moreover, is not consistent with the picture of the personality of the average stutterer.

Activities in Which He Achieves Social Success Should Be Selected for the Stutterer. In addition to calling the roll of the stutterer's assets, capabilities, and special advantages, in order to support his morale, one of the finest builders of confidence is a new activity in which he can excel. Nothing succeeds with a stutterer like success. This activity may be a hobby, a sport, an artistic skill, or even a new job. In the selection of this activity one should bear in mind not only the special talents of the stutterer, but also the special attention-getting property of the new hobby, sport, skill, or job. I am thinking of two stutterers whom I know who got no benefit whatsoever from extensive therapies until this type of occupational therapy was employed; then they improved rapidly, almost suddenly. One of them took up magicianship and was a great success at parties and conventions. The other became an apprentice in a crime-detection laboratory and succeeded so well at his work that he was often called as an expert witness in court. These boys were transformed from social failures to social successes. When they studied their audiences they discovered that in some cases they no longer needed to defend their egos and in others their superiority over their audiences was such as to render unimportant the reactions of the auditors to them. The suddenness of their speech improvement was due probably to the fact that the new therapy brought to fruition all the seeds of thought that had been planted in them over the months and years of apparently futile therapy.

One young physician who had stuttered his way through medical school suddenly awakened to the meaning of his therapist's teachings one hot afternoon on the street in Chicago. He had been sent out on an ambulance call to care for the injured victims in a car accident. He found that the only important factor at the scene of the accident was he himself, his skill and his judgment. Even the policeman took orders from him. The friends of the injured persons paid no more attention to his stutter than to the smudge on his white coat. That he was a stutterer was quite insignificant. As his orderly was binding one of the victims on a litter, the physician had a vision of his place in society which has remained with him ever since to give him social courage. The part of stuttering that was caused by fear of it has gone.

In choosing an activity to serve as occupation therapy the therapist must not make the mistake of selecting one that gets favorable social attention to the patient and at the same time excuses him from speech. To be good speech therapy it must employ speech, but employ it in a new setting. Speech must be associated, not with social failures, but with social successes. To select a job for a stutterer because it places a minimum requirement upon speech is disastrous. If the young man is of professional capabilities, he will never be satisfied with any vocation but a profession, and there is no profession that does not demand speech. Speech is the most important tool of any profession. The stutterer of professional potential, therefore, must take the calculated risk of selecting his vocation as would anyone else, without regard to his speech.[22]

The Stutterer's Attitude Toward Stuttering Must Be Changed. Before one can assail successfully the castle of secondary stuttering he must gird up his loins and attack the dragon that guards the castle, the dragon of moral perfectionism. Without at least slicing off his tail, the battle cannot be won. The tail of the dragon is the stutterer's first precept: Thou shalt not stutter; for stammering and iterations and head-bobbings are an abomination unto the Lord and a sign of Beelzebub. The therapist must convince the stutterer that this commandment is baseless, spurious, and without authority. He must show the patient that the term "stutterer," like any other generic name, is loaded with whatever meaning the users of the word read into it or apply to it. Any class name—Republican, Presbyterian, blonde, Aryan, Norwegian, widow, bachelor, diabetic—may be used either to gain or to alienate one's sympathy. In many situations a Republican would do well not to parade his politics, or a diabetic his medical record, not from a feeling of delinquency or guilt or constitutional inadequacy, but for reasons of expediency. The stutterer should be trained to substitute this principle of expediency of conduct for that of avoidance of shame. He should be told that of course stuttering is unpleasant, cumbersome, and uneconomical in communication, but that it is not something that must be hidden, something from which his hearers might infer that he possesses other related weaknesses and delinquencies. It is difficult for a nonstutterer to realize the moral effect of expressed and unexpressed anxieties of the mother and father of the stutterer as they agonize with him and pray over him in the early years of his life. He may never completely recover from the suasion of this moralizing, but the therapist must do what he can to minimize the effect of it upon the patient's speech.

[22] It must be faced realistically that stuttering is a professional *impediment.* This word came into English from the Latin. Every reader of Caesar's *Gallic Wars* will remember how frequently he complained that *impedimenta* (baggage transport) reduced the striking power of his forces. In English, the word "impediment" was formerly used to signify "that which obstructs bodily functions" (Webster's New International Dictionary, 2nd ed., G. & C. Merriam, 1939). This use of the word has become obsolete except to indicate "obstructions of speech." The dictionary thus records the general opinion that a speech disorder is baggage that slows up the march of thought or reduces its effectiveness. Many a parent says of his stuttering child, "he thinks faster than he can talk." But Caesar could not, or did not, leave all his impedimenta behind; and many stutterers carry baggage into their professional campaigns. Employers—such as boards of education, personnel managers, and office supervisors—often restrict the employment of stutterers. These restrictions are generally more numerous and inclusive than necessary for the protection of the stutterer and his professional clients. Additional restrictions need not be considered by the stutterer himself.

The Stutterer's Ethics Must Be Put on a Realistic Basis. The next attack upon the castle of moral perfectionism is to discover other unrealistic commandments the stutterers may attempt to follow. With each patient a different pattern of moralism will appear. Each requires careful analysis, exposure, and modification or refutation. The problem is to accomplish this without seeming to be a delinquent oneself. If the therapist is not careful, the stutterer will make a perfectionist out of him. I remember one stutterer who was sure that most of what went on between boy and girl alone on a "date" was bad, if not in act at least in thought, and consequently unworthy. To attempt to convince him that he himself should try dating almost put me in the position of contributing to the delinquency of a minor, and caused me to wonder what would happen if what he said about dating turned out in his case to be as he predicted. The stutterer is resistant to change of code, and his defense is almost impregnable because it is based upon moral principles. Though he sometimes falls into what he calls sin, he maintains his moral code, and he is likely to reject the person who assails that code. The therapist may find himself debating the undebatable.

The stutterer holds so firmly to his moral code that he overlooks the implications of another body of moral teachings that serve to temper the first. He fails to observe reforms in the law and modifications to make adjustments to the life of the community. He fails to notice that the staunchly orthodox are often shunted aside in the march of progress, that there is a difference between his conscience and that of the hero he thinks he is copying. To say that it is difficult to get the stutterer to think straight in this ambivalence of moral teaching is a gross understatement.

The stutterer makes moral issues out of habits, conditions, and states that are strictly unmoral. He contemplates with shame characteristics for which he, as a living soul, has no responsibility and also those that are common to all men, good or bad. He broods over his physical appearance, his clothes, his study habits, his family standing, his past social blunders, his religion. He attaches excessive moral significance to his sex drives, to masturbation, and to his friendships with both sexes. He has qualms of conscience about his obligations to members of his family, his employer, his teacher, or his customers. He blames himself for adversities in business, in school, in the shop, or for physical accidents.[23]

[23] The question arises: Is the unrealistic ethical attitude *always* absent in the nonstutterer? Of course not; sometimes it is conspicuously present. But this attitude is *often* absent in the nonstutterer and *seldom* absent in the stutterer. Its presence is therefore significant when seen in stuttering. The reader should remember the difference in moral background between Johnson's Indians and those of Lemert, the nonstuttering and the stuttering.

A frequent source of guilt uncovered in the history of stutterers is that associated with enuresis. It appears often in case histories of stutterers, and one suspects that were it not for the sensitiveness of the patients about enuresis it would appear oftener. One suspects also that enuresis may have a double connection with stuttering: (1) it may be a common source of social anxiety, and (2) it may be an evidence of basic inhibitory weakness of the central nervous system. In other terms: (1) the patient may stutter because he is embarrassed about his enuresis; and (2) both his stuttering and his enuresis may be reactions that he cannot inhibit. Whatever the connection is, the stutterer's communicational attitude is adversely affected by his many painful experiences with wetting his bed and his clothes. He finds it difficult, in conversational contact with others, to view his listeners objectively while he suspects or fears that they may be thinking about his present or past shortcomings. He cannot stop stuttering until his attitude of guilt has been eradicated. The therapist may have to help him think it through and talk it out.

With adult patients who possess real insight, it is not always necessary to expose all the areas of guilt in conversation with the therapist. Once the patient has caught the principle of this part of the therapy, he can be left to make the applications of it to matters that are not revealed to the therapist. Ruthless exposure of the patient's inner life may defeat the purpose of the therapy by causing fresh humiliations. Every device in the therapy of stuttering should be selected on the basis of two ancient criteria: *primum non nocere, et semper dignitatem vitae humanae sustinere* (in the first place to do no harm, and always to uphold the dignity of human life).

One of the best devices to offset the morbid puritanism of the stutterer is humor. The stutterer must be taught to laugh at his unrealistic standards and at his exaggerated concern about his speech failures. This sense of humor, however, cannot be developed by having the therapist laugh at the patient. That would only "set the dye" of the puritanism. The stutterer may learn this attitude of laughing at himself if he sees other stutterers laughing at their own shortcomings. He will usually tolerate jokes about himself as a stutterer if they come from another stutterer. Hence the justification for, and purpose of, the Stutterers' Club. There is really little else to be gained in such an organization, for the blind cannot lead the blind. But the stutterer will accept criticism from another stutterer, provided it is given with a smile. As far as is possible, the organization of the club should be left to the patients themselves. Too much direction by the therapist will defeat the purpose of the club. The meetings should be devoted largely to speeches and discussions about stuttering, stressing humorous talks. If the group is willing, it is beneficial to hold an annual banquet to which nonstuttering guests are invited and at which the toasts are given by the stutterers and introduced by a toastmaster selected from their own group. The motif of this banquet should be to instruct the guests on the proper attitude toward the stutterer and toward his speech impediment. This motif can, of course, be better expressed by indirection, illustration, and anecdote than by direct expository moralizing.

Formal Exercises in Relaxation May Be Used. We discussed the futility of direct and formal relaxation exercises in cases of beginning stuttering. With the cases we have been discussing in this section, however—i.e., those we expediently label secondary stutterers—we may employ formal relaxation exercises, provided the patient has sufficient insight into what is intended in this therapy. By relaxation we do not mean a somnolent or hypnoidal state, or a condition of sleepiness. Quite the contrary; we mean a status that depends upon mental alertness and a keen awareness of the whole environment. We mean also a voluntary control that quite supersedes any volition that is involved in an overt motor process. In the central nervous system the functions of the spinal centers are largely positive and excitatory, while those of the highest gradients of the cerebrum are negative and inhibitory. These latter functions are employed in relaxation. Relaxation[24] is the highest form of voluntary control. It is difficult for many persons to learn.

Relaxation not conditioned to accompany speech is of no avail to the stutterer. The patient is taught first to relax his hands, arms, and shoulders. The best way to teach him this control is by having him lift and manipulate the arms of someone who can relax. If the therapist cannot be an exemplar here, perhaps he should confine his training to other phases of the speech correction. After the patient has learned to relax, he should learn to count or say the alphabet while relaxing. After that he may attempt conversational speech with real communication in it, relaxing the while. This should be continued until he can do it sitting, standing, or walking, and until it becomes habitual. He should be instructed to remember this device and put it to use when he gets in a tight spot in conversation.

"Distraction" Should Be Used with Discretion. The more the patient stutters, the more he fears it, and hence the more he stutters. How can this vicious cycle be broken? We have suggested above that one of

[24] Shall we call relaxation a *process,* an *act,* a *motor pattern,* or what? Clearly, if we can will it, it should have a class name. It may be that it is only a *status,* and perhaps that is why it is difficult to will.

the ways of interrupting this reflexive chain of cause and effect is to reduce the intensity of his fear of stuttering, by changing his attitude toward communicative failures. Getting him drunk, let's say, will reduce the fear of stuttering and hence reduce the stuttering. This treatment, however, is hardly feasible for everyday wear. It has side effects of considerable disadvantage. Another way to break the cycle is to distract the patient's attention from his speech. What he is unaware of he no longer anticipates in fear. This treatment is called therapy by distraction. If the therapist teaches the stutterer to center his attention upon something other than the coming words, the anticipatory fear is reduced and the stuttering is lessened. It makes little difference whether this substitute for the fear of stuttering is logically connected with speech or not, so long as it is dramatic enough to hold the patient's attention. He may visualize a *K* the size of the Empire State building when he fears a coming block on the sound of that letter; he may swing his right hand back and forth at a constant rhythm; he may click steel balls together; he may crawl on his hands and knees. Any of these things may reduce his stuttering—for a time. There are two disadvantages of the distraction therapy: (1) It is effective only so long as the device is being learned; when it has been automatized it has no more effect upon the stutter than walking while talking. (2) When its effectiveness has ceased, it is likely to leave in its wake a trace of the pattern of the distraction device, adding a tic to the constellation of spasms and blocks that make up the picture of the stuttering.

It should be remembered that some distractive devices appear to be other than they are; they may seem to be fundamental therapy, directly aimed at the basic cause of stuttering. There are three situations in which this mirage appears: (1) that in which both therapist and patient are fooled by the device; (2) that in which the therapist recognizes the distractive nature of the device and misrepresents it to the patient or knowingly allows the patient to be self-deceived; and (3) that in which both therapist and patient recognize the distractive nature of the device in question.

It is obvious that in the first situation distraction is often futile and dangerous. It has, moreover, an unfortunate effect upon the therapist, since it may fool him into believing that something very fundamental and basic is being accomplished by the therapy. To give an extreme example: suppose the therapist is strongly convinced that stuttering is due to a failure of visual imagery, and hence he uses the device of the giant letter and the stuttering is lessened. The success of his therapy seems to support his theory of etiology. Before he has waited long enough to observe the permanency of his "cure," he adopts the device as a universal technique for use with all stutterers. His patients suffer the disillusioning effect of false confidence in temporary gains.

In the second situation the only justification of the distraction device is its employment for its suggestion effect—to give the patient a few experiences with stuttering-free speech and after that to discard the device and go on to more basic therapy. Its continued use, or advice to the patient to make any distractive behavior a permanent feature of his speech pattern without warning him that the device is purely distractive, is quackery and charlatanism.

In the third situation the aim of the therapist may be the same as in the second. Moreover, there may be an advantage in the therapy in sharing with the patient the knowledge of what distractive techniques are being employed. The sharing of the knowledge at least shares the responsibility. The patient should be informed that at best the distractive device is a palliative, a treatment of symptoms alone. To prescribe a palliative when a cure is asked is ethical only when the patient knows the nature of the prescription, and when a cure is wholly and certainly unattainable. The therapist would do well, therefore, to examine all the tricks in his bag to make sure which of them are distractive in effect. If he uses any of these devices, it must be with a clear understanding of their nature and their purpose in the overall strategy of the therapy.

Direct Speech Correction May Be Undertaken. In the first section of this monograph the essential facts about stuttering were listed, sixth among them being that, in addition to the convulsive interferences of speech, the majority of stutterers also show phonetic lapses and sometimes real dysarthrias. Time was when it was heretical to advocate making any comment on, or corrections of, the speech of the stutterer, even though you avoided all mention of the stuttering per se. May I venture to suggest that what many stutterers are sensitive about is their general ineptness of articulation. To eschew the formal training of diction not only does not help the stutterer overcome his spasms but it deprives him of improvements in his personal front that would build his morale and give him confidence in his speech. As bracing a weak ankle reduces stumbling, so cleaning up a boy's diction reduces anxieties in his conversational attitude. An analysis should be made, therefore, of his phonetic lapses, and a systematic program instituted to cover them one by one, affording such correction as the patient is able to effect. Diction drill itself does not harm the stutterer, only such drill administered with an attitude that implies that the thing being corrected is wrong. The concepts of right and wrong should be studiously avoided in this training. The stated motive for the correction should be to achieve two things: conformity with the arbitrary code of speech of the community, and grace and beauty in the utterance of the code.

An aspect of the general muscular tenseness of the stutterer is the flatness of his voice, its lack of graceful and emotionally meaningful inflection. In voice, as with diction faults, improvement can have beneficial effect upon his stuttering. Just as in diction the stutterer learns to take pride in the niceness of his pronunciation, so he should be motivated here to present to the world a more pleasant voice. Particularly is help in voice control beneficial for stuttering boys who are passing through the pubescent voice change at the time of therapy. The voice is admirably suited to express the change of attitude that should take place in the stutterer under therapy. With a new voice the stutterer often gets the feeling that he has shed the old stuttering personality and has donned a new one. This is no mere pretense. What he pretends long enough, he becomes.

The Personal Qualities of a Good Therapist

Earlier in this monograph I have referred to the fact that stuttering yields, at least temporarily, to practically any therapy in which the patient has faith. We come then to the subject of the faith-inspiring qualities of the therapist. These are, of course, quite varied: his professional reputation, the certificates on his office wall, the attitude of the patients in his waiting room, etc., but above all, that subtle, difficult-to-define thing called personal magnetism. This is a complex of impressions made upon the patient. The therapist possessed of this ability to impress the patient seems to be frank but tactful; penetrating but understanding; professional but kind; confident but humble. In my professional lifetime I have seen several supreme examples of therapists so equipped. Some of them have succeeded in spite of the fact that such magnetism is almost the entire equipment of their therapeutic armamentarium. Personalities that are long in magnetism and short on knowledge are undesirable members of our profession. I do not begrudge them their successes. What is unfortunate, however, is that, insofar as they succeed, they have authority to write books, make speeches, and teach courses to explain to beginners in therapy how it is done. Usually what these human magnets think they are doing is not what they actually do; and what they do by way of technique of therapy is insignificant in comparison with what they accomplish by means of personal magnetism. Such therapists generally serve their patients well, and they would do little harm in our professional world if they could be prevented from attempting to tell others how to practice. They are great artists; they cause trouble only when they think, or pretend, that they are scientists. What such an artist possesses in therapy is tremendous, but it is not negotiable. It does not outlast him. His disciples try to imitate him, but they have only the rationalized explanations of the master's technique. It is as though a child were to watch a magician draw a card from a rabbit's ear and then attempt to repeat the trick. He does everything that he saw the magician do, but no card; for the child did not see the only important thing that the magician did. I do not mean to imply that these artists in the field of therapy are consciously hiding what they do and how they do it. Most of them are trying sincerely to explain their successes, but they cannot verbalize what they do not themselves understand. What their followers may nevertheless get is a bag of futile tricks.

The great therapist is one who combines science and personal magnetism. By "science" I do not mean my brand of science, or Eisenson's, or Johnson's, or Van Riper's, but rather a working theory that satisfies him, the therapist. He has a rationale, a method based upon reason, and he knows what he is doing. As to his personal magnetism, he may be born to it and thus come by it without effort, planning, or self-discipline; or he may attain effectiveness of personality partly by a humble search for his social deficiencies and assets, to eradicate the former and enhance the latter, and partly by so adjusting his life that stresses, pressures, and frustrations will not be greater than he can safely carry. If the therapist cannot be a hypnotic psyche, at least he can become, provided he has the brains to understand and the will to strive, what in these latter days we have learned to call the well-adjusted personality—stable, earnest, realistic, humble, but above all possessed of an abiding interest in people.

I hope that such a therapist will give my blueprint for the management of stuttering a vigorous and thorough trial. If it succeeds it may not prove much; but if it does, at least some children who stutter, and their mothers and fathers, will have richer and better lives.

Suggested Readings

The listing below contains only articles or books, *not actually referred to in the text*, that are of special significance as reading parallel to the text. The special aspects of the subject of stuttering for which the author commends these references is indicated by the classes in which they are listed.

Concerning the stutterer's basic physiology:

Berry, M. F., "A common denominator in twinning and stuttering," *Journal of Speech Disorders*, III, 1938.

Despert, J. L., "Psychosomatic study of 50 stuttering children," *American Journal of Orthopsychiatry*, XVI, 1946.

Concerning the heredity of stuttering:

Wepman, J. M., "Familial incidence in stammering," *Journal of Speech Disorders*, IV, 1939.

West, R., Nelson, S., and Berry, M. F., "The heredity of stuttering," *Quarterly Journal of Speech*, XXV, 1939.

Concerning diagnosogenesis of stuttering:

Johnson, W., "The Indians have no word for it," *Quarterly Journal of Speech*, XXX, 1944.

Snidecor, J. C., "Why the Indian does not stutter," *Quarterly Journal of Speech*, XXXIII, 1947.

Concerning the iterations of stuttering:

Davis, D. M., "The relation of repetitions in speech of young children to certain measures of language maturity and situational factors," *Journal of Speech Disorders*, IV, 1939, and V, 1940.

Eisenson, J., and Pastel, E., "A study of the perseverating tendency in stutterers," *Quarterly Journal of Speech*, XXII, 1936.

Concerning the personality of the stutterer:

Bender, J. F., *The Personality Structure of Stutterers*, New York, Pitman Publishing Corp., 1939.

Moncur, J. P., "Parental domination in stuttering," *Journal of Speech and Hearing Disorders*, XVII, 1952.

Concerning the therapy of stuttering:

Moore, W. E., "Hypnosis in a system of therapy for stutterers," *Journal of Speech Disorders*, XI, 1946.

Van Riper, C., "The effect of devices for minimizing stuttering on the creation of symptoms," *Journal of Abnormal and Social Psychology*, XXXII, 1937.

A PERSEVERATIVE THEORY OF STUTTERING

JON EISENSON, Ph.D.

Professor of Speech and Director of the Speech and Hearing Clinic, Queens College; Lecturer in Otolaryngology, College of Physicians and Surgeons, Columbia University; Fellow of the American Psychological Association (Division of Clinical Psychology); Fellow of the American Speech and Hearing Association; author of The Psychology of Speech, Basic Speech, Examining for Aphasia, *and* Improvement of Voice and Diction; *coauthor of* The Psychology of the Physically Handicapped (*with Pintner and Stanton*), Speech Disorders (*with M. F. Berry*), *and* Speech Correction in the Schools (*with M. Ogilvie*).

A Perseverative Theory of Stuttering

I. PERSEVERATION AND ITS CORRELATES

THE purpose of this paper is to demonstrate that there is a causal relationship between the tendency of some persons to stutter and the parallel tendency of these persons to engage in more than a normal amount of perseverative behavior. Stuttering will be explained as a perseverative phenomenon, or, more specifically, as perseveration manifest in speaking. For the most part, this manifestation will be explained as a constitutional tendency, related to perseveration in aspects of behavior other than speech. Nonconstitutional perseveration, that which arises as a result of psychogenic factors, will also be considered.

At the outset the writer presents his thesis relative to stuttering as a perseverative phenomenon. A majority of stutterers (from 55 to 60 percent), he believes, are predisposed to a manner of oral language behavior called stuttering because they are constitutionally inclined to perseverate to an extent or degree greater than is the case for most speakers. A minority of stutterers (under 50 percent) include persons who at the moment of speaking are confronted with factors and influences that cause them to perseverate.

Perseveration, for the time being, may be considered the tendency for a mental or motor act to persist for a time longer than normal after the stimulus which brought about the behavior is no longer present. Early concepts of perseveration referred to a tendency for a continuation of neural and mental processes for a time presumably longer than normal following original stimulation.[1]

To hold that stuttering is a perseverative phenomenon amounts almost

[1] For a review of concepts of perseveration see 32:ch. 15, and 27.

to making a self-evident assertion. Whenever a speaker who thinks of himself as a stutterer blocks, repeats, prolongs sounds, or engages in any repetitive ticlike mannerisms associated with stuttering, he is perseverating. What needs to be determined is the relationship of this speech and speech-associated behavior to stuttering.[2] Does the stutterer develop anxieties about speech because he anticipates that in given situations he will not be able to speak without perseverating? Or are the perseverative manifestations the consequences of his anxieties about given speaking situations? Does the speaker who perseverates also show inclinations beyond the normal for perseverative behavior in nonspeaking activities? Is there a relationship between perseveration and personality or in other behavioral attributes that some clinicians believe to be associated with "the stutterer"? Is there any relationship between sex and perseveration in the population at large, and among stutterers in particular? These are some questions this paper will try to answer. At the outset, the reader would be correct in guessing that for many of the posed questions an affirmative answer may be anticipated.

The writer has for some time believed that there is a causal relationship between excessive perseveration and stuttering. The evidence for this belief will be presented and examined so that the reader may come to his own conclusions. In any event, perseveration as an aspect of behavior will be reviewed and its implications for stuttering theory and therapy considered.

Concepts of Perseveration

The tentative definition just given considers perseveration as the tendency for a mental or motor act to persist for a time longer than normal after the stimulus which brought about the behavior is no longer present. An implication of this concept of perseveration is that it is normal for neural and mental processes to continue to influence an individual for some time following the original stimulation. Otherwise it would not be possible for a reacting individual to establish a *set* or attitude necessary for the determination of the appropriate response to the stimulating situation. Perseveration refers to the *persistent effect (for a time longer than normal) of the no-longer-present stimulating situation.* Without some degree of perseveration we could have no consistency of thought, feeling, and action. An excessive amount of perseveration may, however,

[2] Stuttering may be defined functionally as a transient disturbance in *communicative, propositional language usage.* The disturbance is characterized overtly by hesitations, repetitions, prolongations, and hypertension. Covert reactions include apprehension, anxiety, and avoidance drives related to the act of speaking.

exercise interfering and disruptive influences, in that appropriate responses to changing situations are impeded.

According to Spearman (32:165), there are several aspects of perseveration. These include:

1. *Persistence, or secondary function*—"the persistent effect of a presentation after it has quitted consciousness."
2. *Hindrance*—the degree of interference or "the degree of hindrance which the perseverating effect of past mental activity causes to a new one of the same kind."
3. *Recurrence*—the tendency for an act to recur when it is no longer appropriate to the situation.
4. *Inertia*—a generalized effect of resistance to change basic to perseveration in all its aspects.

Some psychologists prefer to use the term *central factor* for perseveration. Central factor is considered to be the normal ability of an individual to establish and maintain "set." It implies "some sort of perseverating neural substrate which is relatively independent of afferent stimulation."

In his monograph Levine (27) hypothesizes some possible psychological and neurophysiological determinants of normal and abnormal influences of "central factor." Some of these will be considered later. For the present, however, let us merely emphasize the point that whether the factor be called perseveration or central factor, it may exist in individuals as either a normal or an abnormal component of intellectual and/or motor functioning. Without some degree of persistence, an individual is not able to maintain a "set" or continue to attend as occasion demands. With an excessive degree of persistence, an individual is not readily able to shift his attention or to modify his set as occasion demands. He seems to be overresponsive to inner drives or determinants and insufficiently responsive to immediate external or environmental stimulation. We will return to the implications of this aspect of perseveration or "central factor" when the relationships of perseveration to factors of personality and of intellect are discussed more specifically. For the present an understanding of the phenomenon of perseveration will be furthered by reviewing types of tasks and "classical" testing techniques for measuring this function.

Tasks and Tests to Measure Perseveration

In general, experimental situations are constructed on the hypothesis that once a situation has been presented the response is determined by something else besides or beyond what was just presented to the subject for reaction. Whether we use the term "perseveration," "central factor," "inertia," "neural lag," or "stimulus trace," we are dealing with a common element. According to Hebb (19:5–6): "That element is the recognition that responses are determined by something else besides the immediately preceding sensory stimulation. . . . All these things have the same property of an activity that has a selective effect on behavior without being part of the present afferent excitation."

Sensory tasks measure, in general, the aftereffects of sensory stimulation. For example, after exposure to light of a given intensity, the time needed for adjustment to near-darkness would serve as a measure of perseveration. Another typical task is to use a color wheel to determine the time needed for flicker to disappear or the colors of the wheel to fuse.

Motor tasks characteristically call for a relatively rapid shift from one pattern of response to another within the same general type of response. A test requiring the subject to alternate between drawing horizontal and vertical lines, or requiring him to draw either line according to a presented but not predetermined order (– – | – | | – – – |), is an example of a motor task of perseveration.

Another type of motor perseveration task calls for "creative" effort. Such tasks call for the modification or breaking away from established habit patterns and require that an old act be performed in a new way. The writing of numerals or letters in mirror-image fashion is an example of a "creative" effort task. Another is the rewriting of a paragraph omitting dots over the *i*'s or crosses for the *t*'s.

Testing for *dispositional or attitudinal* rigidity has been approached by several experimenters through the use of alternating motor and creative-effort tasks. Dispositional rigidity implies that an individual has difficulty or is reluctant to break down old, established habit patterns and to perform according to the immediate needs or requirements of a situation. It implies that the performing individual experiences difficulty in acquiring or shifting to new sets or habits that conflict with old, well-established patterns of response.

Relationship of Perseveration to Other Factors

Intellectual Functioning. Spearman considers perseveration to be a factor related to intellectual functioning. Perseveration, or *p*, represents *mental inertia.* It exists as a general factor that may be distinguished from the factor *G* which represents the amount of mental energy possessed by a human being.[3]

[3] Spearman (32:191) postulates three general factors of intellect related to mental energy: "The G would represent the amount of that energy, *p* would represent its inertia, and O would measure the facility of recuperation after effortful expenditure."

In his *Abilities of Man* (31:ch. 17) Spearman observes that the perseverative tendency is stronger among males than among females. This, if true, is of great importance in our understanding of stuttering. Another observation in the same volume is that perseveration tends to increase along manic-normal-melancholic lines.

Mental Stability. The factor of mental stability is related both to intellectual functioning and to personality as it influences such functioning. Spearman and Jones (32:158–159) observe that ". . . stability is favoured neither by low degrees of perseveration, nor still less by high degrees, but rather by medium ones." In support of their observation, they cite the work of Lankes, Pinard, and Clarke with children and adults, in which the results of batteries of tests of perseveration were correlated with "character" traits and judgments of personality.

Pinard (29) rated school children on a fourfold basis according to a battery of tests of perseveration. The ratings were: extremely perseverative, moderately perseverative, moderately nonperseverative, and extremely nonperseverative. He found that a large majority (75 percent) of the children characterized as "difficult and unreliable" rated as extremely perseverative and about 25 percent as moderately perseverative. In contrast, he observed, "The very opposite holds for the self-controlled and persevering children."

Pinard carried out the same experiment on a group of 116 patients at the Maudsley Hospital and found that they tested along the same general lines as did the children. He characterizes perseverators as tending to be abnormally nervous and sensitive. Spearman and Jones (32:158–161), in reviewing experimental research on perseveration, cite several studies which tend to corroborate their own bias and that of Pinard. In general, "difficult" children, those we would tend to characterize as being emotionally unstable, are apt to be either extreme perseverators or extreme nonperseverators. The writer's own prejudice directs attention to one additional study, that by Ewen (16), who investigated the perseverating phenomenon in normal and epileptic patients. He found perseveration to be a feature of the peculiar mental state of epileptics between attacks. This observation may be especially significant in the light of the observations of Robert West, in this *Symposium,* on the similarity of stutterers and persons with epileptic tendencies. Landis and Bolles (25:512) observe that "Some epileptic patients during a psychic seizure or a furor are unable to shift a line of voluntary action or an entire determining tendency which has been set in progress. They cannot readjust this tendency even when new circumstances arise which demand reconsideration."

Volition. Abnormal or excessive perseveration is viewed by some psychopathologists as representing a disturbance of volition. "From the point of view of a disturbance of volition, perseveration occurs when the determining tendencies for a given task are overcome, blocked, or diverted in some fashion by inhibiting events or ideas" (25:507). According to Landis and Bolles, the individual who is perseverating is attempting to make a response and to execute the performance he recognizes as required or expected of him. The act does not succeed, however, because the circumstances which would favor goal achievement are not present, or not sufficiently strong to overcome other resistant forces. As a result, previously performed behavior is continued, but "without the formation of a new determining tendency."

Although perseveration seems to be associated with some morbid states, such as epilepsy, depression, excessive fatigue, some drug influence, and brain damage, these are not necessary for a perseveration tendency to become manifest. Perseveration may occur whenever the usual means or avenues of access to a goal are blocked. "If a person has the intellectual capacity for appreciating the consequences of his own determining tendencies and persists toward his goals despite blockage or deviation, we say that he is determined. When there is a lack of elasticity and adaptiveness with respect to other inhibiting and facilitating factors, determination becomes inflexibility" (25:507).

Attitudinal Rigidity. Several references have been made to dispositional or attitudinal rigidity as an aspect of perseveration. Dispositional rigidity is expressed in difficulty in acquiring or shifting to new habits or sets that conflict with previously established response patterns. Perseveration may be interpreted as a specialized form of mental or attitudinal rigidity. In some patients with organic brain damage, rigidity or inflexibility may dominate much of their behavior. But rigidity may also be noted in patients with psychopathologies. Paranoid patients, for example, tend to approach many or most situations in the light of an established determining motive. Compulsive-neurotic persons also tend to approach, evaluate, and respond to new situations in the light of a previous evaluation or overevaluation determined by individual motivation.

At the opposite pole of attitudinal rigidity is the behavior of the so-called psychopathic personality. Individuals under this broad category of abnormal persons include delinquents, criminals, and individuals who in general display little "moral consciousness." Unlike neurotics and psychotics, psychopathic persons seem to be untroubled by what they think or do. They are a trouble to their families and to society at large, but seem to be indifferent or uncaring about their own behavior and its effects on others. As a group, psychopaths appear to be unable to maintain a line of action or to work consistently toward any goal or objective. They respond to the immediate, are constantly vacillating, and show an abnormal lack of ability to maintain a set or an attitude.

Cattel (6, 7), a prolific investigator of perseveration as related to personality, found that persons with low perseveration scores include many who resemble the so-called psychopathic personalities.

Personality. Directly or indirectly, in the immediately preceding pages we have been discussing personality and its relationship to perseveration. We may, like Spearman, look upon perseveration as a general behavioral factor, influencing all behavior. Or, in a related way, we may accept Cattell's theory that perseveration as measured in a test situation is the difference between the effects of two "opposing" factors. One is dispositional rigidity; the other is will (the marshaled force of the ego) trying to overcome the effect of lag or rigidity imposed by dispositional rigidity.

Most students of perseveration, this writer included, are inclined to think of perseveration as a general factor normally present to some degree in all of us and quantitatively different for most of us. The extremes of perseveration are associated with disturbed personalities. An absence of the perseverative tendency seems to be found in individuals who are overactive (the manic) and who are not able to attend to situations long enough to make appropriate or socially expected or approved responses (the psychopathic personalities). Excessive perseveration seems to be associated with excessively withdrawn, obsessive, depressed, and paranoid individuals.

Organic Factors. In our earlier discussion of attitudinal rigidity the relationship between brain damage and perseveration was suggested. The student familiar with the literature on aphasia has undoubtedly been able to observe how frequently the term "perseveration" is used to denote a behavioral characteristic of aphasic persons (12:8–9; 1:393–394). We have also referred to the observation that epileptic persons tend to manifest excessive perseveration. The action of drugs such as alcohol and opiates also is associated with an abnormal increase in perseverative behavior.

Nonorganic Factors. We would be loath to leave the impression that excessive perseveration is invariably an organic component or a product of constitutional predisposition. Certainly, temporary increase in perseverative behavior may be brought about by essentially psychological rather than organic conditions. Earlier we indicated that the person who is perseverating is attempting to make a response and to perform in a manner he assumes is required of him. In general, perseverative behavior is likely to occur when the motivating forces or determining tendencies for a given act are in some way interfered with (blocked, diverted, or overcome) by counterforces or inhibiting events or ideas. These inhibiting events or ideas may well have a psychogenic basis. They may arise, as Glauber and Sheehan point out elsewhere in this volume, from competing forces to act and not to act in regard to a specific situation. The inhibiting events or ideas may arise as a result of recalled and/or anticipated penalties which may result from the expected performance. They may also arise out of a sense of insecurity as to the degree of appropriateness of the performance. Isolated or situational and infrequent episodes of perseveration are therefore not necessarily related to any morbid condition or process or with any relatively constant trait of personality of character. Habitual or generalized perseveration is another matter, even if the perseverative behavior as a habitual approach to a situation had an original psychogenic onset.

II. STUDIES OF PERSEVERATIVE TENDENCIES IN STUTTERERS

During the past quarter century several investigators have designed experimental situations to determine whether stutterers tend to manifest perseveration to a greater than normal degree in nonspeaking situations. The results, though by no means consistent, in general support this writer's view that, taken as a population, stutterers do perseverate more than nonstutterers when they are called upon to perform in situations that do not call for overt speech. Some of these investigations will now be reviewed.

In 1935 Eisenson (13) administered items from the Maller-Elkin Attention Test for the Measurement of Perseveration to a group of 30 male stutterers and a matched group of 30 male nonstutterers ranging in age from 10 to 16. The test situations were arranged along the following lines: (1) A situation was presented (copying of letters, easy arithmetic calculation) in which the subject was required to perform as directed for a given period of time. (2) A variation of this situation was presented in which the subject was required to make a different response for an equal period of time. (3) A third situation, consisting of a combination in random order of both original situations, was then presented. The subject was then required to change his responses quickly and relatively frequently. Failure to make the required changes was interpreted as a failure to respond readily and appropriately to new and changing situations.

The results indicated that stutterers as a group made more errors (continued to respond to situations that were no longer present, such as adding when multiplying was required, or writing upper-case letters when the situation called for lower-case) than did the nonstutterers. In addition, the stutterers slowed down more (completed fewer items) than the nonstutterers. Interestingly, when the experimental situation called for the continuation of the same response to a nonchanging situation, the stutterers worked more rapidly (completed more items) than the nonstutterers.

In a later study, Eisenson and Winslow (15) experimented with a group of 15 Brooklyn College students in therapy at the College Speech Clinic and a control group of 15 nonstuttering students. The experimental situation called for the subjects to respond to (1) an original situation consisting of an arrangement of colored squares on a card exposed through the aperture of a tachistoscope and (2) variations of this situation in the form of new colors not presented on the first card and the elimination of colors shown on the first and subsequent cards. The subjects were required to respond to the color cards by noting the total number and the different colors observed.

The results indicated that there was a significant difference between the stutterers and nonstutterers in their responses to color cards. The stutterers were influenced more than the nonstutterers by stimuli (colors) which were once present but no longer physically present at the moment of the called-for response. Stutterers continued to respond to and "see" colors in new situations which had been presented only in previous situations.

Sheets (30) used visual stimuli to investigate perseveration in stutterers. He measured the reaction time needed for his subjects to perceive changes in light from (1) darkness to a green light, and (2) a red light instantaneously changing to green and from green to darkness. Although the differences in reaction time were smaller than the amount presumed necessary for statistical significance (Critical Ratios from .994 to 1.88), the differences, we think, suggested a tendency for stutterers to perseverate more than nonstutterers.

In an experiment along similar lines, Goldsand (18) measured perseveration by the reaction time for perception of a dim light after her subjects were exposed to a bright one. She concluded that stutterers as a group made higher scores (were more perseverative) than nonstutterers. She observed also that stutterers were more variable in their responses than nonstutterers.[4]

Falck (17) investigated perseveration as one of several traits in a group

[4] The factor of variability observed by Goldsand and others is consistent with the present writer's findings. Even when group differences between stutterers and nonstutterers are statistically significant, they should not alone become the basis for predicting how an individual stutterer, or a normal speaker for that matter, may behave. At the outset we indicated that not all stutterers are constitutional perseverators. Variability in regard to perseveration, or of any factor that might be interpreted as "constitutional," should not be surprising.

of stutterers ranging in age from 5 to 59 years. Although he found no consistent pattern of behavior which might describe or characterize all stutterers, he did find that perseveration correlated positively with the tendency of the stutterer to demonstrate tonic blocks.

An investigation of several areas of perseveration was undertaken by King (24). Specifically, he set out to learn whether stutterers differed from nonstutterers in the areas of alternating motor perseveration, dispositional rigidity, and sensory area. He also compared male and female (boy and girl) stutterers with one another as well as with nonstutterers. He employed a series of tests designed to measure (1) alternating motor perseveration, (2) dispositional rigidity in a motor task, and (3) sensory perseveration. His subjects included 72 stuttering males, 8 stuttering females, 82 nonstuttering males, and 55 nonstuttering females.

King's main finding was that stutterers showed significantly more perseverative tendencies in general than nonstutterers. The tests which seemed to be most discriminative for the two groups were those which required a rapid and contiguous change of set.

Some of King's other findings, especially those related to sex differences, are also worthy of note. Boy stutterers are significantly more perseverative than boy nonstutterers. While the same contrast is found between girl stutterers and girl nonstutterers, the differences are not as great as for the boys when the individual tests are considered. However, when the test results are pooled (the probabilities combined) the cumulative difference approaches statistical significance.

On tests of dispositional rigidity, which measure the subject's ability to break away from old, well-established habits to perform according to the needs of the test situation, King found boy stutterers to be more perseverative than boy nonstutterers. Girl stutterers, however, were not found to be more perseverative than girl nonstutterers. In general, though the results of the King experiments do not establish clear-cut sex differences in perseveration between boys and girls who do not stutter, some individual tests do show that such a difference exists.

We do not wish to leave an impression that King found uniform and consistent differences relative to perseveration between stutterers and nonstutterers. Like other investigators, he found considerable variability among stutterers. In some of the sensory tasks there were no significant differences between stutterers and nonstutterers. Nor does King feel that his findings can support a contention such as has been made by Spearman that perseveration exists as a general behavioral factor. King did find, as indicated earlier, that stutterers are significantly more perseverative than nonstutterers in motor- and mental-test situations that call for a rapid and contiguous change of set.

From the point of view of the present writer, the difficulty stutterers manifest in test situations calling for constant change of set is highly important. Conversational speaking, which calls for changing thought and linguistic content that cannot be readily anticipated and for which general but not specific preparation is possible, requires rapid and continuous change of set. Such speaking contrasts with the evocation of memorized content, or the repetition of content previously evoked. The latter speech situations, calling for relatively little change in set, are among the "easy" ones for most stutterers. We shall return to this point later. For the present let us report an additional study relevant to the thesis under discussion.

Doust and Coleman (10), in an article supporting a neurogenic basis of stuttering, report the results of a flicker-fusion experiment with 46 adult stutterers and 131 adult nonstutterers. They found the mean critical-flicker-fusion (CFF) threshold for the stutterers to be significantly lower than for the nonstutterers. The stutterers' mean number of cycles per second for flicker-fusion was 37 compared with 41 for the fluent speakers. Stated otherwise, they found that on the average the color wheel had to be slowed down five cycles for stutterers to perceive flicker.

Although the experimenters were not primarily concerned with establishing differences in perseveration (differences in change of perception from constant color to flicker and vice versa), the writer thinks that their results may be so interpreted. On the basis of their findings, Doust and Coleman observe that "It is . . . interesting to speculate on the relationship of communication, consciousness, and the CFF and the nature of the dysplasia existing between these variables in the stutterer. If each is correlated with the other, and if discriminatory awareness is impaired outside the expressive end of the communicative spectrum, then it is probable that more than a single aspect of the process of thought may be affected."

The present writer does not know whether we can accept differences in flicker-fusion as presumptive evidence of neurogenic differences; such differences may also be a manifestation of anxiety. He does hold, however, that regardless of whether the critical flicker-fusion difference is neurogenic or psychogenic, it probably is related to perseverative lag in a visual-perceptual function.

III. STUTTERING AND COMMUNICATIVE RESPONSIBILITY

It has long been recognized that almost all stutterers show considerable variability in their tendency to stutter. This observation has puzzled the stutterers themselves, their relatives and friends, and students of stuttering. The apparent variability and inconsistency of the stutterer's ability to speak with normal fluency or normal nonfluency has led many students of stuttering, including contributors to this *Symposium* to regard stuttering as essentially a psychogenic problem or a problem resulting from the young speaker's attempts to meet the standards of excessively perfectionistic members of his home environment. The present writer does not believe that this conclusion is necessarily justified by the evidence. Many brain-damaged persons suffering from aphasia show considerable variability in their linguistic ability and even in their ability to articulate proficiently. Few students of aphasia would argue that this disorder is essentially a psychogenic one, or an environmentally induced one, or a disorder resulting from the diagnosis of aphasia by some person presumed to be an authority or in an authoritative position. On the other hand, there is an increased recognition that the impairments of the aphasic are aggravated and in some instances maintained because of psychological factors. This is probably a tenable position for about half of the stuttering population. For this portion of the stutterers the writer accepts the observation that some situations are more conducive to stuttering than others. Many of the situations conducive to stuttering can be generalized and anticipated; they will be considered in a moment. Those stutterers who stutter without pattern, who may stutter at any time, or overtly at no time, or too much of the time, we would be inclined to consider as belonging to a nonorganic group.

Conditions Associated with Increased Stuttering

Stuttering, as suggested, is largely predictable. For stutterers both as individuals and as a group, though not without exception, the incidence of stuttering can be predicted or anticipated. Such prediction is based on experimental findings as well as on nonexperimental observation. The factors conducive to stuttering are related to specific but recurring situations associated with the speaking situation and with the nature of the linguistic content called for by the situation.

In several studies Brown (4) found that stutterers tend to have *verbal cues* which are related to increased stuttering. These verbal cues include (1) initial words in sentences, (2) longer words in sentences, (3) accented syllables within sentences, and (4) nouns, verbs, adverbs, and adjectives, as opposed to other parts of speech. He concluded from these findings that stutterers interpret these verbal cues as threatening and anxiety-producing, and therefore conducive to increased stuttering. But another evaluation of the findings may also be in order. Verbal cues related to stuttering—word position, word length, and parts of speech—are generally those that carry the burden of meaning in communicative speech. Longer words may be anxiety-producing because of the stutterer's lack of familiarity with them. They may also be those which, because of lack of occurrence and practice, do not provide a basis for familiar or habitual articulatory set. They may also be the significant words in the sentence in terms of what the speaker is trying to communicate.

Eisenson and Horowitz (14) found that stutterers experienced increased difficulty in oral reading as the intellectual significance or meaningfulness (propositionality) of the material was increased.[5] Three selections of varying propositional value were used: a simple list of 130 words, a nonsense selection of 130 words, and a meaningful paragraph taken from a letter written by Franklin Delano Roosevelt. Each of the three selections contained the same set of twenty adjectives, ranging in length from one to five syllables. The number of other parts of speech (nouns, verbs, prepositions, etc.) was determined for the propositional selection and the same number was used for the first two selections. The subjects, 23 male and 3 female college students, were in attendance in the speech clinics of Brooklyn College and the City College of New York.

Some of the specific findings of the study included the following: (1) An increase in the propositional value of an oral-reading selection was accompanied by an increase in stuttering on nouns, verbs, adverbs, and adjectives. (2) In contrast, there was a decrease in stuttering on words conventionally classified as pronouns, conjunctions, and articles. There was no significant difference with reference to prepositions. (3) There was a greater difference in total percentage of stuttering between a meaningful and nonsense selection than between a nonsense selection and a list of words. In general, Eisenson and Horowitz observed that "The content of the reading selection determines whether an utterance is composed of a series of sounds or a series of semantic units. As meanings and the responsibility for communicating meanings become prominent, stuttering increases. . . . The stutterer has greatest difficulty in the utterance of propositional speech."

The earlier-mentioned studies by Brown, and Eisenson and Horowitz, and the observations of Bluemel (3:chs. 3, 9) suggest strongly that many if not most stutterers experience difficulty in communication, in saying something meaningful and expected in terms of the overall situation.

[5] A *proposition* is a unit of meaningful linguistic content. Nonsense material, oaths, and utterances expressive of strong feelings and emotions are nonpropositional. Language that occurs in regular sequence, such as counting and reciting the alphabet, may be considered as having low propositional value.

From the point of view presented here, stuttering will not be understood unless we evaluate the linguistic component in the speaking situation. Most stutterers can speak nonsense if they are not expected to make sense. When not suffering from stage fright they can speak from memory better than impromptu. But memorized content does not call for intellectual organization and linguistic formulation as do impromptu and conversational speech. Stutterers can speak alone, to themselves, because there is no challenge to what they have to say and no response from a listener that may call for a quickly formulated linguistic response from them. In this situation they are not engaged in meaningful, propositional language usage but in an exercise in the use of word-forms that resemble phonetically, but not semantically, real word usage. This is the case also when stutterers "talk" to nonunderstanding animals, or to young children who have not arrived at the stage of wanting to know, or daring to ask, what the words to which they were exposed are supposed to mean.

In choral situations, when the stutterer shares the responsibility for this artificial and pseudocommunicative situation, most stutterers also speak with comparative fluency. Here again we are dealing with a situation in which, to say the least, the stutterer shares but does not carry the individual responsibility for what is said.

In contrast to these relatively easy situations for most stutterers, we can generalize the difficult situations along the following lines: The incidence of stuttering for most stutterers increases when the individual finds himself unequal to the demands of the speaking situation. In such a situation the stutterer suffers from a temporary breakdown or disorganization of propositional language usage. The linguistic disturbance becomes most apparent in situations that normally require that the speaker (1) formulate the language symbols (the propositional units), (2) evoke the proposition orally,[6] audibly, and individually, and (3) anticipate an immediate specific response, oral or otherwise, appropriate to the situation and to the stutterer's initial evocation. Under these conditions, the stutterer cannot maintain an established linguistic set. He must expect to make continuous changes consistent with the demands of the changing linguistic situation. He must anticipate that he will utter not just one linguistic unit, for which he may prepare, but additional units for which specific preparation is im-

[6] There is some evidence to suggest that the written-language productivity of stutterers is also impaired in impromptu essay writing. In an early study the author found that a group of 15 stuttering male college students wrote fewer words and made more errors in writing than did a control group of nonstuttering students. The errors included repetitions and crossing out of words. The results, we thought then, suggested that the stutterers experienced more difficulty in organizing and sustaining coherent thought than the nonstutterers. (See J. Eisenson, "Some characteristics of the written speech of stutterers," *Journal of Genetic Psychology,* L, 1937, pp. 457–458.)

possible. He may have difficulty with his first formulated linguistic unit because of his anxiety in anticipating the need for not-yet-formulated linguistic units. Under this general condition, the stutterer who is also a constitutional perseverator has his greatest difficulty in speaking. The difficulty may be aggravated by anxiety, but it originates because of the stutterer's basic tendency to perseverate to a more than normal degree in situations not normally conducive to much perseveration for most speakers. We shall return to this point later.

Modification and Reduction of the Incidence and Severity of Stuttering

Let us now review two types of studies relative to the reduction of the incidence and severity of stuttering. The first group deals with the nature of different speaking situations and the reaction of the stutterer to these situations. The second deals presumably with "controlled" speaking situations in which the stutterer modifies his speech with repeated responses to the "same" situation.

In 1950 Bloodstein (2) reported on a study in which he sought to determine the conditions under which stutterers report their stuttering to be reduced or absent. He presented a list of 115 conditions reported in the literature as being relatively easy for stutterers. Some of these conditions, such as speaking to an animal, speaking nonsense, and reciting from memory, have been discussed earlier in this paper. Bloodstein found that for the main group of his subjects, 50 adult stutterers, it was possible to specify 100 conditions under which a fairly large proportion reported substantial reduction in stuttering. He classified these specific conditions into six general conditions: reduced communicative responsibility, reduced need to make a favorable impression, absence of unfavorable listener reaction, changes in speech pattern, associated activity (speaking while walking, speaking to a set rhythm), and intense or unusual stimulation.

Bloodstein notes that despite the strong tendency for uniformity of conditions under which stuttering is reduced or absent, there was considerable variability: "In part, this variability is probably an artifact of the wording of the item. For example, it is obvious that 'ordinary conversation with your mother' involves very different objective stimulus conditions depending upon whether the behavior of the mother tends to be critical, distressed, sympathetic, indifferent, or understanding." In general, probably, variability can be accounted for by differences in the subjects' evaluations of the speaking situation, whether it is a mother, a stranger, a policeman, or a formal audience.

Among other studies of interest on the reactions of stutterers to speaking situations is one by Trotter and Bergmann (36). They compared the ratings of a group of 50 stutterers (41 male and 9 female), mean age 22 years, with the ratings of 100 nonstuttering members of a college psychology class. The Speech Situation Rating Sheet for Stutterers, developed by Johnson, was used to rate 40 speaking situations. A comparison of the findings for the two groups indicated that:

1. Stutterers tend to avoid speaking situations more, and enjoy speaking less, than nonstutterers. However, a considerable number of nonstuterers were more avoidant of speaking situations, and reported that they enjoyed speaking in them less, than did many stutterers.

2. Those nonstutterers who avoid speaking situations most enjoy speaking in them the least. They are also the most nonfluent of the nonstuttering speakers.

3. There is a tendency for stutterers and nonstutterers to agree in a relative way in their reactions to different kinds of speaking situations. With the important exception of the use of the telephone, situations most avoided by nonstutterers tend also to be avoided most by stutterers; those enjoyed least by nonstutterers are also enjoyed least by stutterers; those in which the nonstutterers are found to be most nonfluent are the ones in which stutterers have greatest difficulty. In regard to use of the telephone, all such situations were ranked much higher in avoidance by stutterers than by nonstutterers. For instance, "telephoning to inquire about a price, train fare, etc." was ranked second in avoidance by stutterers and nineteenth by nonstutterers.

On the basis of the Trotter and Bergmann findings we may conclude that, in general, the difference between the reactions of stutterers and nonstutterers to many speaking situations is one of degree. Those situations which are difficult or not pleasant for nonstutterers are more so for stutterers. The interesting exception is the telephone situation, which appears to be considerably more disturbing for most stutterers than for most nonstutterers. This finding supports the impression most clinicians have that the telephone is a bugaboo for stutterers. Could the reason for this be that when a person initiates a telephone call, he is expected, at least at the outset, to say something, to reveal or communicate the purpose of his call?

Adaptation Studies

A series of studies at the University of Iowa was concerned with the "adaptability" of the stutterer to recurring speaking situations. The general problem considered was the effect of repeated utterances of the "same" linguistic content in reading and in self-formulated speech. Johnson and Knott (22, 23) demonstrated that when stutterers read a given passage several successive times there is a decrement in the incidence of stuttering between the first and fifth consecutive readings. As a rule, marked decrements are found as early as the second reading of the passage. Leutenegger's procedure (26) varied from some of the earlier adaptation studies in that different time intervals (20 minutes, 1 hour, and 24 hours) took place between successive readings of the same passage. The subjects were 36 adolescent and adult stutterers (31 male and 5 female, ranging in age from 15 years 6 months to 37 years 5 months, with a mean of 22 years 2 months).

As indicated, Leutenegger found evidence of significant adaptation (reduced incidence of stuttering) as early as the second trial, and continued evidence of adaptation with successive trials. Beyond this, he found that the stutterers showed recovery from adaptation (tendency toward resumption of stuttering) directly as the time interval between reading trials increased. He points out the analogy between the recovery from adaptation (recovery of the stuttering response) and experimental extinction of a conditioned or learned response as a result of a weakening of reinforcement. The present writer would like, for the sake of his theoretical position, to suggest related but alternate interpretations of the results. First, the amount of mental and motor set required that has to be reestablished in the oral reading of a passage varies directly with the time interval between successive readings. Second, immediately repeated readings reduces the intellectual significance of what is read. By the time of a fifth or sixth successive reading, word-forms rather than semantic word units are being uttered. Increasing the time intervals restores the intellectual significance of the material the subject has to read aloud. He is reading for meaning, or looking for meanings as he reads, rather than acting as a transformer of visible signs to audible signs. Later in our discussion we will return to this argument and its implications. For the present, let us consider evidence of the effect of repeated evocations of self-formulated speech rather than of the reading of prepared written materials.

Newman (28) compared the severity of stuttering of a group of 20 stutterers in an oral-reading and a communicative-speaking (self-formulated speech) situation. In the first situation the subjects read prepared descriptions of a set of picture sketches; in the second they formulated their own oral descriptions of the sketches. In the oral-reading situation the greatest decrement of stuttering took place on the second trial; in self-formulated speaking, the largest decrement took place on the third trial. Newman also found that the reduction in stuttering (adaptation effect) was always less in self-formulated speech than in oral reading.

We do not, at this time at least, care to take issue with any of the many experimenters and students who have studied the so-called *adaptation-effect*. Whether subjects experience reduction in anxiety, or get rid of their anxieties, or gain whatever satisfaction they need by stuttering in one trial so that the severity and/or incidence of stuttering is reduced in successive trials when the "same" content is involved, may all be moot points. However, it is naive to overlook the extremely small likelihood that in a normal speaking situation anybody ever repeats the "same" content, even though the same word-forms may be used. Successive utterances of any linguistic word-form content, whether it be in reading aloud or in self-formulated speaking, modifies the intellectual significance or propositional value of the utterance. In reading aloud, unless we are directed to read for meaning and for communication, as the subjects of Eisenson and Wells were,[7] many of us are inclined merely to utter the sounds we have associated with the signs we call written words. Our responses are different when we are required to read to search out and communicate meanings. In essence, mere reading aloud is subpropositional; reading for meaning is propositional. But the reader, unless he happens also to be the writer, is not responsible for the intellectual content but only for the transmission of the content. Repeated or successive readings, especially when they are immediately successive, reduces the propositional value of the content. One reason for this is that, except for occasional school situations, we do not often have to read aloud successively. If we do, it is to commit content to memory, and so in effect to establish an articulatory and vocal set that approaches the automatic in preparation for a special situation.

If we are not preparing to read aloud for a special situation, and if we can continue to listen to ourselves as we read a passage five or six times, we are likely to find that something along the following lines takes place: (1) We may begin to slur, and to increase the rate of utterance with successive readings. (2) We may change the stress of words, and actually to modify word-forms so that they are phonetically different in successive readings, especially by the time of the third or fourth reading. (3) We may, if our ability to memorize is good, begin to read from memory with only occasional cues from the written passage. (4) A combination of 1, 2, and 3 may occur. In any event, it should be apparent that though the spellings of the words we read aloud in successive trials remain the same, the words we utter, their meanings and phonetic patterns, are modified from reading to reading. That is why quotation marks were used sev-

[7] J. Eisenson and C. Wells, in "A study of the influence of communicative responsibility in a choral situation for stutterers," *Journal of Speech Disorders,* VII, 1942, found that 8 of 19 subjects increased their stuttering when the element of communicative responsibility was introduced in a choral-reading situation.

eral times when reference was made to the assumed "sameness" of the term "same" in evaluating adaptation studies.

Modifications in self-formulated speaking parallel those for oral reading. In a normal speaking situation we rarely repeat what we have said exactly as we said it in the first instance. Even when we are asked to "say it again" by someone who did not quite hear or understand us, we usually change some of the words we use. Exact repetition of self-formulated content is an artificial speaking situation. It is a situation that may occur as part of an experimental design but is not likely to occur in real life. Repeated utterances of material not conventionally read occurs in acting, but it is of interest that actors refer to "the reading of their lines." If, then, we find experimental evidence that even in an artificially created situation repeated self-formulated speech shows reduced stuttering, we should not be at a loss for an explanation. To begin with, self-formulation takes place only on the first trial. On this trial the speech is propositional—the subject is saying something in the presence of somebody, if not to somebody, with words formulated and selected as appropriate to the situation. On the second trial, if the subject is directed to repeat what he has said, he is no longer formulating and selecting propositional units. Instead, he is recalling and evoking, as far as he can remember, what he previously uttered. The task has changed from formulation of linguistic units, as in normal communicative speech, to one of recalling and evoking what has been previously formulated. If the experimental subject has a good memory, or if for reasons inherent in his relationship to the experimental situation, he is not anxious or apprehensive or wanting to put on a good show, he begins to perform in a speaking situation that is nonpropositional and noncommunicative. In such general situations, we know, most stutterers can speak with comparative fluency. The situation calling for successive utterances of initially self-formulated speech proves to be no exception. It is significant that there is less reduction in stuttering in repeated self-formulated utterance than in repeated readings. This is probably because there is greater deviation in repeated utterance from trial to trial than there is in repeated readings. Both initially and in successive evocation there is greater propositional value in self-formulated speaking than in oral reading. To be sure, "repetitions" reduce the propositional value for spoken utterances as they do for reading, but the process is slower, and so therefore is the reduction in the severity of the stuttering.

Summary of Results of Stuttering Relative to Changes in Incidence and Severity of Stuttering

In the immediately preceding pages day-to-day speaking situations and experimental-laboratory speaking situations have been reviewed for their varying effects and relationships to the incidence and severity of stuttering. In spite of considerable individual variability, general tendencies could nevertheless be observed for stutterers taken as a group or a special population. These tendencies may be generalized, according to the writer's viewpoint, along the following lines:

1. Stuttering increases as the semantic significance (propositional value) of the linguistic content is increased.
2. Stuttering increases as the speaker is required to formulate the linguistic content.
3. Stuttering increases as the speaker becomes aware of, and accepts responsibility for, a communicative effort.
4. Stuttering increases as the speaker must modify his set—intellectual, linguistic-articulatory, and vocal—to immediate and changing speech situations.

The above generalizations could of course be written as converse statements about circumstances associated with a decrease in stuttering. We would like, however, to add the following conditions which are associated with a decrease in stuttering:

1. Stuttering decreases in situations in which the speaker feels little or no need to make a favorable impression.
2. Stuttering decreases in situations which permit the speaker to modify his usual speech pattern so that he no longer speaks as his usual self.
3. Stuttering decreases as the speaker assumes a role instead of speaking as his usually recognized self (reading, acting, and role playing in general).

IV. STUTTERING AS A PERSEVERATIVE PHENOMENON

The first two sections of this paper presented some concepts of perseveration and its correlates as aspects of human behavior in the population at large and the stuttering population in particular. The third section presented the relationship between the nature and significance of oral linguistic content and its implications for perseveration and stuttering. We shall now be concerned with perseveration as an etiological correlate of stuttering.

According to the viewpoint presented here, stuttering *is a transient disturbance in communicative, propositional language usage.* Speech, the medium for oral language usage, becomes involved because the symbol-tool of speech, language, is temporarily disturbed. The articulatory aspect of speech may show impairment as an associated involvement, especially if the speaker had defective articulation as part of his developmental speech history. The basic involvement, however, is in the linguistic component of speech.

Propositional language is language used meaningfully and intentionally. The term "proposition" is used here in the sense in which it was employed by Hughlings Jackson (**20**): a proposition is a meaningful arrangement of *speaker-formulated words,* or a meaningful unit of speech. When we use words propositionally, we indicate significance and relationship of the words within the unit, and of the unit for the speaking situation in general and for the listener or listeners in particular. When, as listeners, we comprehend a proposition we perceive and understand word relationships and their meanings for us.

To appreciate the significance of a propositional unit—which may be a word, a phrase, or a sentence—we must understand the difference between words and word-forms. Human beings are unique in their ability not only to use words as symbols, but to use word-forms in nonsymbolic or nonpropositional ways. When, for example, we swear, or say sweet nothings, or respond to a social gesture such as "How do you do?" with the very same "words," we are speaking either nonpropositionally or subpropositionally. The difference, from the point of view under discussion, is one of degree. Swear words, "coo" words, and the language of strong affect in general we regard as nonpropositional. Its use has little relationship to the presumed listener. Often there is no listener, and the speaker evokes the affective expression to ventilate his feelings without any regard to the situation, the literal or figurative meanings of the individual words, or the outpouring of sounds which resemble words. Sometimes the speaker may direct a verbal outpouring at a listener, who may return in kind. It is highly unlikely that either party to this verbal interchange is at all concerned with the semantic and biological inconsistencies that would be involved were the word-forms to be evaluated as words and interpreted as if meaning rather than feeling were intended. The reader may determine for himself what he really means when he uses his favorite term of affective language, his invective if he is inclined to use invective, or his term of endearment if this is more consistent with his inclination. Such an exercise should help him to understand the difference between words and word-forms, and the difference between propositional and nonpropositional language usage. As an additional immediate exercise the reader should distinguish between the meaning of "How are you today?" when he hears these words spoken by a passing acquaintance, a good friend, a relative, and by the family physician when he is visiting his office as a patient.

We recognize that most stutterers who have a vocabulary of affective terminology are usually fluent in its use. Fluency, however, should not be expected from stutterers who have relatively small and infrequently practiced affective vocabularies. We should now also be able to recognize that particular situations and the relationship of the speaker to the situation make for differences in the significance of the linguistic content for the speaker. The situations reviewed in the previous section that are conducive to decreased difficulty for the stutterer are in general situations in which propositionality is reduced or absent. In these situations communicative responsibility is also reduced.

On the dual and related bases of reduced propositionality and reduced communicative responsibility we are able to understand why few stutterers have difficulty in singing, especially in a group, in choral speaking, or in speaking to pets or to children who do not understand or would not be inclined to ask what the speaker really meant by the words he used. This situation also helps us to understand why a change in the manner of speaking, such as speaking in a singsong manner, altering the pitch or the rate, or speaking without voice, helps temporarily to reduce the incidence and severity of stuttering. When a speaker concentrates his attention on his manner of speaking rather than on his communication of content, on sounds rather than words, he is less concerned with meaning, with words, and more concerned with sounds and word-forms. Linguistic content has been reduced in propositional value, and speaking tends to become easier and more fluent.

The Etiology of Stuttering

Early in this discussion the writer presented his basic thesis that a majority of stutterers, from 55 to 60 percent, are predisposed to a manner of oral language behavior called stuttering. It was indicated there that this proportion of the stuttering population is constitutionally inclined to perseverate to an extent or degree greater than is the case for most speakers. A minority of the stuttering population includes persons who, at the moment of speaking, are confronted with factors and influences that are conducive to perseveration. This point of view will now be elaborated. A distinction will be drawn between the organically predisposed and the functional or nonorganic stutterer and the suggestion advanced that both are products of perseveration.

Organic Stuttering

The writer believes that the tendency for constitutional perseveration, and its associated tendency for more than a normal amount of blocked and repetitive speech, has its etiology in differences in the neurological make-up of the speaker. The differences may arise because of peculiarities of cortical development, possible competition between the cortical centers for control of language function, or between the cortical and subcortical centers for such control. In some instances neurological damage before birth, during the act of birth, or at a later time, usually before language control is normally established, may be the underlying causal factor.

Some supportive data for this assumption of neurological difference may be found in the research of Travis and his students employing electroencephalographic techniques (9, 35). Unfortunately, this technique was not continued. It might well be that if it were, it would afford us a basis for distinguishing the organic from the nonorganic stutterer. In any event, we should not expect to find uniform or relatively uniform encephalographic (EEG) readings in all or even in a preponderant majority of stutterers in a given age group. We should expect to find, however, and the evidence tends to support the supposition, that EEG readings differentiate many stutterers from many normal speakers, as well as stutterers from one another.

Clinical observations of adults with known brain damage—those who have suffered cerebrovascular accidents, tumors, or penetrating head wounds—frequently show repetitive speech as a specific aspect of their behavioral modifications. This is true both for persons who have suffered right brain damage without aphasia and for those who have incurred left brain damage with or without aphasic involvements. The tendency for increased perseveration is almost universal among the brain-damaged. Perseveration may be manifest in all dimensions of behavior, including speech in its articulatory and linguistic aspects. Among the brain-damaged who become linguistic perseverators, some respond with frustration and for a time strongly resemble chronic stutterers. Others seem not to show as much awareness, or respond with less frustration to their awareness of perseveration, and repeat without any apparent accompanying specific anxiety or struggle. These individuals continue for a time—some for an indefinite time—to be perseverative speakers. In the absence of excessive anxiety and struggle behavior, of fighting against a tendency they cannot control, they sound like repeaters but not like stutterers.

Differences in the overall responses of the brain-damaged to their modified states may be at least in part a result of their premorbid personalities. Those who have habitually responded with anxiety to difficult situations may be the ones who begin to sound like stutterers. Others, who have habitually responded with a more philosophic "wait and see" attitude, may sound only like perseverators. The writer's investigations of aphasic patients suggest strongly that premorbid personality traits are an important factor in the recovery of these patients. It is likely that personality traits and established attitudes and modes of responding to illness and injury are important in determining the sequelae of these events.

From Perseveration to Stuttering. Whether a constitutional perseverator becomes a stutterer is probably determined by circumstances that permit perseveration and speaking efforts to become associated. Among very young children for whom repetitive (perseverative) behavior is normal, speech is characterized by a considerable amount of repetition. The general tendency is for repetitive behavior, including repetition in speech, to decrease with age. Between the ages of 24 and 62 months, a crucial period for the organization and integration of language function, Davis (**8**) found that the average child repeats 45 times per 1,000 words spoken in a free-play situation. In order of occurrence, repetitions were found to be more frequent for phrases than for words and syllables. Interestingly, boys tend to repeat syllables more often than girls.

With available clinical techniques and scientific devices it may not yet be possible to distinguish the potential stutterer from the normally fluent child in terms of repetitive speech behavior. It is possible, however, that among the vulnerable 1 percent or less of children who become stutterers we may have a majority who cannot prevent themselves from being and continuing to be perseverative speakers, but who try to do so. The reasons for their trying may lie in part within themselves and in part be present as a result of their reactions to environmental pressures. It is possible that some of the children who become stutterers, who begin to be apprehensive and manifest anxiety and struggle behavior about their tendency to be repetitive in speaking, are among the more sensitive and have greater awareness about their behavior than other children who are merely repetitive or nonfluent. Beyond this, it is possible that children with greater sensitivity and awareness have the effects of these inclinations heightened by adults who at a crucial time respond to these reactions and so strengthen them. It may well be that during the period of language development some children respond more intensely than others to adult reactions to their speech. The same children who are verbally encouraged to "speak up" may meet with considerable competition from the adults who "asked" them to do so. Despite the negative influence of many adults on the speech of their children, most children survive this untoward influence and become normal speakers. A few, however, are not equal to the pressures, demands, and negations to which they are exposed.

Is it possible to distinguish the children who are likely to become stutterers, the less than 1 percent of the population, from the remaining 99 percent plus? Johnson, most of us know, argues that it is not: "So-called stuttering children are not different from children not so diagnosed, with respect to birth injuries, other injuries, diseases, and general development as indicated by such indexes as age of beginning of speech, sitting and standing without support, and teething. They are not different with regard to intelligence. In general they are normal children (**21**:233).

Other points of view, presented elsewhere in the vast literature on stuttering, suggest that some research workers believe that children who stutter are in some constitutional ways different from most children who do not stutter.[8] Other authorities, including at least one represented in this *Symposium,* emphasize differences in psychological traits. Certainly the difference West emphasizes in the sex ratio among stutterers is one that cannot be ignored. It is undeniable that there are more males than females among stutterers, and that the ratio difference is not the one found in the population at large. Here, to be sure, we have an organic difference that makes a difference. The effect of the difference may be explained by unequal environmental pressures on boys and girls in terms of their readiness for speech and their linguistic abilities when the pressures are exerted. Evidence was presented earlier in this paper that there are differences in perseverative tendencies along sex lines. Combined, the constitutional predisposition toward perseveration, the responses to specific environmental pressures as well as cultural pressures that more often affect male children adversely than female children, may explain the onset of stuttering in children as well as the sex ratio among stutterers.

Van Riper (**37**:344) holds that children who are likely to become stutterers may be distinguished from those who are not in one of the following ways:

1. They may have low frustration tolerance.
2. They may have speech environments with an excess of fluency disruption.
3. They may have a constitutional predisposition (dysphemia) to prolonged nonfluency or to stuttering.
4. They may have parents who misevaluate their speech or for some other reason react to their nonfluencies with anxiety or penalty or both.

[8] For a review of this literature, see **1**:ch. 11.

5. They may be ones for whom dysrhythmic, nonfluent speech may be a manifestation of an underlying emotional conflict.
6. They may be victims of some combination of the above.

Van Riper's list of criteria for the stuttering child includes many possibilities, organic and psychogenic. If the term "perseveration" were substituted for "nonfluencies" in criteria (3), (4), and (5) the writer could accept Van Riper's criteria with little or no reservation. His own interpretation of the Van Riper criteria for distinguishing from other children the child predisposed to becoming a stutterer is that the child predisposed to stuttering is one for whom the combination of constitutional and external factors transform a tendency to an abnormality. The tendency is for repetitive, dysrhythmic, nonfluent speech[9] to be present on the basis of perseveration. The abnormality is a derivative of the child's reaction to his speech efforts. It is related to his attempts, arising from internal and/or external pressures, to be the kind of speaker he cannot succeed in becoming. This type of deviant speech most of us call stuttering.

To the list of Van Riper's predisposing factors for stuttering the writer would like to add some of his own. In effect, these are a spelling out of what is meant by the terms "constitutional predisposition" and "dysphemia." The factors listed below are based on his own clinical experience and on published research that appears to him to be valid and reliable.

1. Children are more likely to become stutterers if there are more stutterers in their immediate families and in collateral branches of their families than are to be found in the population at large.
2. Children are more likely to become stutterers if they, and other members of their families, are or were lacking in clearly established laterality by school age. Occasionally these members are referred to as ambidextrous. A better term for them may be "ambi-nondextrous."
3. Children are more likely to become stutterers if their early developmental history is suggestive of delayed speech.
4. Children are more likely to become stutterers if they have difficulty in reading and writing (spelling) in their early school years.
5. Children are more likely to become stutterers if their developmental histories include more than a normal amount of allergic involvements and upper respiratory illnesses.[10]

[9] The writer does not wholly accept repetition and so-called nonfluencies as aspects of dysrhythmia. His own emphasis is to look upon perseveration (repetition) as an attempt to maintain rhythm not present in the normal speech flow. Unless linguistic content is memorized or occurs as a serial sequence, as in reciting the alphabet and in counting, normal speech flow is likely to be marked by abrupt pauses and frequent hesitations. In other words, smoothness and maintained rhythm in free, self-formulated speech is the exception rather than the expected.

[10] For a more detailed review of factors associated with stuttering, see 1:ch. 11.

What we now need to consider is how the symptoms of stuttering become reinforced so that the speaker and the members of his environment begin to think of him as a stutterer rather than as a repetitive speaker. Part of the behavior of the full-fledged stutterer, the so-called secondary stutterer, includes facial tics, contortions, tremors, tonic spasms, and associated signs of stress and struggle during some moments of speaking. Anxiety about these, apprehensions of speaking, and wish to avoid speaking are internal reactions to some speaking situations. These overt and covert reactions probably become associated with some speaking situations along the following lines: The stutterer, because of his strong emotional reactions to his manner of speaking, is not in a position to judge objectively which part of what he does helps him to get through his blocks or to stop repeating. He tends to interpret two events of behavior as cause and effect merely because they are sequential. (Such confusion and error in judgment is not peculiar to the stutterer; it happens, however, to be more costly for the stutterer.) The sequence of events that becomes confused is usually the block in speech and the spasm, tremor, contortion, forcing, or struggle behavior which begins to take place just before or during the block. There is little likelihood that the associated overt behavior which apparently is the cause of so much annoyance and distress to the stutterer has anything to do initially with the termination of the stuttering block. Unfortunately for the stutterer, these overt manifestations are almost always terminated at the given moment of stuttering by the utterance of the blocked sound or word. So, as Van Riper points out (37: 373), "No matter what silly gyrations his mouth goes through, finally the word comes out. When it does, the panicky fear belonging to that word subsides." As a result, because of the reduction of fear and anxiety, and probably because of the disturbed state immediately preceding and accompanying the block, the stutterer mistakenly concludes that his struggle behavior was directly responsible for the evocation of the word and his release from anxiety. Thereafter he repeats a gross and complicated act to overcome a spasm and secure momentary release from anxiety. What he did worked, so he does it all again. This kind of behavior is generally found in animals. It is also found in emotionally disturbed human beings. At the moment of stuttering many, if not most, stutterers behave like disturbed human beings. In a sense, this is again a case of Charles Lamb's boy who burnt his entire house down to get the fire for roasting a pig. It took the boy a little time to learn that the fire can be confined and the pig roasted more effectively in something like a pit, a fireplace, or an oven.

There are, of course, alternative explanations for the significance and maintenance of the oral manifestations and associated mannerisms of stuttering, some of them considered elsewhere in this *Symposium.* In the organic stutterer, at least, it is probable that oral satisfactions or the satisfaction derived from the realization of morbid expectations, if they exist, constitute secondary gains rather than primary causes of stuttering. The organic stutterer may have some secondary gains in common with the nonorganic stutterer and stuttering may be maintained by some organic stutterers because of these gains. Whether this is true probably depends on the stutterer and his needs as an individual. If, even as a young child, he needs to punish an adult, he may find his stuttering an excellent weapon for such punishment. The stuttering may also be used as self-punishment, if this answers the individual's need. It may also be used to keep listeners waiting and anxious, uncomfortable and yet reluctant to break away from the verbal clutch of the stutterer. In short, stuttering may take on values and meanings for the individual unrelated to its etiology or its onset, some of which may serve to maintain stuttering and to intensify and complicate the therapeutic problems of the stutterer. This aspect of stuttering will be considered later in this discussion. For the present, let us review the steps that transform some constitutional perseverators to stutterers.

Stuttering as a perseverative manifestation may take place whenever the speaker finds himself unequal to the demands of the speaking situation. For a young, normally perseverative child, and even more so for a child with a constitutional predisposition for excessive perseveration, an overdemanding speaking situation may be ever present in the form of unrealistic parental expectations. Such expectations may arise either because the parents are perfectionistic and generally high-aspiring persons or because they are making comparisons that seem reasonable but are not. Parents whose first child is a girl may be comparing and expecting her younger brother to follow his sister's schedule. Unless the boy is precocious, he is not likely to meet this schedule. If he is normally perseverative but is looked upon as an excessive repeater or hesitator by his parents, who do not recall the sister having spoken in this manner at a particular age, the boy may suffer the results of parental memories and comparisons. If he is excessively perseverative, the comparisons are likely to be even more damaging in their effects.

It is probably fortunate that not all children who are more-than-normal perseverators are equally sensitive to the reactions and expectations of their parents. If they were, the incidence of stuttering in the population would be considerably higher than 1 percent. Some children, regardless of their degree of nonfluent or repetitive speech, may pay little attention to the reactions of their parents. Perhaps, because of their early health histories, these children may assume that parents are anxious persons and so take them in stride. Other children may simply be unaware of their parents' attitudes and so develop according to their own inclinations and despite the anxieties and drives of their parents. The writer believes that the perseverative child who becomes a stutterer does so because of a constitutional predisposition which combines with intelligence, sensitivity, and awareness of environmental expectation. The combination of factors, operating at a crucial period, usually between the years 3 to 5, makes for the stuttering. In the absence of any of these factors, most speech-perseverative children are likely to grow up to be speech-perseverative adults—the hesitant, repetitive, "uh . . . uh" type of speakers. If they do not try to become more fluent than they are capable of being, they run little risk of becoming stutterers as adolescents or adults. If they make an attempt to increase their fluency, possibly because of the pressure of a teacher or a friend, and decide that the effort is beyond them, they are certainly not likely to become stutterers. In all walks of life, teaching and speech pathology included, we have speakers who are repeaters and hesitators. Most of these persons do not consider themselves stutterers, and most of them are not. They would become stutterers if they responded to their hesitancies and repetitions with anxiety and apprehension rather than with mild annoyance or a vague wish that they could speak better or differently. But most do not, and so most of our so-called nonfluent speakers are just that rather than stutterers. A few of these perseverator-speakers may feel the need to have something especially worth listening to when they engage a listener, and so most of us are the gainers for this felt need. Unfortunately, a few others may try to compensate for their perseverative tendencies by entering fields that demand more than a normal amount of fluency and ready articulateness. They try to become politicians or lawyers or salesmen who use language as the tool of their trade. Some, perhaps most of them, are destined to fail. In their attempts to achieve aspirations inconsistent with their native capacities they may develop personalities and meet with problems that could have been avoided had their potentials been evaluated early enough, and guidance been given and accepted. In many respects these preseverator-speakers develop traits, attitudes, and problems similar to those of nonorganic stutterers.

Nonorganic Stuttering

In his *Handbook of Speech Pathology* (33) Travis includes stuttering in a section headed "Speech and Voice Disorders Unrelated to Organic Abnormalities." The chapters included in this section present points of view considerably different in basic premise and in therapeutic implications for the stutterer.

The writer wonders, and readers should wonder, whether the various authors and authorities on the subject of stuttering are talking about the same disturbance. It may well be that they are using a common word-form to talk about different disturbances that share some speech symptoms considered undesirable by most speakers. Travis, for example, says "Both introspective and objective observations convince us that most people stutter." He goes on to say that "Only a few people are sufficiently miserable over their speaking relationships, however, that they bring their problem to therapy under the label of stuttering." Interestingly, both in the Travis *Handbook* (33:918) and elsewhere, the authors and authorities Wendell Johnson and Lee Travis seem to be in agreement that stuttering —whatever it may be—most probably arises as a result of the child's attempts to make adjustments to parental expectations and behavior. Somehow, out of the child's attempts to adapt to his parents in particular and his culture in general, the child becomes a stutterer. This form of deviant speaking had somehow to be learned. Elsewhere in this *Symposium* a theory is presented on how an individual learns to stutter. Another very important related question is: "What kind of a child is it who has to learn to stutter in his attempts to relate to his home and outside environment?"

An answer to this question has been presented here for about half the stuttering population in terms of constitutional predisposition and perseveration. Now an explanation is in order for nonorganic stutterers.

Members of this nonorganic group, we think, include persons who begin to stutter on an imitative basis and then continue to stutter because of the psychological value and "secondary gains" associated with their manner of speaking. The nonorganic group also includes persons for whom stuttering is a manifestation of a basic emotional disturbance usually having its origin in early childhood. This group may be termed psychogenic stutterers. One theoretic explanation for this subgroup is presented in this *Symposium* by Glauber.

Situational Difficulties for the Psychogenic Stutterer. The writer's impression is that psychogenic stutterers have their greatest difficulty in situations in which they are required to give verbally of themselves, to "speak themselves" without pretending, role playing, or through the employment of another person's language. On the surface, the situations appear to be the same as those presented earlier for the organic stutterer. Propositional, communicative, self-formulated language usage is difficult for stutterers in general. The dynamics of the difficulty for the psychogenic stutterer distinguish him from the organic stutterer. Because of his inability to give of himself, he cannot readily evoke words. Unforunately, the psychogenic stutterer cannot always escape the need to talk. Beyond this, he does not always wish to avoid talking. If, however, he is conditioned and his reactions generalized, he may experience anxiety and apprehension in many speech situations not logically related to early ones which may have been anxiety-producing or penalizing. His need or drive to speak and his difficulty in giving verbally of himself produce a state of ambivalence which is characterized by perseverative speaking.

Earlier in this paper it was indicated that perseveration may occur whenever the determining tendencies for a given task are overcome, blocked, or diverted in some manner by inhibiting events or ideas. Perseveration may occur whenever the usual means or avenues of access to a goal are blocked. The goal of the psychogenic stutterer is to say something. The counterforces may be the conditioned habitual fears of the consequences of saying something, or the inhibiting force of not wishing to give of one's self. It may be the fear that if the speaker gives a little he may be expected to continue to give more and still more to a point beyond his needs or his wishes or his immediate capabilities.

Through the process of generalization, unsagacious and often irrelevant, the psychogenic speaker may spread his anxieties from saying something to somebody to the act of talking as if he were saying something. Through this process the seriously disturbed psychogenic stutterer is likely to have considerably more difficulty with nonpropositional language than the organic stutterer. His difficulty may become generalized to include speaking to pets, to nonunderstanding persons, to counting, reciting, and even to speaking and singing in chorus. In a sense, the difficulty becomes one of oral evocation, regardless of the significance of the evocation or of the responsibility for communication. We may at this point have arrived at a difference between organic and nonorganic stutterers. *For organic stutterers the basic problem is one of linguistic formulation and production; for nonorganic stutterers the problem is one of production. For organic stutterers stuttering is primarily an intermittent disturbance of propositional language usage. For nonorganic stutterers it is a speech disturbance, a problem of the expression of the self.* For this subgroup, we are able to accept Johnson's characterization of stuttering as *an anticipatory, apprehensive, hypertonic avoidance reaction* in a speech situation.

Predisposing Factors for Nonorganic Stutterers. Whether one assumes the position of Johnson, Travis, or Glauber relative to the origin and onset of stuttering, we still have to arrive at some explanation as to just what there is about approximately 1 percent of the population (one-half percent from the writer's point of view) that predisposes it to stuttering. Is there any special trait in this group that causes its members to react to their environments with stuttering? We know that most members of this group will begin their speech difficulties as children. We also know that more of them will be males than females. Are there any other significant common-denominator predisposing factors? Glauber presents in his paper a family constellation that accounts for the child's predisposition to stuttering. Johnson emphasizes that normal children were subject to pressures by somewhat perfectionistic, unrealistic parents. These children, in attempting to relate and adjust to their parents, became victims of expectations which they could not meet but nevertheless tried to meet. They accepted their parents' interpretations of their normal nonfluencies as deviant speech, accepted the attributes of their parents, and began to think of themselves as stutterers. In doing so, or thinking so, they became stutterers.

Travis also attributes the essential fault to parents. In earlier writings, however, Travis held that the children who became stutterers had somewhat different potentialities from nonstutterers and so were predisposed to their difficulties. In 1946 Travis (34) held that there was a somatic variant which served as a pathological subsoil of stuttering. This variant presumably is a tendency for the brain hemispheres of the child to be more nearly equal in potential and control of speech functions than is true of nonstutterers. Given this deviant if not pathological subsoil, stuttering itself develops because the child cannot quite cope with the demands of his (Western) culture in which ". . . an early, harsh, complete and uncushioned renunciation of infantile and childish behavior works in conjunction with the somatic variant possessed by a few infants and children to produce stuttering. Stuttering may be considered then as a failure of the child to deal successfully with a given life demand, a failure to find socially acceptable gratification for subjective needs under given circumstances."

More recently Travis (33:918) spelled out some of the characteristics of the stutterer and of the environment to which the stutterer is maladapting: "These people, as children, had no tolerance for the delay of the satisfaction of their needs. They could not yet learn to wait, to reason, to hope, to plan. Rather, they were compelled by all-consuming drives, tensions, and discomforts to action—crying, twisting, flaying. . . ."

Travis argues that such children developed possibly "tumultuous relationships" that furnished the subsoil for "unverbalized and hence unconscious emotional conflicts." Unfortunately, because the stutterers as children were treated with less rather than more indulgence than their needs and drives required, they became stutterers. "Their savage drives should have been kept at the lowest possible level by the attentiveness of their parents. Every supportively encouraging effort should have been made by the parents to teach the child to talk and to think in order that he might in turn learn to wait, hope, reason, and plan."

Instead of the indulgent treatment these children needed, they were, according to Travis (33:919), treated as if they were emotional and intellectual adults. "Adult powers to control their drives and feelings were assumed. Incompatible demands were made and utterly impossible checks and tasks were set. Unlearned and at times unlearnable discriminations were expected. Heavy sanctions were applied for mistakes and failures."

Common Factors in the Background of Nonorganic Stutterers. In our search for unity amidst diversity relative to the evaluation of the background of stutterers, we are able to find several traits, or at least several common labels, attributed to children who become stutterers. The term "ambivalent" is recurrent. Though ambivalent may not have precisely the same meaning for Sheehan as it does for Glauber or for Travis, there is a common core of meaning that is probably important. The stutterer, beginning as a young child, seems to have strong conflicting drives in regard to the same situation. Sometimes the tendencies are toward speaking. He wants to speak, but fears speaking. He needs to speak, but immediately becomes apprehensive about the penalties of speech. The young stutterer or stutterer-to-be wants to relate to adults, and particularly to his parents, but fears that his attempts will be futile, or that he may be rejected or punished. So he develops ambivalent attitudes about adults and others to whom he may need and wish to relate. Ambivalences continue because his drives and needs continue. These persist because they are drives and needs that cannot be successfully repressed. Human beings are expected to talk, and even little children, however well-behaved they may try to be, must also sometimes talk.

Another factor common to children who are stutterers or potential stutterers is a tendency for overgeneralization. As suggested earlier, children generalize their ambivalences, their conflicting needs, from parents in particular to adults in general. They generalize from one situation with which the original difficulty or conflict was associated to many situations having only incidental resemblances to the original. They generalize from particular words associated with their difficulties to words semantically or phonetically or orthographically resembling the first "particular" words.

So they become victimized by a second unique behavioral tendency—to generalize as we learn. Without the ability to generalize, human learning would be specific and an accumulation of individual situational reactions. With the ability to generalize, we can respond to new situations in terms of old ones. But we also are occasionally victimized by our capacity to generalize, by doing so when the situations are different in some important essential or essentials, and a different response is required. The young stuttering child, and the child who continues to stutter into adult life, apparently falls victim to his generalizing ability because he is not in a condition to discriminate wisely or well. Because of this, his stuttering spreads from situation to situation instead of being confined to those early ones with which his difficulty was initially associated. This, for example, is why the stutterer who insists that the sound *p* is a difficult one for him may also stutter on the words "pneumonia" and "psychology."

"Repression" is another recurring term applied to stutterers by theorists who do not believe in an organic etiology. For reasons related to theoretic positions, stutterers are described as repressing their feelings and their thoughts and the words that might express them if they were to be released. So Travis (33:919) describes and explains the nature of repression as follows: "Stuttering may be defined as an advertisement of strong, unconscious motives of which the stutterer is deeply ashamed. Repression falls on the verbal expression of these motives and may fall on all words and sentences lest they might lead to these motives. When any person stutters, he is blocking something else besides what you and he might think he is trying to say; something else that is pressing for verbal expression but which will be intolerable to you and to him alike should it be uttered."

Regardless of what we believe the stutterer is repressing, the starting and stopping of words may be considered as specific oral manifestations of this tendency. Through the process of generalization, or overgeneralization, the stutterer may begin to repress words that have little direct relationship to the original drive or motivation that was associated with the repressed verbalism.

Underlying the positions of theorists as diverse as those represented in this *Symposium* is the common assumption that somehow the environment did not treat the stutterer as he should have been or needed to be treated. Adults, and particularly parents, were harsh, or rejecting, or perfectionistic, or misevaluating of the behavior of the children. To be sure, the adults were more conforming to the environment than the children they adversely influenced. The children, however, needed different treatment, more permissive and accepting adults, than our culture seems to provide. In this unfortunate relationship of the stutterer, or potential stutterer, to the adults in his environment, two tendencies become evident. One is that the child is unable to meet the needs of his environment; the second is that the adults are unable, for a crucial period at least, to meet the needs of their child.

The tendencies and traits just considered are among those the writer considers predominant in the common background of nonorganic stutterers. He has made no attempt to be exhaustive. Emphasis has been on the presentation of factors and influences that many theorists consider important. The fact remains, however, that the same factors may be present for children who do not become stutterers. There is still need to find out why stuttering, rather than some other deviant behavior, becomes the behavioral manifestation. We are not entirely satisfied that we have as yet arrived at a suitable answer unrelated to constitutional predisposition for stuttering as a symptom choice. In brief, we need more research, and perhaps more soul searching to arrive at the answer to the key question in stuttering: "What kind of a child is it who responds to his environment, and to himself, with stuttering?"

V. THERAPEUTIC APPROACHES AND THEIR IMPLICATIONS FOR THE THEORY OF PERSEVERATION

Except for these therapists who advocate psychoanalysis as the treatment of choice for stutterers, most others include some form or forms of symptomatic therapy as part of their overall treatment program. The degree of emphasis varies considerably, not only according to the stutterer's apparent and deep-seated needs, but also according to the training, inclinations, and abilities of the therapist. In his survey of symptomatic therapy for stuttering, Van Riper (33:ch. 27) points out that such therapeutic approaches fall into two categories: those that have as their goal the prevention of the occurrence of stuttering, and those that have as their goal the modification of the stuttering symptoms. ". . . the first tries to teach the stutterer to talk without stuttering; the second tries to teach the case to stutter in a fashion tolerable to both society and himself."

We have by now reached a point in our treatment of stutterers where the question is no longer whether a stutterer should be exposed to symptomatic treatment, but rather what kind of symptomatic treament he should receive. Van Riper, in his contribution to this *Symposium* and in the chapter referred to in the *Handbook of Speech Pathology,* does an excellent job of reviewing the types and values of symptomatic treatment. The present writer agrees with Van Riper's preference that symptomatic treatment for stutterers should enable them to *express rather than repress* their speech symptoms. Further, that whenever possible the symptom treatment should be such as to help the stutterer to evaluate himself and his symptoms and what they may mean for him. Still further, the clinician and the stutterer should, if at all possible, evaluate the therapeutic approaches and what the therapist and patient are trying to accomplish through their use. The "if at all possible" reservation is one that should be determined by the patient's intellectual capacity and emotional readiness. There is no point in verbalizing for a patient reasons or rationale that he cannot assimilate. On the other hand, there is little justification for a clinician competent and confident in his techniques and the overall objectives of his therapeutic procedures to hold back information and insights from his patient.

An additional point in regard to symptomatic treatment should be emphasized. The assumed reason for the efficacy of an approach is not necessarily the real reason, or may be only part of the real reason, for its efficacy. For example, the therapist who directs his stutterer to chew his breath, or his words, to overcome his stuttering block may do so on the assumption that by "chewing" the patient returns to a basic biological use of his oral mechanism that has been "forgotten" by the stutterer when he tries to speak. Chewing, however, may have other values that may be more or less momentarily therapeutic. First, because in our culture it is not considered polite to chew as we speak or speak as we chew, the patient is permitted to do something conventionally tabooed. This may satisfy a need he dare not ordinarily express, and so it may be good for him. Second, the technique may serve as a distraction device. We know that any technique which shifts attention from what is said to a manner of speaking serves, temporarily, to reduce stuttering. Third, the patient who is busy "chewing his words" may actually be envisioning a person, possibly even the therapist, he is "chewing out." This too may satisfy a need and hence be therapeutic. Fourth, the kind of linguistic content a patient may be verbalizing while chewing may have little or no propositional value, and so the situation may become a relatively easy one for the stutterer. This listing by no means exhausts the possibilities of what goes on within the patient when a specific technique is employed, but it should suggest that whatever is going on may be very different in the thinking and feelings of the stutterer and those of the clinician. With this in mind, let us examine some of the current symptomatic approaches from the point of view of the perseverative theory of stuttering.

Negative Practice. When Dunlap (11) directed a stutterer to imitate his own stuttering, he did so on the assumption that the stutterer was thereby becoming aware of a habit and learning to control it through the technique of *negative practice.* This, of course, may well be true. It is also possible, however, that what might be taking place is that the stutterer is permitted to repeat as long as he needs to repeat, to perseverate according to his need, rather than to avoid doing what he is inclined to do. In effect, the stutterer is given encouragement and approval to *be himself.* If the stutterer is a constitutional perseverator, this is excellent therapy. If, on the other hand, the stutterer is a neurotic individual who has become victimized by a habit, the approach is still good therapy.

Voluntary Stuttering. The foregoing comments on negative practice also hold for the technique of voluntary stuttering. The emphasis given by Bryngelson (5) on the importance for the stutterer to see himself as well as his speech symptoms objectively points again to the therapeutic implications of not only permitting but approving the expression of an inclination. Bryngelson began to train the stutterer to speak repetitively whenever he felt that he might stutter. Through repetitive speech the stutterer was helped to face speaking situations rather than to avoid them. Struggle behavior became reduced. When the stutterer could not voluntarily repeat, he was encouraged to stutter without inhibition, to express rather than repress his inclinations. From the writer's point of view, Bryngelson helped stutterers to go a long way to the goal of self-acceptance of the need for repetitive (perseverative) speech in certain situations. The situations generally are those calling for communicative responsibility and the use of propositional language.

Easy Repetition. Johnson (21:291) recommends a form of voluntary, easy repetition as a therapeutic goal for the stutterer. Johnson observes that when the stutterer is working toward reduction of tension and development of control over stuttering behavior and a sense of choice over how he is to stutter—"the result tends to be that the stutterer, in performing his stuttering behavior more and more simply and easily, either repeats or prolongs the initial sound or syllable of the stuttered word." In this observation it seems to the writer that Johnson recognizes that nonfluency (repetition) is an essential aspect of the speech of the stutterer. To be sure, nonfluency is also an essential aspect of the nonstutterer's speech. In any event, if an individual who cannot help repeating (perseverating) wins approval rather than penalty for his manner of speaking, he is in effect encouraged to perseverate in his speech according to his need. In further therapy, the stutterer may reduce the number of his repetitions (perseverations) according to his immediate situational needs. In this way the perseverative speaker who becomes a stutterer can be helped to resume his constitutional status as a perseverator rather than to continue as a stutterer.

Prolongation. When we teach a stutterer to prolong a sound rather than to repeat, we are probably accomplishing the same result in terms of symptom treatment. If the stutterer prolongs a sound as he moves from one articulatory position to the next, he is probably perseverating covertly rather than overtly. What we may be helping him to do is to maintain a set until the neural lag is gone. Then, without struggle, he can move on to the next sound or the next word.

Cancellation and Pseudo-Stuttering. The technique of *cancellation* is introduced by Van Riper when his case shows that he is ready and able to stutter openly and without inhibition. Cancellation, according to Van Riper (33:889–890), ". . . consists of coming to a complete halt after the stuttered word has been finally uttered, pausing a moment and then attempting to say the word again with even less struggle and avoidance. The case is not to try to say the word without stuttering. Even when the fear and threat is gone and he knows he can say it without having any symptoms, he deliberately does some pseudo-stuttering on the cancellation. This pseudo-stuttering should not be a facsimile of the original symptoms, but represent a modification of them in the direction of normal nonfluency."

Van Riper believes that during the moment of pause—the pause in cancellation—the stutterer is supposed to scrutinize the symptoms and feelings that he experienced immediately before his block. This scrutiny takes place in the light of the newly found insights into the dynamics of his behavior. Also, "During the interim between the original stuttering and the new cancelling attempt, the stutterer finds himself altering his sets and making plans for the subsequent modification of symptoms" (33:890).

Van Riper indicates several psychotherapeutic implications of the cancellation technique. Among them is that cancellation—intentional stuttering—provides a symbolic goal. "The stutterer realizes that a form of stuttering similar to that which is demonstrated in the cancellation would be tolerable to both himself and other people. It demonstrates to the stutterer that it might be possible to stutter in another way, that he might be able to stutter and still communicate, that stuttering need not be catastrophic."

Here is probably another instance of a therapeutic technique that permits a stutterer to become a perseverator without penalty, and so helps him overcome his reactions to stuttering. Beyond reasonable doubt, other things go on when a stutterer is permitted to repeat. He has the approval of a therapist, an authority figure, to be himself instead of struggling to avoid being himself. He can improve his self-esteem, and in so doing overcome some of the feelings that may aggravate his reactions and lower his self-esteem. He may even, if this happens to be the case, entertain some of the secondary gains of stuttering until he is ready to surrender them because they are no longer essential to his needs. He can have all this and perseverate too. This, unquestionably, is potent symptom therapy as well as psychotherapy. We recommend it!

Adaptation. The technique of adaptation, that of having the stutterer repeat on linguistic content read aloud or self-formulated, has been evaluated in the earlier part of this discussion. The assumption there was that when a stutterer repeats what he has previously read or spoken, anxiety is reduced with successive utterances. As a result there is a reduced stuttering. There is, of course, no argument with the assumption that anxiety is reduced with repeated utterances of the same material. However, as indicated earlier, repeated iteration of any linguistic content reduces the intellectual significance and the propositional value of the content, and so speech may become more fluent.

Easy Articulation. Some therapists teach the stutterer new patterns of articulation that call for less articulatory tension, for less "sticking" on some sounds than most of us employ in speaking. Perhaps what these therapists are helping their cases to accomplish is a manner of articulation that does not require a firm motor set. If the perseverative tendency is in part related to inertia, the less firm an articulatory position is, the smaller the amount of energy that will be needed to modify or change the position. Speaking that is reduced in normal articulatory tension may be a way of avoiding the onset of a perseverative state.

Rate Control. Most therapists who employ rate control usually ask their patients to speak more slowly rather than more rapidly. In this slower rate of speaking, we may be helping the stutterer to adjust to his capacity for linguistic formulations and their articulatory expression. In effect, we may be teaching him how to avoid obvious perseverative behavior which would become evident if he were to speak at a rate more like most speakers. At the modified, slower rate, the stutterer is afforded the time he needs for changing his mental and motor sets according to his inclinations.

This symptomatic treatment of stuttering seems to have two goals: the immediate goal of self-acceptance of stuttering symptoms, and fluent "stuttering," the intermediate goal for some and the final one for others.

From the writer's point of view, whether fluent stuttering is an intermediate or a final goal depends upon whether we are dealing with a constitutional perseverator or with a nonorganic psychogenic stutterer. For the constitutional perseverator, repetitive speaking relieved of associated anxiety, apprehension, struggle, and its inner and overt manifestations is all that we can hope to accomplish. The individual, with the help of as much insight and self-acceptance as he can gain through direct or indirect psychotherapy, learns to speak in a manner and with an attitude consistent with his constitutional predisposition. The constitutional perseverator can also be considerably helped through a recognition of situations, such as those analyzed earlier (see pp. 235–243), which are conducive to increased perseveration. Such recognition should help to prepare the speaker to adjust to situations without apprehension. If needed, he can get set for the use of techniques that enable him to continue his communication rather than to block and struggle.

The psychogenic stutterer may possibly be helped beyond the point of voluntary repetition. He may be helped to speak with only a normal amount of so-called nonfluency—perhaps better described as speaking with normal fluency, which includes some repetitiveness and dysrhythmia suggestive of nonfluency and of stuttering.

Although some symptomatic treatment may serve the same functions for psychogenic stutterer as for organic stutterer, much of the treatment may serve different purposes. What some of these may be was indicated in the first part of this section. Beyond symptomatic treatment, regardless of the significance of this therapy for the psychogenic stutterer, avowed psychotherapy may be in order. In some instances this may be to determine the underlying cause and meaning of the symptoms for the stutterer. The goals, nature, and extent of psychotherapy are matters to be determined by the needs of the individual stutterer. The factors determining these objectives will be considered in the discussion that follows. For the moment, however, the writer should like to indicate that he does not believe all psychogenic stutterers fall into a common category and stutter for the same reason, nor that all neurotics who stutter ought to become exposed to the same psychotherapeutic techniques.

Psychotherapy

Any good relationship between a patient and a therapist is in part psychotherapeutic. This incidental psychotherapy takes place regardless of technique. Sometimes it takes place despite the symptomatic technique employed. For some stutterers who have not developed additional or associated maladaptive behavior, only incidental psychotherapy is necessary. This may well be the case with young stutterers. Of course, considerably more therapy may be necessary for the parents and other adults in the stutterer's environment. It is likely that the more effective therapy is for the adults, the less direct psychotherapy the child will need. If this is not possible, therapy for the child must in part include helping him to accept the adults as they are.[11]

Adolescent and adult stutterers, regardless of the genesis of their stuttering, are likely to need more that just incidental psychotherapy. Any moderately intelligent individual who is aware that an important aspect of his behavior is significantly different from most others in his environment is likely to develop some reactions to this behavior that will need treatment. Within this *Symposium* considerable attention has been given to this viewpoint. The present writer's emphasis is that we cannot ignore the symptoms of stuttering, especially if the stutterer's history suggests a constitutional predisposition for his disturbance. Neither can we overlook the need many stutterers have for psychotherapy.

Adolescents and adults, especially intelligent ones, are likely to make some use of their handicaps. If the handicap is stuttering, it can be used to excuse them from social situations that may be unpleasant for reasons quite unrelated to their speech. As suggested earlier, stuttering can be used to make others uncomfortable, to punish persons deemed by the stutterer to be in need of such punishment. It can be a stand-by alibi for failure, for not trying because there may be a failure, and for a host of other purposes that only a resourceful human mind can anticipate. These uses make stuttering a way of life. They must be dealt with if therapy for the stutterer is to be successful.

Just how much psychotherapy the adolescent and adult stutterer needs depends upon the individual. Some adult stutterers may have worked through their problems themselves and be ready to give up—or have given up—the secondary gains when they come to a therapist. In such instances there may be a danger of too much rather than too little psychotherapy. Symptomatic treatment may be all that is indicated. Other adults may be reluctant or unable to accept the notion that stuttering is without value. They come to the therapist with the presenting symptoms of stuttering and "want no messing around" with their personal lives. For these adults, symptomatic treatment may be of some help, and incidental insight may be attained if the therapist is understanding and patient. Some patients begin to ask questions that suggest there is growing doubt, and perhaps an inkling of insight, as symptomatic treatment progresses.

[11] For the author's views on therapy for the young stutterer see 1:ch. 12.

Clinicians as well as stutterers reach a point in therapy when the question of the need for deeper psychotherapy must be faced. The clinician must then determine whether his training and inclination are sufficient to permit him to be of further help to the patient. If not, a referral is in order to a therapist with competence in psychotherapy, and if at all possible, one who has had successful experience with stutterers.

Review of Therapeutic Approaches for the Organic Stutterer

Earlier in this section some of the symptomatic and psychotherapeutic approaches for stutterers were evaluated, with indication of how these may have efficacy for the stutterer with a constitutional predisposition toward his difficulty. At this point a more positive approach is in order, with an outline of a therapeutic program for the stutterer whose difficulty is related to his tendency toward excessive perseverative behavior.

This writer believes it important to secure evidence that may establish the likelihood that we are in fact dealing with an essentially organic rather than a functional speech disorder. Specifically, we ought to determine whether there is a basis for believing that the individual stutterer with whom we are dealing is inclined to excessive perseveration and so has become a stutterer, or whether he is stuttering and perseverating for psychogenic reasons. A clinical history and the criteria considered earlier for perseverative tendencies should be of help. (See p. 250.) Beyond this, specific and appropriate tests of perseveration may be administered. Some of these were described in part I of this essay. Medical information—especially information suggestive either of atypical neurological development or of neuropathology in early childhood—should also be presumptive of a tendency for the existence of excessive perseveration.

Some words of caution are in order. We do not know precisely what neurological differences cause perseveration. We do know that persons with brain damage are strongly inclined to perseverate. Even these persons, however, reduce their perseverative inclinations as their general physical condition improves and as they adjust to the limitations imposed by the conditions. Excessive perseveration may be a temporary state; the physical correlates of perseveration should therefore be checked and reëvaluated periodically. The excessively perseverative child need not be an excessively perseverative adult—the physical conditions may have changed for this individual. If this, indeed, turns out to be the case, we may be dealing with a habit of perseveration rather than constitutional perseveration. For such an individual new insights and a different set of objectives should be in order.

If we are satisfied that at the time the stutterer comes to us for therapy, we are dealing with a constitutional perseverator, then therapeutic approaches toward the following objectives are indicated:

1. To help the stutterer toward an acceptance of himself as a functioning organism.
2. To weaken the nonorganic causes that tend to increase conflict, ambivalence, and other attitudes associated with psychogenic perseveration.
3. To modify, control, and if possible eliminate stuttering blocks and the secondary symptoms of stuttering.
4. To help the stutterer to speak in a manner consistent with his constitutional predisposition, to repeat as often as necessary, to modify rate, and otherwise speak so that the effort is devoid of anxiety, conflict, struggle, and the covert and overt characteristics of stuttering.

Except for emphasis on organic or constitutional factors, these objectives are such as to be acceptable to any but strongly psychoanalytically inclined therapists. The reader will recognize that within this *Symposium* therapeutic programs toward these objectives have been presented.

Self-Acceptance. To an extent determined in part by the age and intelligence of the individual the stutterer needs to be helped toward an objective evaluation of himself, his stuttering, and his reactions to his stuttering. Many stutterers need to be helped to accept themselves as persons who will continue to be repetitive or hesitant to an extent greater than most of their associates. At the outset they must confront the realities of their stuttering. If they can pause to stop and look at themselves, literally as well as figuratively, at their moments of stuttering and ask "What is this about?" instead of "Why is this happening to me?" they will probably get better answers to both questions.

Many therapists stress the need for more rather than less speaking at the outset of therapy, regardless of how much stuttering takes place. By speaking more, the patient is presumably not trying to avoid situations that might betray him. Instead, he is going out of his way to reveal himself so that there will be no fear of being found out.

By speaking more, and stuttering more, the individual can make note of the situations conducive to his stuttering, as well as those associated with nonstuttering. Through such awareness the individual may begin to look upon himself as a stutterer under one set of conditions and a relatively fluent speaker under another set. He may through such an evaluation look forward to some situations while getting over apprehensions and anxieties about others. When the stutterer is enabled to make the distinction between stuttering and perseveration, he may be able to adopt an attitude of "Sufficient unto the situation is the perseveration thereof." In the author's therapy, when he feels that he is dealing with a constitutional perseverator, he stresses the point that repetitions and hesitancy constitute perseveration. The addition of anxiety, apprehension, and struggle behavior to repetitions and hesitancies transform perseveration into stuttering. Perhaps this is what Johnson also means when he has patients evaluate the "normal nonfluencies" of speech. The writer, of course, regards perseveration as excessive recourse to so-called nonfluencies. So he does not try to convince the stutterer that he too can be a perfectly normal speaker if he reëvaluates his nonfluencies. Instead, he emphasizes the need for objective evaluation and acceptance of the amount of perseverative oral language usage the stutterer seems to require in specific situations and types of situations. Through this approach, he helps the stutterer to self-acceptance—to accept himself for what he cannot help being rather than to try to be somebody he is constitutionally unable to become.

Weakening of the Nonorganic Causes of Perseveration. The therapeutic approaches considered under the headings of symptomatic treatment and psychotherapy all help toward the objective of weakening the nonorganic causes of perseveration. Any forces that help to reduce ambivalence and to increase the drive toward speaking will serve this end. Acceptance of the stuttering, and later of perseveration, help to reduce the psychological overlays associated with avoidance and refusal to accept the reality of stuttering. A strengthened wish and willingness to speak may become too strong for any residual fear of speaking. So the determining tendencies for speaking become greater than the inhibiting force, and the requirements for perseveration on the basis of a volitional disturbance no longer pertain. With a reduction in struggle behavior, the amount of perseveration existing on an organic basis need no longer be reinforced by nonorganic perseveration. The result may be a marked decrease in repetitions and hesitations, with speech beginning to approximate the normal.

Modification and Control of the Secondary Symptoms of Stuttering. Several of the techniques considered in this discussion of symptomatic treatment of stuttering are recommended as entirely appropriate for the modification and control of secondary symptoms. The nonverbal mannerisms, the ticlike behavior that is superimposed on the oral blocks, require awareness and voluntary control for their modification and eventual elimination. The techniques of negative practice, of *voluntary reproduction of the whole act of stuttering,* are pertinent for this objective. These have already been considered (see p. 261) and so need not be discussed again.

Establishment of a Manner of Speaking Consistent with Constitutional Predisposition. When we help the stutterer to become aware of how much perseverative behavior he normally (for himself as a perseverator) needs to exercise in a speaking situation, we are helping him to approach normal speech. There can, of course, be no prescription for all stutterers in terms of constitutional predisposition. The needs of A are not the needs of B, because the constitutions of A and B are not the same. Even if they were, since their reactions are not the same, the overall effects are different.

A stutterer must learn how slowly or how quickly he must speak in a given situation. He needs to learn with what appropriateness he can generalize from specific situation to situation. He must be helped to repeat only as often as he needs to repeat and then move on to the next utterance. He must learn not to yield to repetition for repetition's sake, yet not to regard a moment's pause as an unbearable hiatus. When the stutterer learns this, and begins to speak in the light of this knowledge, he is beginning to leave stuttering behind and to be a perseverator. When the perseverative utterances are reduced to a minimum without discomfort and anxiety, the speaker is no longer a stutterer. In some situations there will be no need for perseveration. In others there may be comparatively little perseveration, little enough to be considered normal nonfluency. In a few situations there will be greater than normal perseveration. But this will be greater than normal only when the constitutional perseverator compares himself, or is compared with, so-called statistical norms. What we try to establish, however, is the norm or norms the individual is to observe for himself. When this objective is achieved, the speaker will have established a manner of speaking consistent with his constitutional predisposition for perseveration. The individual will no longer be a stutterer but a speaker who is an occasional perseverator. If he accepts himself as such the battle over stuttering has been won.

References

1. Berry, M., and Eisenson, J., *Speech Disorders*, New York, Appleton-Century-Crofts, 1956.
2. Bloodstein, O., "A rating scale of conditions under which stuttering is reduced or absent," *Journal of Speech and Hearing Disorders*, I, 1950.
3. Bluemel, C. S., *The Riddle of Stuttering,* The Interstate Press, Danville, Illinois, 1957.
4. Brown, S. F., "The loci of stutterings in the speech sequence," *Journal of Speech Disorders*, X, 1945.

5. Bryngelson, B., "Stuttering and personality development," *The Nervous Child,* II, 1943.
6. Cattell, R. B., "The riddle of perseveration: II. Solution in terms of personality structure," *Journal of Personality,* XIV, 1946.
7. Cattell, R. B., and Winder, A. E., "Structural rigidity in relation to learning theory and clinical psychology," *Psychological Review,* LIX, 1952.
8. Davis, D. M., "The relation of repetition in the speech of young children to certain measures of language maturity and situational factors," *Journal of Speech Disorders,* IV, 1939, and V, 1940.
9. Douglass, L. C., "A study of bilaterally recorded encephalograms of adult stutterers," *Journal of Experimental Psychology,* XXXII, 1943.
10. Doust, J. W. L., and Coleman, L. I. M., "The psychophysics of communication," *A.M.A. Archives of Neurology and Psychiatry,* LXXIV, 1955.
11. Dunlap, K., "The technique of negative practice," *American Journal of Psychology,* LV, 1932.
12. Eisenson, J., *Examining for Aphasia,* New York, Psychological Corp., 1954.
13. Eisenson, J., "A note on the perseverating tendency in stutterers," *Journal of Genetic Psychology,* L, 1937.
14. Eisenson, J., and Horowitz, E., "The influence of propositionality on stuttering," *Journal of Speech Disorders,* X, 1945.
15. Eisenson, J., and Winslow, C. N., "The perseverating tendency in stutterers in a perceptual function," *Journal of Speech Disorders,* III, 1938.
16. Ewen, J. H., "Perseveration in the insane epileptics," *Journal of Mental Science,* LXXI, 1930.
17. Falck, F. J., "Interrelationships among certain behavioral characteristics, age, sex, and duration of therapy in a group of stutterers," Ph.D. dissertation, Pennsylvania State University, 1955. (Reported in *Speech Monographs,* XXIII, 2, 1956.)
18. Goldsand, J., "Sensory perseveration in stutterers and non-stutterers," *Speech Abstracts,* IV, 1944.
19. Hebb, D. O., *The Organization of Behavior*, New York, Wiley, 1949.
20. Jackson, H., "Selected writings of J. Hughlings Jackson," H. Head (ed.), *Brain,* XXXVIII, 1915.
21. Johnson, W., *et al., Speech Handicapped School Children,* rev. ed., New York, Harper, 1956.
22. Johnson, W., and Knott, J. R., "The distribution of moments of stuttering in successive readings of the same material," *Journal of Speech Disorders,* II, 1937.
23. Johnson, W., ed., assisted by Leutenegger, R. R., *Stuttering in Children and Adults: Thirty Years of Research at the University of Iowa,* Minneapolis, University of Minnesota Press, 1955.
24. King, P. T., "Perseverating factors in a stuttering and non-stuttering population, Ph. D. dissertation, Pennsylvania State University, 1953.

25. Landis, C., and Bolles, M. M., *Textbook of Abnormal Psychology*, rev. ed., New York, Macmillan, 1950.
26. Leutenegger, R. R., "Adaptation and recovery in the oral reading of stutterers," *Journal of Speech and Hearing Disorders*, XXII, 1957.
27. Levine, A. S., "'Perseveration,' or 'The Central Factor,'" *Psychological Reports*, I, 1955.
28. Newman, P. W., "A study of the adaptation and recovery of the stuttering response in self-formulated speech," *Journal of Speech and Hearing Disorders*, XIX, 1954.
29. Pinard, J. W., "Tests of perseveration: II," *British Journal of Psychology*, XXXIII, 1932.
30. Sheets, B., M. A. thesis, University of Utah, 1941.
31. Spearman, C., *The Abilities of Man*, London, Macmillan, 1927.
32. Spearman, C., and Jones, L. W., *Human Ability*, London, Macmillan, 1950.
33. Travis, L. E. (ed.), *Handbook of Speech Pathology*, New York, Appleton-Century-Crofts, 1957.
34. Travis, L. E., "My present thinking on stuttering," *Western Speech*, X, 1946.
35. Travis, L. E., and Knott, J. R., "Brain potentials from normal speakers and stutterers," *Journal of Psychology*, II, 1936.
36. Trotter, W. D., and Bergmann, M. F., "Stutterer's and non-stutterer's reactions to speech situations," *Journal of Speech and Hearing Disorders*, XXII, 1957.
37. Van Riper, C., *Speech Correction: Principles and Methods*, 3rd ed., New York, Prentice-Hall, 1954.

EXPERIMENTS IN STUTTERING THERAPY

CHARLES VAN RIPER, Ph.D.

Professor of Speech and Director of Speech and Hearing Clinic, Western Michigan University; Fellow, American Speech and Hearing Association. Author of Speech Correction: Principles and Methods, Speech Therapy, Speech in the Elementary Classroom, Teaching Your Child to Talk, *and* Casebook in Speech Therapy. *Coauthor of* Casebook in Stuttering *(with Leslie Gruber)*, Introduction to General American Phonetics *(with Dorothy E. Smith), and* Articulation and Voice: Abnormal and Normal *(with John V. Irwin). Contributor to professional periodicals including the* Quarterly Journal of Speech *and the* Journal of Speech and Hearing Disorders.

Experiments in Stuttering Therapy

The Origin of Stuttering

IN THIS paper I have no new theoretic position to present as to the etiology of stuttering. My position continues to be the one I held earlier—that stuttering probably has a multiple origin.[1] Varying with the individual, stuttering may emerge out of backgrounds of emotional conflict, low frustration tolerance, an early speech environment characterized by an over abundance of fluency disruptors, or by poorly timed coördinations. Stuttering may also emerge as a result of parental labeling of the normal nonfluencies of the child as abnormal, or as a result of the anxiety and stress felt by a child in trying to please his parents by talking in phrases and sentences before he is ready for this linguistic task. Personally, I think that the last factor is the most likely cause for the onset of stuttering.

Whether the individual becomes a stutterer as a result of constitutional or environmental factors, or as a result of a combination of both, stuttering tends to maintain itself once it gets started. It somehow achieves a functional autonomy, a self-reinforcement which keeps it going. Clinicians must be mindful of this aspect of the problem in their treatment of the stutterer. In fact, it well may be that the determination of the original cause or causes of the stuttering may not be as important therapeutically as the determination of the factors that maintain it.

Introduction

In this paper I wish to emphasize stuttering therapy rather than theory. The title of this account, be it said immediately, can hardly be considered entirely accurate, if by experiment we mean a carefully controlled piece of research. This is the tale of one man's experiences in stuttering therapy, in which he deliberately varied his procedures, recorded by means of daily

[1] C. Van Riper, *Speech Correction*, 3rd ed., New York, Prentice-Hall, 1954, pp. 343–350.

and weekly protocols his goals and methods, and evaluated the progress of his cases as objectively as he knew how. It was felt that an account of this experience might have some value for other professional workers in his field.

Since errors of interpretation are likely to occur in any such personal presentation of one's professional accomplishments despite a desperate attempt to maintain objectivity, it was thought wise to emulate the anthropologists and to provide a brief description of the author's history so that the reader might discern any bias which might be present. This account, then, is written by a man, aged 50, the director of a college speech clinic, son of a country physician who rejected him and a mother who protected him, who stuttered severely from the age of 22 months until he was 28 and who still stutters slightly but has adequate fluency, who was shifted successfully from left- to right-handedness, who attended three commercial stammering schools in his early twenties without any but temporary relief, and who has received hypnotic, psychoanalytic, and the Bryngelson-Travis therapy of the early 1930's. The author believes that his present speech adequacy derives from his own efforts to modify his stuttering symptoms so that he could stutter fluently, without gross abnormality or interruption, and from a security derived from a good marriage and professional status. Selah!

Some explanation of the motivation for carrying out such a project over the course of more than 20 years might be appropriate. In 1932, when the author first achieved sufficient fluency to enable him to begin his doctoral studies in clinical psychology, he decided to devote his professional life to the study of stuttering and the improvement of its therapy. He did not know exactly how he had achieved his own fluency and he was appalled at the failure of his fellow stutterers to make even as much progress as he had made. Therefore, upon receiving his doctorate from the University of Iowa in 1934, he spent the next two years there as an experimental therapist and in various researches on the nature and development of stuttering. In 1936, selecting a then small college where he could continue to do therapy, he initiated a speech clinic and therapist-training program. In accordance with his aim, he decided to vary from year to year his therapeutic methods, to keep his regular protocols, and to institute a five-year follow-up program so that he could evaluate the results of his therapy. The last of these aims has not been entirely successful, since it seems impossible to get yearly returns from all of one's former cases. There are always a few who forget or refuse to report. It was also the author's intention to select as his cases, when selection was possible, those whose stuttering problem was severe and whose prognosis was unfavorable.

Group, individual, self, and environmental therapy experiences were seen as possible variables. All cases were to receive therapy for at least one semester, with the number of therapy sessions varying from one to fifteen a week. These intentions have, in large measure, been accomplished, but there have been many instances in which they could not be fulfilled. We shall try to indicate when they could not.

1936–1937

Rationale

In 1936 we believed that the essence of stuttering lay in a neuromuscular blocking or inability to move the paired speech musculatures at a specific moment in time. These blockings, however, were seen as being of extremely short duration, lasting but a fraction of a second, and precipitated by a latent dysphemia activated by situation and word fears. The *greater* part of the stuttering abnormality was viewed as consisting of *learned* reactions to the threat or experience of these blockings, as avoidance or frustration responses. These, it was felt, could be unlearned through proper training methods, thereby decreasing the severity of the disorder. With the severity decreased it was hoped that the frequency would subsequently be reduced, with less unpleasantness in speaking since less fear and frustration would occur. In short, our aim was to "whittle down" the stuttering to its neuromuscular blockings, thereby achieving a fluency adequate for everyday communication.

Influenced by our psychoanalytic experiences and by the concept of a *margin* of cerebral dominance which could operate the speech mechanism fluently so long as it was not reduced by ego-destructive stresses, we felt that any therapeutic program should include activities which would enhance that margin and increase the individual's ego strength. We also felt that the stutterer could be trained and toughened to resist the specific disturbing influences which impaired that margin of cerebral dominance or which reduced that ego strength. Any experience which would do either should decrease the frequency of the stuttering blocks.

It should be noted that the basic assumptions upon which this rationale rested were these: (1) Stuttering consists largely of learned behavior and can be modified and reduced through training procedures. (2) Stuttering consists largely of avoidance and frustration responses, both of which reinforce the stuttering. (3) The stutterer's self-concept can be altered so that less stuttering will occur. Both the stuttering and the stutterer were viewed as being modifiable.[2]

Clinical Routine

Seven adult and three child stutterers received intensive therapy. The adult group met as a group for an hour five days each week, and each individual received individual therapy from the author for one hour each day. Through a series of assignments each adult carried out, without supervision but with written and oral reports, a program of self-therapy tailored to his individual needs. Four of the adults were male, three female. All were college students. Of the children, one, aged 7, was what we would now call a transitional stutterer, without fears or avoidances but with severe frustration responses. The other two, aged 10 and 12 respectively, were severe secondary stutterers. All were boys. Therapy with the children was all individual, consisting of three hours weekly for each with weekly parental conferences. We will first describe the therapy with the adult group.

Group Therapy Sessions

These periods were spent primarily in the clarification of the goals and methods of therapy, in demonstrations by the therapist and the stutterers of their relative ability to resist deliberately contrived stresses, to stutter without avoidance or frustration responses, and to verbalize their feelings about themselves, their fellow stutterers, the therapist, and the therapy. The sequence of the items in the preceding sentence fairly well reflects the emphasis as the therapy progressed. At first the sessions were largely confined, though not entirely, to the exposition and demonstration of goals and methods. Toward the end of the second semester most of the group sessions consisted of the verbal sharing of feelings in a fairly permissive atmosphere. The therapist's role, however, was definitely authoritative; he was the teacher, the leader, the prescriber, and sometimes the punisher. Despite this, a strong group feeling was established which carried over into social activities outside the clinic. One girl, however, was unable to join this group and remained outside it, a scapegoat and rejected. The other six members also paired up in subgroups for therapy and social

[2] That this rationale is not a backward projection of the author's present thinking is evidenced by his articles in the literature of 1937. "A symptomatic treatment of stuttering," *Proceedings American Speech Correction Association,* VII, 1937; "The preparatory set in stuttering," *Journal of Speech Disorders,* II, 1937; and "The growth of the stuttering spasm," *Quarterly Journal of Speech,* XXIII, 1937.

activities. Two of the males formed a close but healthy friendship, and the other two males paired up with the other two girl stutterers.

A description of the therapy methods would now seem to be in order. To reduce the dysphemia which we then presumed to exist in all stutterers, all of them were taught new unilateral skills: ping-pong, tennis, shorthand, engraving, etc., and all bimanual activities were reduced. Thus one male, an excellent flute and piano player, was shifted to the trumpet. One-handed typing of reports was insisted upon. No case was changed in his handedness, since testing had revealed that all but one were thoroughly right-handed. The latter individual, highly ambidextrous, was asked to use his right hand exclusively.

Experiences in simultaneous talking-and-writing were strongly emphasized. The cases began with a minimum of 5 full pages of talking-and-writing per day and within 3 weeks had increased this daily quota to at least 15 pages. A few individuals turned in as high as 30 pages daily. This technique was thought to accomplish several things; it might increase the basic margin of cerebral dominance so that fewer neuromuscular blockings would occur; it maintained the speech mechanism in action on a highly voluntary level rather than on an automatic one (shades of feedback theory!); it trained the stutterer to make a sudden and direct attack upon words which often were feared; and finally, as Travis once said, if the benefit derived from its use were due only to suggestion, well then use it for that purpose. We now feel that talking-and-writing has another utility far beyond any of those mentioned, but we shall describe that in its proper place.

Essentially, in doing this simultaneous talking-and-writing, the stutterer was required to write the first letter of the word very suddenly and to time the utterance of that word so that it coincided exactly with the dominant stroke of the letter being written. Between words, one came to a state of rest both in writing and in talking. Each writing and utterance was therefore a sudden, staccato, all-out attempt, with no holding back, temporizing, or avoidance. The stutterer was urged to speak with a strong voice and strongly articulated jaw movements. For three months this talking-and-writing was not used for purposes of communication. Stutterers read material from articles on stuttering and mental hygiene or verbalized their feelings in self-talk. Little stuttering occurred, but when it did the stutterer merely encircled the word, wrote out on a separate sheet of paper his description of the stuttering behavior, and then continued. Most of the talking-and-writing was done outside the clinic when the case was alone, but occasionally group sessions began with this activity so that the therapists could check the adequacy of the technique. All sheets of the quota were handed in to the therapist each day. The stutterer's performance could be judged fairly well from the characteristics of the script alone. These experiences with talking and writing, with their need for self-discipline, contact with the self in purposeful activity, and undergoing temporary unpleasantness for future good, often gave rise to hostility, self-disgust, self-pity, and other feelings which, with the help of the therapist, enabled the stutterer to understand his basic reactions to his problem.

Another technique which was used daily as a major part of the therapy was "voluntary stuttering." This phrase has had so many meanings that we must describe it. Essentially it meant, in 1936, that the stutterer was to *substitute* a highly voluntary and deliberate repetition of the first sound or syllable of the word on which the individual expected to stutter involuntarily and with his characteristic abnormality. This was not the effortless, rhythmic, automatized "bouncing" recommended later by the Iowa therapists. The stutterer had to resist the impulse to use any avoidance or struggle responses. He had to fight for the control of the self. He had to confine his utterance to the first sound or syllable, eliminating all extraneous postponement and starter devices. He had to continue the production of these voluntary repetitions until all of his anxiety had subsided and he was sure that he could say the word without any struggle or tremor appearing. The repetitions were not to be rhythmic or automatic but conscious, slow, and deliberate. In the syllabic utterance, the stutterer was required to use the phonemes appropriate to the normal utterance of the word; i.e., he was not to say "buh-buh-boot," but "boo . . . boo . . . boot" and variations in the number of repetitions per word were the rule rather than the exception. When a single sound was uttered, as in "apple," the stutterer was urged to repeat it with the next sound (the *p*) in mind, so that actually syllabic utterance served as the basic unit of voluntary stuttering. He would say, "aap . . . aap . . . aap . . . aap . . . apple" with the *p* sounds postured but not exploded. With blends the second phoneme was similarly postured. No attempt was made to simulate normal nonfluency. When one voluntarily stuttered, all within earshot knew that the individual was fighting for mastery of his problem, that he was not pretending to be a nonfluent normal speaker. He was a stutterer, actively coping with his difficulty, sometimes failing, sometimes succeeding, but never surrendering. The stutterers learned this substitute way of responding to the threat of stuttering in the relatively safe climate of the clinic and gradually brought it into "stranger-situations" and finally into their everyday communication. At this time, 1936, voluntary stuttering was to be used only upon the words whereon the case expected difficulty. No pseudo-stuttering was used.

Some fairly superficial psychotherapy was also given. The stutterers and the therapist alike gave verbal excerpts from their autobiographies each day, and the group was encouraged to comment at any time. Stuttering was disregarded during this period. Stutterers were also required weekly to turn in a five-page written conversation between their clinical and stuttering selves summarizing their problems and their needs. Many of these were very revealing. Each week the stutterers were given the opportunity of taking the therapist down town into difficult speech situations where he was required to stutter voluntarily while they enjoyed the procedure. Five minutes of each group period was set aside for the verbalization of hostility and this was always accepted by the therapist as natural and valid, in view of the battle for self-control which was taking place. The group sessions were used for giving information, for clarifying goals, and for reporting experiences and insights.

Results

By the end of the first semester, six of these adults were experiencing marked fluency in the large majority of speaking situations. One of the original group, the girl who was rejected by the others, was completely fluent and left the clinic. Two of the other six had occasional severe blocks in sudden critical speaking situations. The other four showed miniature replicas of the old symptom patterns in their unguarded casual speech when hurried, but spoke very well in stress situations.

By the end of the second semester, during which the group-therapy sessions were discontinued and the individual-therapy sessions confined to twice or thrice weekly, two of the four above-mentioned stutterers had "relapses" and began to avoid and struggle with their speech as before. The others improved or maintained their new fluency and improved attitudes, took part in outside speaking activities, and showed a marked growth in social adjustment.

These seven members were followed up for five years or more. The two who relapsed became as severe stutterers or worse than they had been upon acceptance in the clinic, and one other stutterer also regressed. The scapegoat female stutterer had some intermittent psychotic episodes but recovered completely both from them and from the stuttering. This girl and one of the male stutterers became completely fluent. Two others, both males, have had excellent speech but reported that they stuttered occasionally under great stress. It was no longer an important problem in their lives. Score: two free; two satisfactory; three no change or worse.

Child Therapy

All of the three children were given some play therapy, in which nonsense speech, animal talking, vocalized gestures, and fantasy talk were stressed. We attempted to give them experiences in pleasant talking free from strain. We also played with repetitive stuttering and some easy prolongations of sounds. Stuttering was looked at in mirrors and heard through megaphones as signals to have a pleasant experience such as ringing a gong, escaping from a wastebasket, token-hurting the therapist, or eating a peanut. Stuttering was rewarded and frustration was released. The parents were also treated, the mother only in one case. They were given some education concerning stuttering, methods for removing pressures, and freeing the child from penalties. We also had them attend some of the adult stuttering sessions. We provided the child with parent report cards which listed parental errors such as interruption, impatience, anger, etc. The children marked these cards and the parents knew it. We also visited each of the children's homes in the evening and at a mealtime to suggest changes in environment. Two of the parents coöperated very well; the third resisted our "prying" and discontinued therapy after one month. One of the other children (the transitional stutterer) made an uneventful and complete (five-year) recovery. The third child became worse and we finally terminated therapy, suggesting that the parents return after adolescence had been completed. Five years later he was much worse, but reluctant to have any further therapy.

1937–1938

Rationale

During the summer vacation preceding this school year, we drew up the following quaint document to guide our efforts. It is submitted with some reluctance.

STUTTERING TREATMENT, 1937

This next year we are really going to improve our treatment of stuttering. Last year's results were pretty lousy. Only half of the cases really did the job they should. You've got to drive them harder. You've got to build a conscience about making all of their speaking feared words a voluntary act. You've got to inspire them, to put steel in their souls. They made the clinic and your presence too much of a safe harbor. They've made babies of themselves. They've got to be toughened to stand fear and penalty. You've got to build strength. Make them do their talking and writing strongly while shouting. Make them do their voluntary stuttering so the whole world knows they are working on their speech. Insist that they enter the toughest speech situations that you can contrive, whether they succeed or fail. You've been too soft and sympathetic, too weak as a therapist. You've got to be strong and lead them out of their weakness. Every clinical experience should be aimed toward building strength and rejecting weakness.

At the present writing, 1956, we wince a little at the revelation of these words. Perhaps we were being affected by Adolf Hitler, who was regenerating a defeated, weakened German nation with heady doses of the same folly. But we followed out the spirit of this little document to the letter, using the same basic techniques of the preceding year but organizing the therapy with a precision which would have done justice to a Prussian drill sergeant. There was no self-therapy. All assignments were done in pairs with some other stutterer or student therapist as observer, checker, and reporter. Quotas of pages of talking-and-writing were demanded, with expulsion from the clinic threatened for failure to meet the daily quota. They did shout their talking and writing, which this year was done bilaterally, using a vertical board so as to produce mirror script with the nonpreferred hand while the preferred hand simultaneously guided the speaking mouth and wrote the symbol correctly. Strong sudden movements and much staccato shouting was employed. Ambivalence was penalized.

In the area of voluntary stuttering certain changes were also made. As a penalty for failing to use true voluntary stuttering successfully on a feared word, the stutterer was required immediately to stutter voluntarily on the next five words whether he feared them or not. This seemed to produce immediate increments in fluency and in case morale. Avoidance tricks often disappeared; the more bizarre contortions diminished, and the cases became more willing to work on their feared words. We can see now that this prevented the abnormality from serving as a release-reward and associated some form of stuttering with decreasing anxiety, among other factors, but to us it was viewed simply as a penalty for weakness, for surrender. In the later stages we decreased the number of subsequent words from five to one as vehicles for this penalty, and found that the single word seemed to have as much effectiveness as the magical five. In the course of therapy we experimented with other penalty retrials. There was one day, for example, when each stutterer was required to stutter voluntarily on the next 50 words as a penalty for failing to use the technique on one he feared. The difficulty with this was that we always ran into new feared words within the subsequent 50, so that finally all words spoken were stuttered upon voluntarily with more or less efficiency, usually less. At any rate we finally settled upon the single reiteration of the word upon which failure had occurred as the vehicle for the penalty stuttering, and it seemed to have the same effect. This was the forerunner of the cancellation technique of the present day.

The group sessions, we regret to say, became almost revival meetings, with much exhortation, strong suggestion, confession, resolutions, and fired-up team spirit. The leader was vividly present. He led his charges into battle. He stuttered with them in the drug stores, over the telephone, in the market place. He set them the example of stopping strangers to inquire concerning the location of a mythical store which carried the name of the stutterer's bugaboo, voluntarily stuttering, pseudo-stuttering to be sure, but done bravely, confidently, and with assurance. Urged to identify with the leader and under his demanding eye, the stutterers did undergo these experiences with a surprising amount of triumph. Probably the basic healing characteristic in this activity was the fact that the therapist identified with the case rather than the reverse, and that the stutterers did get some reward for touching the emotionally electrified grid of stuttering. At any rate, a large majority of the stutterers showed rapid gains and attained a high degree of nonstuttering fluency within two months. Unfortunately, during the Thanksgiving holidays they all relapsed completely when they were out of contact with their peerless leader, who was deer hunting. Renewed efforts for the three weeks prior to the Christmas holidays, coupled with a most ingenious reporting system of penny post cards with detailed questions to be filled out by the stutterer and mailed to the therapist at the end of each day, demonstrated that the same relapse, utter and complete, occurred again, and the rest of the semester year was spent in molting some of the fine feathers of authoritarian therapy and making the best of what remained to us. It was not a satisfactory year but an educational one, at least for the therapist.

Results

Of the eight adults who participated in the intensive program—two female, all college students—one was booted out for insubordination in the third week of therapy, another quit after Thanksgiving, and two others failed to return after the Christmas holidays. Of the remaining four cases, two were having only occasional blockings at the end of the second semester and those under great stress. These after five years were still in much the same condition and quite reconciled to stuttering as a minor nuisance which played no important part in their lives. The other two were individuals who seemed to oscillate, all through the second semester and thereafter, from periods of real fluency to periods of pronounced stuttering. It seemed as though the stuttering had to increase to a certain degree, whereupon they would confront it, do some talking-and-writing, enter some feared situations and do some voluntary stuttering, whereupon the speech would begin to improve gradually until the minor nuisance level was reached, whereupon the individual stopped working with his speech—and then a decline in fluency ensued. These two individuals often returned to us for help during their periods of marked nonfluency and anxiety, and some token help and reassurance often was sufficient to reverse the cycle.

We had two other adult cases this year with whom we worked differently. One of them we hypnotized, and experimented with a variety of therapeutic procedures: (1) posthypnotic suggestion not to stutter; (2) posthypnotic suggestion to remain relaxed during speaking; (3) massed practice in fluent speech during trance with suggestion that the case would remember the feel of fluency later; (4) training in voluntary stuttering during the trance. The first two techniques produced severe anxiety attacks after some initial fluency, and the stuttering seemed more compulsive thereafter. The third and fourth techniques did show marked effectiveness, but the subject became highly suggestible to all kinds of stimuli, and hence more vulnerable to phonetic, semantic, and environmental cues which have become associated with speech difficulty.

The other adult with whom we worked was also hypnotized, and the therapist and a psychiatrist colleague together in collaboration used the trance to explore the nature of the personal conflicts and early experiences with stuttering. Several traumatic episodes involving speech were acted out and the subject made aware of this repressed material by the psychiatrist's suggestion that he would reëxperience it as a dream to be told to the therapist. This case had been receiving psychotherapy from this psychiatrist for several years previously and had made a quite adequate personal adjustment but was still stuttering severely. At the end of the semester, no improvement was noted in his stuttering as the result of our joint efforts, and treatment was discontinued. Five years later he was much improved though still stuttering. This increment, however, we felt to be due to his marked success in marriage and business which occurred after we worked with him.

We worked intensively with two stuttering children, one, a 4-year-old boy, a so-called primary stutterer with many syllable repetitions per word and per 100 words under conditions which did not seem to be particularly stressful, and the other a very severe secondary stutterer with avoidance and frustration responses, marked tremors, anxiety, and mal-attitudes. With the first child we established a good play relationship in which only Indian talk (gestures and single-word sentences in a hollow voice) was used for all communication. He became quite fluent in these sessions and after initiating his father, brother, and mother into our tribe with much ceremony and teaching them Indian talk, his speech improved markedly at home. Five years later there was no trace of stuttering in his speech.

The other child we tried in vain to work with directly. He was highly suspicious of all father figures and hostile to substitute mothers, and much of our early therapy did little but compound the difficulty. However, one of our students, a man in his early twenties, befriended the boy, took him fishing, broke a few game laws, stole some melons, joined his Boy Scout troop and revitalized it, and, with our counseling, taught the boy to "slide" out of his blocks rather than fight them, to stutter slowly rather than swiftly, to stutter easily rather than with forceful struggle. Our own role was that of the suspicious authority figure, who could not believe that the student therapist was any good, or that the boy could ever overcome his stuttering. We showed glee when the boy stuttered in the old way; we showed disbelief when he demonstrated the easier way of stuttering. We attacked the boy's clinician in his presence, told him he could never help that child, told him he'd better get a different career. The boy worked like a trouper out of friendship for his clinician and because of his dislike for us. At any rate he improved remarkably and though we lost track of him three years later, his speech at that time was excellent, according to reports from teachers and the boy's associates. We were unable to hear him personally. This case was important to us primarily in that it demonstrated that some modification of the stuttering in the direction of normal utterance could be achieved without having to stick to the repetitive ritual of voluntary stuttering. A quotation from one of the protocols of that period might be of interest here: "J. has shown that you can't punish stuttering out of a person. The stutterer needs to learn to be kinder to himself, to stop punishing his mouth and soul. Why can't we tease it out of him, let it leak out, ooze out? Stutterers hurry to stutter. Why don't we teach them to do it in slow motion? There's too much recoil in voluntary stuttering. Why back up and try again and again and again? Why not move forward?"

1938–1939

The stuttering therapy of this year can best be presented by giving an actual case report, which seems fairly typical of those in the case folders of that period. This particular report is of a single day's activity by a college girl who had been enrolled in the speech clinic for three weeks.

I. Unilaterality:

A. I planned to do three five-minute periods of vertical board writing but I only did one. I hate this stuff. It drives me crazy and when I stutter with my hands as well as my mouth I sure don't like it. I know I should fight these feelings but I didn't today. I'll try it again.

B. I did thirteen pages of regular talking and writing, probably to make up for my failure. My hand got cramped and I had to quit or I'd be doing it yet. Hope it did me some good. Didn't stutter much, just once or twice. See encircled letters on the attached sheets.

II. Rhythm control:

A. I did much better on the rhythm machine today. I got scores of 68, 72, and, believe it or not, 91 on jaw bite, and 37, 32 and 44 on the tongue thrust. My jaws still ache.

B. I sent ten messages to Joyce by tongue clicks using the Morse code. I had to put down the dots and dashes on paper first. She got most of the messages o.k. This sure takes a lot of time though. And I can't send them too fast or my tongue gets tangled up. It's better though than it was.

C. Garth and I danced and kept talking all the time as fast as we could. Fell over each other's feet when we got blocked. But not too bad. I like this.

III. Eliminating avoidance:

A. I planned to call home long distance but I lost my nerve. I was afraid my mother would be disappointed or think I hadn't been working enough. I don't know if I'll ever be able to talk to her. If only my dad were home alone, I could call. But I failed on this assignment and feel ashamed and scared. How can I ever get better if I'm so weak.

B. I asked the Co-op clerk for some cards I had to have after I had first asked my roommate to get them for me. There's a star for me.

C. I kept practicing tongue twisters with those nasty *s* sounds I'm so scared of. My roommate says I'm getting her so she stutters on them. She's kidding.

D. I pre-wrote two phone calls, one to the Burdick where I asked for myself. Is Elaine registered there? I almost hung up before my name I was so petrified, and I stuttered so bad the clerk must have almost hung up after I started it. But I did it, word by word, just like I wrote it. No detours. And I felt good. The other phone call wasn't so good. I got a crabby old witch at the train station who kept yelping at me. I don't know what I said but it wasn't what I'd planned.

IV. Self-improvement:

A. Planned to study and concentrate without looking up while eating a sandwich at a busy drugstore counter. Performance: Did this but it was very hard and I looked up twice, thinking that everybody was looking at me. Nobody was. I kept at it for about ten minutes and actually did concentrate probably about four minutes of that time. How's that for a scatterbrained kid?

B. I to talked to M. about sex and boys and what they want. This is a real trophy for me. I have never talked about it to anyone. I didn't put this down as a planned assignment but I thought of it when we were working out our self therapy plans yesterday in group meeting and put it out of my mind. I found I could ask questions about it for the first time.

V. Eradicating shame:

A. Planned assignment: Read aloud in the hall outside the clinic while classes are passing. Performance: I did this to Fred Bilkey for five minutes at 3:00 P.M. I was embarrassed when some of them stopped and looked at me, and I giggled too much and clowned a little to hide how I felt at first. I did better later but I still felt ashamed. I should do this again. I'm like Peter who denied our Lord Jesus three times. I deny myself and that I am what I am, a stutterer, one thousand times but believe it or not, Doc, I do stutter.

B. Planned assignment: Two fifteen-minute periods of pseudo-stuttering on every word. Performance: I only did this for five minutes and, then I got bored with it. I don't think this does me any good. But I know I should have carried out my plan, only I shouldn't have planned so much of this stuff. Maybe I should do only one minute of it in front of a mirror. I don't mind stuttering when I have to, but when I don't have to it half kills me. I feel so repulsive.

C. Planned assignment: Talk to three people you don't have to. Performance: I talked to five of them, including one older lady. Older women are always hard for me to talk to, maybe because my mother is hard to talk to. I faked to her too until she got upset and then I did too but I felt especially good about doing it.

VI. Psychological barriers:

A. Resist three interruptions and do not hurry was my planned assignment. But no one would interrupt me, so I had to interrupt them. I did it to three other people and stole their conversation from them. But I tend to hurry. Must fight that.

B. I told one clerk she didn't have to feel sorry for me.

VII. Study of stutterings:

A. Planned assignment: Find what my eyes do when I stutter. I put up a mirror in front of me when I was phoning. I blink and kind of flutter, especially when my mouth is fluttering at the same time. Then I squeeze my eyes just before the word comes out. Kind of hard to be sure, but I think that's it.

B. I read the first chapter of Appelt's book. It made me scared. There have been so many ways to treat stuttering. How do I know this one here will work?

VIII. Speech controls:

A. Planned assignment: Make fifteen phone calls and mark with pencil how many of your blocks you can change from involuntary to voluntary ones. Performance: I changed this because it was too long and hard. Instead I made it fifteen minutes of phoning. I got four phone calls done in this time. I kept track in two columns, one for those I didn't or couldn't make voluntary and the other for those I could and did. In the failure column I had 14 and in the success column I had 9. And there were some stinkers on the phone too. I felt that I had done pretty good. My big problem is that in the middle of a stuttering I can't think or stop or anything. I just get scared out of my reasonable mind and do things that don't make sense. But on nine of them I did keep my wits.

IX. Thoughts to talk about in group meeting:

A. On being afraid to hope.

B. On my wishing I weren't a girl stutterer but liking to be a girl. I would rather be a boy stutterer than a girl stutterer if I had to.

C. On using tongue twisters in treating stuttering. They might be good.

D. On being angry with myself.

There were 11 stuttering adults in this year's program, 3 of whom were girls. All were college students except two men who were in their twenties. All were intelligent and all were very severe stutterers. The early group meetings were spent by the therapist largely in briefing, in clarifying the goals and methods. He personally took each of the cases individually into speaking situations and by demonstration and supervision showed each of them the type of performance which would be appropriate to each of the above nine areas of therapy. This basic training or briefing period lasted two weeks, whereupon the self-therapy structuring of therapy was instituted. No individual therapy with an individual clinician was done. Daily group sessions of two hours were used for purposes of reporting only the trophy experiences, i.e., those experiences which they had planned and carried out and of which they were proud. A written report of the type given above was turned in to the therapist who made written comments upon it and returned it to the stutterer. He often indicated which items should be reported to the group. In the first of the two group sessions the therapist played a subordinate role, confining his efforts to assisting the stutterers to make their experiences vivid to all participants. The stutterers were also to analyze verbally if they could why the trophy was a trophy. A good amount of self-analysis came out in these report sessions. Most of these report sessions were closed to student therapists or outsiders, and they often turned into periods of emotional release and insightful discussion.

The second of the daily group sessions was used for the construction of self-therapy assignments. The stutterers took each of the nine areas in turn and wrote out an assignment for themselves or for one another under that heading. These were then read orally to the group as a whole, and each stutterer could select from those provided by his fellows the one which seemed most to fit him. The therapist often verbally edited some of the assignments so that more reasonable quotas, energy and time expenditure, and ease in checking or reporting could be achieved. In cases where some of the stutterers refused or shirked the responsibility for making these self-therapy assignments, the group usually took care of the problem in its own self-interest. Several of the brighter and more highly motivated ones occasionally assumed the therapist's role. The individual stutterers were not as fluent or as much in control of their stuttering or avoidance behavior by Thanksgiving as those of the year before, but only one of them showed a marked regression after that holiday. The same situation occurred after the Christmas holidays. The therapist made no attempt to advise policies or practices over these holiday periods. Most of the stutterers however did some self-therapy during the vacation, though during the longer Christmas holiday the amount of self-therapy markedly decreased and became more of a token therapy. They were glad to return to the clinical routine and improved swiftly upon doing so.

Some explanation of the variations in treatment should be provided here. We added daily experiences in what became called "rhythmic improvement." This was done because we noted that even in the normal speech of severe stutterers the temporal pattern of syllables was broken. There were gaps, pauses, unusual prolongations of unstressed phonemes. The carrier waves of consecutive speech seemed different. Inflections were muted. And so, in the absence of definitive research, we again experimented with therapy. Stutterers listened to recordings of normal conversation until they knew the content well, then attempted to speak in unison with the speakers. They attempted to repeat such utterances in sequence with the recordings, trying to duplicate the temporal, pitch, and intensity patterns exactly. We had previously carried out a little pilot therapy along this line with two stutterers who used this as their only therapy for a period of two weeks and had made some striking gains in fluency. So we tried it on the whole group for an entire semester. As always, there were too many other factors present to enable us to assess the value of this specific type of therapy, but our clinical impressions were that, if used, it should be employed in terminal instead of intensive therapy.

Included in our rhythmic training was an apparatus we devised from an old phonograph, which carried discs with make-and-break contacts so that various temporal patterns of clicks could be produced and repeated at different speeds. This was connected with a clock counter and with a device which the stutterer held in or against his mouth so that he could jaw-bite or tongue-thrust. If his jaw-bite was made absolutely in unison with the clicks produced by the phonograph's contact discs, the counter was activated. If the stutterer's timing was off, the counter did not count. We thus had an apparatus which we could use to train the stutterer in rythmokinesis. The stutterers called this the rhythm machine and tried to improve their scores during a certain time limit and at a given speed. Some of them made gains which seemed to us almost incredible and these gains seemed to be reflected in improved fluency. Others, however, who made little gains in rhythm scores also improved in fluency. We used this for several years, but finally discarded it. There was magic in it and suggestion, and we wanted to minimize both.

Another of the techniques we used in rhythm therapy was the dance. A member of our faculty had been a professional dancer and had studied abroad with experimenters in free dance forms. She worked with our group of stutterers—and their therapist (who has sacrificed much for his profession)—to break down the inhibitions and enhance fluidity of movement. All of us stuttered with our feet, arms, and torsos in the early stages of this therapy but gradually improved. Your author's only real triumph came just once, when he came to the evening session with his ego slightly oiled and extemporized to candlelight (and wild applause) the Dance of the Wild Cucumber. We still feel that these techniques had real merit as speech therapy, but unfortunately, the necessity that the therapist identify with his cases in the dance, with or without veils, became too heavy a burden. We felt there must be easier ways of doing stuttering therapy. In later years we tried the dance technique again with two cases and the dance instructor as the therapist, requiring that the stutterers verbalize freely as they danced. This produced marked but temporary gains in fluency and freedom from fear. We have not made the verbal dance an integral part of our present therapy but invite our dignified colleagues to do so. It was good for the soul but bad for the bones.

Another of the basic areas of therapy dealt with the elimination of avoidance. We had previously been stressing that the stutterer should cease his avoiding and postponing of speech attempts on feared words. We had, heretofore, penalized this avoidance behavior. The emphasis during this year's therapy was more positive. The stutterer was urged to search for the speaking situations and words in which the urge to avoid, withdraw, or postpone could be found. These were identified before the group and then all of the stutterers sought them out, entered these situations, used the words deliberately in conversation repeatedly, compared notes, and by sharing the fears pretty well reduced them and the avoidance devices which maintained them. In one form or another, we have continued this practice to the present day.

The other main areas of therapeutic activity are fairly well illustrated by the sample case record given earlier. It will be noted that for the first time we attempted to have an activity therapy which attacked the problem from many angles, that the stutterer was given the basic responsibility for planning and carrying out his therapy, that the speech experiences provided an opportunity for group analysis and sharing, and that the therapist identified closely with the group without being its dominator.

Results

By the end of the first semester all but one of the individuals were speaking very fluently and with little fear. Occasional stutterings under pronounced stress still occurred in all but two, who were completely free. These were the individuals whose stuttering had been very overt and severe frustration strugglings but with little avoidance behavior. Indeed, the group was so successful that we disbanded at the end of the semester and had no terminal therapy. We had wished for some time to determine whether the terminal-therapy period was or was not essential. It was. Within two months, five of the stutterers came in and asked for a reconstitution of the group meetings, saying that they had missed them greatly and had felt the loss of group support very keenly. Three of these five were stuttering more frequently than at the end of therapy, but none of them had regressed to their old patterns of stuttering. One of them moved away and wrote only once, reporting that she was stuttering as badly as ever. We could never check her progress later. One other individual failed to report after the end of the second semester, joined the Canadian Air Force, and was killed. His speech had been excellent.

We were able to get the five-year reports from the other nine individuals. Two of these were then severe stutterers again; two others were worse than when they left the clinic but much improved over entrance; three claimed to be normal speakers with only a very rare avoidance or stuttering; two others were fluent except in occasional situations of stress, where they still used voluntary stuttering. We were able to interview four of these cases and found no discrepancy between their reports and their actual speech. One of the men became a salesman and was very successful. Apart from the sudden termination of therapy and the mistake of not providing for immediate terminal therapy, we felt that this year's work was pretty successful.

1939–1940

This year we used exactly the same plan of therapy as we had used for 1938, but we had different stutterers. Half of them (five) were handled as before with group sessions and self-assignments. The other half were given only individual therapy, their clinical hours being equal in number to those of the stutterers receiving group therapy. About half of the time was spent with the therapist and half with the stutterer's clinician. We tried to keep the emphases upon goals and techniques equal for all stutterers and tried to match them for severity of symptoms and amount of situation and word fears. Don't think we were successful, but we tried.

In terms of all the measuring times: pre-Thanksgiving, post-Thanksgiving, pre-Christmas and post-Christmas, and the end of the semester, the stutterers who received group therapy progressed much faster than those who received only individual therapy. They assumed more responsibility for planning and carrying out their assignments; they showed less resistance and sabotage; they avoided less and worked more; they showed markedly greater gains in social poise and adjustment. They became much more fluent both in their ordinary life situations and under stress. By the end of the first semester all but one of the cases receiving group therapy were beginning to think they were cured, always a sad moment for the discerning therapist who knows of the flight into health. The single exception had been pretty much of an isolate; he had made little progress after the first four weeks, and felt pretty bad about it but not bad enough to try very hard.

At the beginning of the second semester, as we had previously announced, we terminated all therapy except for monthly checkups. Some of the stutterers receiving group therapy did continue to eat together occasionally for a few weeks, but within a month this association too had disappeared. We were surprised to find that those receiving group therapy reacted much more poorly to the discontinuance than did those receiving individual therapy. The latter individuals showed only minor setbacks; three of the former group had real relapses, stuttering very severely for a week or two before they began to make some headway and regain a fluency level not as high as before but fairly adequate to their needs. Some of this might be attributed, we felt, to the better fluency which those receiving group therapy had attained. They may merely have had farther to fall. Nevertheless, it was our impression that certain values were inherent in the individual-therapy relationship which lent stability to the changes which did occur. We also were convinced that some kind of terminal therapy had to be devised for the second semester.

The results of our five-year checkup were as follows: We had returns or reëxaminations for four of the five receiving group therapy. Two of them had sustained their gains in fluency and were at about the level of their dismissal in June. One was much improved over entrance but was avoiding, and some of his voluntary stuttering had become habitual, although his previous "spasm pattern," as we called it then, was that of strong silent fixations of tongue, jaws, and lips accompanied by fast tremors. He felt that he had improved a lot but needed more. The fourth stutterer was stuttering as badly as he had upon entrance and was pretty bitter over our failure to help him.

Of the five stutterers who had received only individual therapy, we were able to contact three. These had shown no gain or decline from their level at dismissal. They were much improved over entrance but still mildly handicapped in stress communication. One of them reported that the other two missing stutterers had corresponded with him within this five-year interval and had experienced complete relapse.

1940

The therapy for the adult stutterers this year was organized much as in the group therapy for 1939, with the same nine divisions of activities being used—namely, unilaterality training, rhythm practice, eliminating avoidance, self-improvement, decreasing shame and embarrassment, erecting psychological barriers, the study of the disorder and its symptoms, and self-understanding. Daily activities and experiences in each of these comprised the therapeutic regime. The major variation instituted was the early cessation of formal assignments. Instead, the stutterer was given a daily report blank on which he was to record and report his achievements in each of these areas. These report blanks were turned in to the therapist by eleven o'clock of the morning of the therapy days, which were reduced to three—Monday, Wednesday, and Friday. This provided time for the report blanks to be scrutinized for use in the group meetings, which lasted for two hours. Individual conferences with the therapist were scheduled so that each stutterer had two hours weekly for discussion of his individual progress and problems. In these conference periods, the therapist conducted a relatively nondirective interview, but he also used the period to provide a realistic evaluation of the stutterer's performance in terms of the nine items on the report blank. In other words, he was listening not only to the content and attitudes being expressed but to the manner in which the stutterer was working on his speech problem. Each session ended with an objective summary of the latter.

The group meetings differed from those of the preceding year in that they were not group-centered but therapist-centered. The therapist dominated the proceedings, analyzing the performances of individual stutterers, clarifying the methods and goals of therapy, suggesting experiences, exposing resistances and sabotage, directing, advising, exhorting, and demanding a fair day's work of each stutterer. At the same time he closely identified with his cases and gave sufficient evidence of understanding their difficulties and accepting their frailty so that rapport was excellent—or so he thought at the time.

We have said that in the early weeks of therapy, definite assignments were given in each of the nine divisions. These were constructed by the therapist and their performance was supervised and evaluated by student clinicians who reported orally to the group as a whole. These early group meetings with the stutterers and their student clinicians, and the evaluation of therapeutic activity, generated plenty of emotional fireworks, which the therapist attempted to accept and interpret so as to define the nature of the disorder and its therapy. Much of the stutterers' hostility was aimed at the student clinicians, who required almost as much counseling as the stutterers themselves. Nevertheless, within four weeks of these daily assignments and group meetings, the stutterers seemed ready to enter the second phase described above wherein no assignments were given but triweekly reports of their therapy activities were returned and evaluated in both group and individual sessions with the therapist. In this second phase, the student clinicians became merely companions who shared an hour a day with their cases. The students could be exploited by the latter in any way they desired save that of the libido. They reported to the therapist only when the stutterer asked them to do so. This sudden shift in status helped to overcome the very strong initial resistance to do any self-therapy, a resistance which appeared at the beginning of phase 2.

Results

Two female and six male stutterers of college age made up the experimental group. All were very severe stutterers, two of them so nonfluent that no avoidance mechanisms or symptoms were apparent. They would proceed immediately into a severe tremor and struggle violently until utterance was achieved, then plunge inevitably into another. All but one had little social life. It is impossible in this paper to describe each stutterer's individual problems but none were psychotic or homosexual. All had anxieties centered chiefly about communication and audience penalty.

By Thanksgiving only two of the group had attained the degree of fluency achieved by the majority of the cases of the year before, but all of them except one were reporting and doing a fairly creditable job of consistent work on their speech, and their speech had improved both in terms of decreased severity, decreased avoidance, and improved intelligibility. Their attitudes toward their stuttering were excellent. They were not willing to stutter but they were willing most of the time to work on it. They stuttered about as much in the clinic as they did in outside situations, which contrasted with the performance of previous groups of stutterers in this regard. During the Thanksgiving holidays they were asked to continue to use their report blanks as before. Upon their return, all save one (one of those who had achieved the greatest fluency) reported improved fluency and they maintained it. They declared that their parents and associates seemed to accept and be interested in their therapy and that they felt less anxiety in their homes than ever before, an experience which surprised them. The one stutterer who had slumped rapidly regained his fluency.

By Christmas two of the stutterers who had achieved the best fluency earlier than the rest were doing very little in self-therapy despite our urgings, admonitions, and suggestions. They felt quite adequate and were sure they needed no more drudgery. Both of these relapsed markedly toward the end of the Christmas holidays though they had perfect fluency at the beginning. They subsequently worked hard and were fairly fluent by February but had to work to be so. The two most severe stutterers continued to progress both prior to and through the vacation period, working steadily, and by the end of the semester had as good speech as any of the others. One of the stutterers failed to return from his vacation and wrote a friend that he had relapsed badly and had given up. We were unable to contact him thereafter. The other three stutterers slipped a little over the Christmas holidays and attributed this to their failure to do sufficient self-therapy. None of these three were able to stutter voluntarily on their feared words during severe stress, either before the vacation or after it, nor had they achieved this ability by the end of the semester. However, their speech was remarkably improved in classwork and social situations, and little avoidance or anxiety was evident in ordinary speaking situations. The group as a whole, perhaps because of the individuals who composed it, or because of the difference in therapeutic regime, did not seem to progress as rapidly or as far as had the group of the preceding year.

One never knows in this type of experimentation what produces what results—there are just too many variables in the equation. Nevertheless, we felt the need to explore a variety of methods and therapeutic regimes in the hope that some happy combination might enable us to hit the target with better consistency than we or others had been able to do. Besides, there is a certain validity to the clinical impression of therapeutic progress which is difficult to define or measure and yet which helps us to know which of two techniques works better. We do not belabor the point or the illusion, whichever you prefer. What has kept us going is the feeling that someone should blaze a trail even if it ends back in the swamp. It is almost as important to know where one shouldn't go, if one is lost, as it is to know the right direction. At any rate, this group did not seem to do as well as the previous group by the February inventory date.

To improve matters, we sought a better terminal therapy. There was no sudden discontinuance of all therapy, though group therapy no longer took place the second semester. Instead, each of the stutterers continued to receive an individual counseling-therapy session with the therapist twice each week for the first two months of the second semester, once a week during the third month, and thereafter as requested by the case. Thus a gradual tapering-off process occurred. No individual report blanks were used, but the sessions still consisted of interviewing and evaluation of the speech during the interview. Of the seven stutterers all showed improvement during this terminal therapy, though several had short periods of poor speech. By June all of them were fluent in ordinary situations but all had occasional nonfluencies consisting of such symptoms as swift and irregular syllable repetitions, tiny tremors, and mouth posturings. These were usually disregarded both by the stutterer and his listener, and they occurred infrequently and usually in nonstress situations. Occasionally some avoidance (such as a postponement) took place under stress. One of the stutterers was very fluent and had no speech fears. Owing to the war and other factors, we were able to get a five-year report on only three of these seven individuals. Two of them reported that they were as fluent as when they left the clinic. The third, whom we examined, was worse than when he left but about as good as he was at the end of the intensive therapy and much better than at its beginning. We did get the opportunity to evaluate the other four cases after an interval of one year. One had relapsed badly to his pretherapy state; two were quite satisfied with their speech but had occasional severe stuttering in situations of great stress. The fourth individual had many nonfluencies in his speech but no contortions or avoidances and felt little concern about his ability to communicate.

During this year, *with other stutterers,* we experimented with several types of relaxation, notably those described by Dr. Edmund Jacobson, Mabel Gifford, and a Hindu Yoga variety which consisted of prolonging the exhalation slightly, rolling the eyeballs upward, and contemplating life as a whole. We were able to produce temporary fluency by these means, especially when strong suggestion that speech could be fluent was also employed, but this fluency broke down under stress so easily that we were not impressed. To ask a stutterer to relax when he experiences fears of words or audience penalty is to deny the validity of fright.

1941–1942

At the beginning of this year we decided to make every fifth year a summary year in which we would do no new experimentation but instead would employ all of the practices which we felt had proved to have real promise. We therefore offer here only an outline of the therapy in terms of practices which have already been explained. The basic method consisted of fulfilling speech assignments formulated by the therapist and his clinician and carried out by the case under their supervision or in self-therapy with written and oral reports. Group, individual, and self-therapy was offered. The penalty for consistent refusal to do these assignments was leaving the clinic, first for a week, and then if the stutterer continued to fail to do his work, expulsion from all clinic services.

In this regard it should probably have been stated earlier that in this clinic no fees have ever been charged for any diagnostic or clinical services, and any stutterer was always free to leave without obligation. We do not feel that this situation is one entirely favorable to therapy. People work harder for things they must pay for, and the guilt from failing to do what was expected was perhaps harder to handle when the case gave nothing in return for the therapist's time, efforts, and devotion to his welfare. The advantage of the free service was that it enabled us to get the severe stutterers we needed as cases and it provided some food for the therapist's ego strength, which frequently needed it. Anyone who specializes in the treatment of chronic stutterers will understand the latter statement.

In brief, then, therapy followed this sequence and employed these practices: The daily group sessions were used by the therapist for providing information, demonstrating techniques, or clarifying goals and also for creating a sense of group belongingness in which stuttering could be accepted as a mutual problem to be solved. The sessions were also used for airing emotional feelings such as anxiety, hostility, and aggression toward themselves, each other, and the therapist or clinicians. In the daily individual-therapy sessions, the stutterers with the therapist or his student clinicians either went out into the city or the college and fulfilled assignments, or they held individual conferences in which their problems in revising themselves or their behavior were discussed in terms of an historical perspective, present conditions, or future goals. The stutterers were encouraged also to formulate and report self-assignments with respect to these goals.

The goals themselves were these: to reduce avoidance of anxiety-laden words and situations; to substitute a highly controlled voluntary behavior in place of the "involuntary" and uncontrolled stuttering behavior; to relieve frustration; to reduce any dysphemia which might be present; to build ego strength in every way and to help the stutterer function as a social being. The basic techniques used this year have already been described. The terminal therapy resembled that of the preceding year.

This was our test year, and as we look back upon it we feel that we gave it all we could. The results were not too encouraging when we checked up five years later. We were able to interview all of these individuals at that time. Only four of the ten stutterers (seven male and three female) were able to satisfy our criteria: (1) normal fluency; (2) nonavoidance; (3) no apparent struggle; (4) adequate socialization. We were satisfied with the progress of these four individuals.

Of the remaining six, two were stuttering as severely as they had done at the beginning of therapy and in our opinion were actually in worse shape for having undergone so intensive a program of therapy. Their sense of failure was profound. The other four cases were markedly improved over clinic entrance: two had excellent fluency except in traumatic stress situations but still avoided occasionally, and a few had strong situation fears with some avoidance; the other two were stuttering quite frequently and avoiding occasionally, but the severity of their stuttering was much reduced. All of these six stutterers except one who had made little progress throughout the year were worse than they had been when they left the clinic, but much better than when they entered it.

In scrutinizing the progress made by these cases in terms of their progress during therapy we were unable to discern many significant predictive factors. The four stutterers who successfully mastered their problem were individuals who had worked harder than the others, who had made fairly slow gains at first, and who, after strong initial resistance, had established a pretty close working relationship with the therapist. None of these had shown the early and sudden and temporary remission of all stuttering which we have termed false fluency, though some of the other six had done so. One of our successful cases we had deliberately kicked out of the clinic during terminal therapy because we felt that he was strong enough to go it alone and was unhealthily exploiting his relationship with the therapist. Besides the false fluency, the only other item which appeared to have significance in "predicting" therapy failure was the degree of regression during Thanksgiving and Christmas vacations. Most of the cases regressed somewhat, but those that were most unsuccessful regressed most during these periods.

In this connection, it might be interesting to review the impressions of the therapist during therapy in terms of the final results of this therapy. When each case was dismissed, the therapist wrote up a prediction of his eventual success with reasons for that prediction, sealed it in an envelope, and did not open it until after the five-year checkup. We found that we had been unduly optimistic (which is probably a good thing in a therapist) in that we had predicted final success for seven of the ten cases, improvement for two, and failure for one. We were correct for this latter case, and for three of the four who were finally successful. Indeed, at the conclusion of this therapy year, we felt that we were pretty good. Nevertheless, we knew that our methods were very crude, inefficient, and infinitely laborious. We doubted that many therapists would be able to have the time or drive necessary to duplicate our practices, and believed that the solution of the problem of stuttering was still incredibly remote. We determined therefore to revise and explore and experiment throughout the next five years.

1942–1943

The therapy program for the first semester of this year for four of the eight stutterers followed much the same pattern as that of the preceding year, with several major additions and one substraction. The other four cases we treated in the old way. With the first group, we instituted a strong program of prewriting the utterances in which stuttering was expected. We also required many experiences in pseudo-stuttering—in faking not only the characteristic stuttering patterns but other types of stuttering, varieties which would be more tolerable to the listener. We stressed the analysis of stuttering behavior in terms of avoidance and release reactions. We also emphasized the necessity for altering the characteristic patterns of stuttering abnormality. Each of these techniques we had used experimentally and for short periods of time with certain stutterers in preceding years and with some apparent success, but this year was the first in which we employed them consistently throughout the intensive therapy. The major item eliminated was voluntary stuttering as a basic technique for speaking feared words. An account of these changes with our reasons for instituting them might be of some interest.

Prewriting, in our preliminary experiments with it, had seemed to produce not only a marked reduction in the frequency and severity of stuttering but powerful resistances which led eventually to a much clearer understanding of the self. The stutterers hated it, not only at first but continuously. Indeed, the task was onerous. They found it highly frustrating to have to write out on a tablet or card every word of the utterance to be spoken and to underline all words which were feared and, after the utterance had been spoken, to encircle or by various symbols to indicate the type of stuttering response which had taken place. Some cases raged; others quietly sabotaged; all protested the inconvenience and silliness of the technique in a social situation outside the speech clinic. Hostility toward the therapist and his clinicians often became intense, and required much in terms of permissive acceptance and understanding. Nevertheless, as a basic part of each day's therapy which the stutterer was required to accomplish or leave the program, enough was done, despite the sabotage and resistance, to produce some effects which we felt were excellent. First of all, it seemed to straighten out the stutterer's confused thinking. Most adult stutterers have ducked and dodged and tentatively tasted so many feared words that they find it difficult to express themselves directly in a straightforward fashion. Their utterance twists and turns and reverses its course so often as they run the verbal gantlet that the verbalization of thought becomes impaired. The larger configurations become broken; phrasing is erratic; the continuity is full of nonsequiturs and unmeaningful pauses. Prewriting seemed to counteract this.

It had other values as well. It shifted the focus of anxiety from listener reactions to the word itself. This might seem to appear unfortunate, but we have not found it so. Stuttering abnormality, the essential carrier of the unpleasantness, after all seems to find its lowest common denominator in the utterance of the sound, syllable, or word. That is where much of the battle must be fought, or so we thought in 1942. It seemed difficult to combat or do much about the vague situation fears which had their roots in past experiences. We could do little with them except through verbalized remembering, a procedure we had used routinely and without much evident effect. The funnel might be full of personal and social anxiety but it all had to come down the spout of the uttered word. At any rate, we found that prewriting did focus much of the anxiety on the utterance of the underlined word itself. All the feelings of helplessness, of surrender to forces more powerful than any the case could summon to combat them, came to the fore, and with a supportive and interested therapist sharing the battlefield, the stutterer, much to his surprise, began to find that he could modify the resulting stuttering behavior.

It was probably at this point that we came again to realize that the solution to the problem of stuttering was not going to be a simple one, that in the utterance of a feared word the stutterer was faced by the necessity of mastering himself, of accepting the responsibility for his own behavior, or of yielding and surrendering to a growing neurosis. We all must fight these battles many times and in many places. The stutterer, by symbolizing all his troubles in his stuttering, chooses as his battlefield the utterance of a word. With a therapist by his side he need not fight blindly or alone. Like England, he may lose a hundred battles and still win the war. But he must not flee the field or surrender abjectly. So we thought in 1942, and, with some slight modification, so do we still.

Prewriting had another value. It seemed to be much better than any facile and superficial attitude of appearing "willing to stutter" which was essentially false or psychotic in a culture such as ours. We had taught stutterers previously to assume such attitudes, to say with Popeye, "I yam what I yam, a stutterer I." We had taught them to mention it casually, gaily, tossing in a stuttering joke or two to show the listener that they didn't really mind it. Many of them used this "objective attitude" as a trick to delude themselves and their auditors into thinking that the assumed attitudes were not phony but real, and by thus gaining a temporary mastery over the situation, they could obtain some temporary fluency. But we have never known a stutterer to be really willing to stutter in a situation where that stuttering was penalized by society, or for that matter in an utterance which became distorted and frustrated by the abnormal speech behavior itself. The need for communicative closure alone makes the stuttering unpleasant even when the listener is most permissive and free from rejection. When our cases brought out their cards, wrote what they were about to say, and then said it, all the world knew that they were individuals trying to master their speech problem. The desired goal so far as attitude was concerned thus became a willingness to work, to battle, rather than to stutter. And this seemed to produce highly beneficial results. Often, in spite of themselves, they would make such comments as, "Well, I had trouble on that word. I've got to encircle that one." And their auditors would immediately become interested and sympathetic and show a surprising respect.

Prewriting also gave the stutterer much needed training in frustration tolerance. Most stutterers react violently to communicative frustration. Even a small repetition sets off massive struggle responses. Interruption by a listener finds them very vulnerable. They plunge from stuttering to stuttering almost blindly, fearful of silence almost as much as of stuttering. Under a mandatory program of prewriting, which certainly was communicatively frustrating, they gradually became resigned to this frustration, and the adaptation seemed to generalize to the stuttering behavior itself.

The program of prewriting was introduced gradually into the assignments; it was first used with the clinician or therapist, then to friends, and finally to strangers in the city. Quotas were increased in terms of minutes, then half-hours and hours, until finally one day a week was set aside as one in which all communication had to be prewritten. We doubt whether any of the stutterers actually fulfilled all of this assigned prewriting, but they did a great deal of it, and it provided the vehicle for much of the other therapy.

This year we also concentrated on pseudo-stuttering, or, as the stutterers called it, "faking." It was used throughout the therapy, both intensive and terminal, in the prewritten utterance and also in the spontaneous speech. We had used pseudo-stuttering for years, in the form of voluntary stuttering, as a replacement for real stuttering. This year we began to use it primarily on nonfeared words. Our purpose was to desensitize rather than to substitute. We had long been impressed by the stutterer's terror of touching the hot stove of stuttering, his need to flee, to avoid, to escape frantically from its unpleasant scorch. Voluntary stuttering we had used primarily as a substitute for the "real" stuttering, using it to battle for control of the self. Pseudo-stuttering or faking we employed as a means of toughening, of fighting the frantic fear of the uncontrollable, of remaining in contact with the unpleasantness. It was used in many ways but always on *nonfeared* words. Our cases used it early in a communicative situation to reduce the situational anxiety which comes from anticipation of the surprise or shock with which a listener responds when the first stuttering shatters the picture of a normal person talking. They thus deliberately created the condition and beat the auditor to the punch. Many of them became very clever at softening a situation by pseudo-stuttering and felt a degree of superiority over the unsuspecting listener by employing the technique to determine his reaction. They would often fake and then mention casually that they stuttered and were working on their speech in the speech clinic, and thus obtained a measure of fluency which would not otherwise have occurred. We did not feel that the exploitation of pseudo-stuttering in this way was entirely wise, since it smacked of trickery and phoniness and enabled the stutterer to escape from battles with the self which had to be fought. Only one of the stutterers used it consistently in this way, however, so we kept it as part of our therapy.

When the stutterers used pseudo-stuttering in the above-mentioned fashion, we observed that seldom did they employ the behavior which typically characterized their ordinary stuttering. What they used was truly pseudo. Therefore we insisted that they employ a form of behavior which closely duplicated their real blockings when they faked. This brought the inevitable resistance, a signal which we had come to recognize as meaning that the basic disorder was being truly affected. In order to create a reasonable facsimile of their real stuttering, they had to study it. They had to hold it in immediate memory in order to reproduce it. Thus they had to come into direct contact with the behavior from which they fled and detached themselves. In order to use it at all, they had to rehearse it and plan it in advance of the utterance. We felt that this analytical contact with the "monster of the mouth," as one stutterer called it, was essentially healthy. After the initial struggle to escape the confrontation of this part of the self, avoidance behavior markedly decreased, and so also did the word fears. The sense of responsibility for one's own behavior grew. The real stuttering seemed to become less uncontrollable. Pseudo-stuttering seemed to have true effectiveness as a desensitizer when used in this way.

We found in it also another unexpected dividend. Although the stutterers were expected to use pseudo-stuttering only on nonfeared words and attempted to do so, it soon became apparent that many of these pseudo-stutterings turned into real ones. We observed the development of this phenomenon. The duplication of certain key features of the stuttering seemed themselves to precipitate tremors which were far faster than those which could be duplicated voluntarily. At times a certain tensed lip posture itself might seem to set them off uncontrollably. Most therapists who have employed pseudo-stuttering of any kind will recognize how quickly faked stutterings can become "real" stutterings when the pseudo form closely resembles the latter. This tendency probably influenced the shape and form of the so-called voluntary stuttering, or bounce, which often had little resemblance to the stutterer's characteristic behavior. Many therapists have felt therefore that close duplication of the characteristic stuttering behavior in the technique of pseudo-stuttering was unwise. And so did we at first. But soon we came to realize that here was another battleground where the individual could fight for mastery of the self, could learn to accept the responsibility for his own behavior. Accordingly, we had our cases record their successes and failures in keeping their faked blockings from becoming real and used these experiences to study the situational stresses and emotional states which seemed to coincide with the failures. Often some of the first progress shown by a given case seemed to date from his ability to keep his pseudo-stuttering in stress situations entirely voluntary.

We experimented in many ways with faking, varying the frequency with which it was used as well as the form. For example, one of our cases used four thousand faked blocks in one day and it almost killed him. One day, usually Saturday, was set aside for the weekly "bath of stuttering" with a quota of fakes which the stutterer had to achieve before going to bed. In the wee hours of the morning, searching for listeners in all-night restaurants and filling stations, the stutterer for the first time found himself wanting to talk and the devil take any audience penalty. We concluded that mass faking was generally unwise, that a few experiences, if vivid and if studied, were much more effective than merely a large number. Pseudo-stuttering we felt had real possibilities when used as a learning situation.

We also experimented with the form of the faked stuttering. In our efforts to get the stutterer to come closer to a true duplication of the real stuttering behavior, we noticed that both he and his listener seemed to have strong preferences for certain forms of faked stuttering rather than others. A pattern in which the phonemic sequence was unaltered, even if dragged out, seemed much more tolerable than one in which repetition occurred. A pattern in which movements were regular, relaxed, and slow seemed much more acceptable to an audience than one which was irregular, forced, or hurried. Out of these experiences in varying forms of their faked blocks, two of the stutterers, to our surprise, began to use a sort of smooth slow-motion word utterance as a replacement for their usual stuttering when attacking feared words. By employing this instead of their old struggling avoidant behavior, they found a remarkable gain in fluency, frustration release, and listener acceptance. We were frankly concerned when this occurred, feeling that this might be another of the innumerable ways in which stutterers avoided the issue of their fears. When we voiced these suspicions one of the stutterers said, "I thought that the evil of avoidance lay in its dodging of fear. But I'm not running away or postponing an attempt on a feared word when I stutter in slow-motion. On the contrary, I'm hunting for situations and words that scare me so I can tackle them differently. Is this bad? It doesn't feel that way to me. It just feels like I'm stuttering sensibly rather than going haywire like I used to. Why is it a sin to refuse to let your mouth jump around in the old way, to let it go crazy, when I can make it do my bidding? Look at all the different kinds of stutterings people have. Why can't I have this kind instead of my old kind? Where's the virtue in the old stuff? I'm not avoiding anything except reacting in a crazy way." We had no ready answer.

We have previously said that this year marked our discontinuance of the use of voluntary stuttering as the basic technique for uttering feared words. We gave it up for several reasons. It tended to become, in too many stutterers, not a real attempt at maintaining true voluntary control but an automatic repetitive postponement mechanism. Despite our efforts to the contrary, the stutterer tended to fall into the practice of saying his feared words with a number of automatic syllable repetitions varying with the word fear. Thus if he expected a long blocking he would say, "muh, muh, muh, muh, muh, muh, muh, muh, moon," whereas if only a little unpleasantness were expected he would say, "muh, muh, moon." He also tended to fall into the habit of using a schwa vowel instead of attempting to make the proper phonetic transition in a forward-moving way. Voluntary stuttering tended to become involuntary, and since its duration varied with the fear, we had here no real hope of reducing the stutterer's essential communicative abnormality or his surrender to anxiety. When used well it was excellent, but it was too often merely another postponement or audience-manipulation trick. Moreover, the final syllable of the series often was the only point at which the battle for mastery occurred. Used in this way the stutterer might as well have said, "a . . . a . . . a . . . a . . . a . . . er . . . moon" or "tra-la-la-moon." What we needed was a technique which would more closely approximate normal utterance.

We therefore experimented again with the types of replacement stuttering we called smooth prolongation and the stop-go, neither of which were entirely satisfactory. The smooth prolongation often turned also into a postponement mechanism in which the first phoneme was held until the anxiety reduction had occurred, and only then was the actual speech attempt initiated. Thus we had merely a continuant rather than a repetitive postponement trick. The stop-go resulted in too many split words. After several weeks of consecutive training in each of these methods for handling feared words, we then turned to a new technique we called "varying" or "dropping." The stutterer was to proceed to stutter on his feared words in his old way but to vary the characteristic pattern by alteration, addition, or subtraction. For example, one of our cases who characteristically stuttered by lifting his head jerkily was trained to do just the opposite, to lower it jerkily. This we would have termed alteration or varying. By subtraction, we mean that the stutterer was to attempt to stutter without one of the dominant features which characterized his usual stuttering behavior. A rather amusing instance of this might be cited. One of the cases attempted all of his feared words by a rhythmic and spasmodic opening of his rounded lips, the duration of which varied with his word fear. We therefore, in addition to much mirror confrontation, had him spend 15 minutes each day watching the goldfish in the aquarium in a Woolworth store down town. If you have observed the mouth movements of goldfish, you will understand why we made such an assignment. By the end of the week, this stutterer had eliminated completely his rhythmic mouth openings. There was plenty of stuttering left (though no new symptoms developed, interestingly enough) but he just couldn't bear the vision of a hundred goldfish joining him in his moment of stuttering. This is what we termed subtraction or "dropping." We also encouraged the addition and incorporation of other grotesqueries (though these had to be constantly varied) within the stuttering behavior. At times the stutterer was trained to use his characteristic sequence of abnormality but to emphasize and exaggerate any one of the more prominent features within it. Thus we attacked the stereotypy of the stuttering response to phonetic fears, feeling that much of the compulsive strength of a response lay in its patterned consistency. We found that these techniques were highly effective in reducing both the severity and frequency of stuttering and in changing the stutterer's helpless passive attitudes toward his problem.

With this group of four stutterers we played down the group work and interaction, though we met together daily for an hour. Each individual had a daily conference with the therapist and another with a student clinician. No self-therapy was required or encouraged, though many of the stutterers of course did some. No exploration of the past history of conflicts was stressed, but the actual behavior of the case as he worked on his speech was used to help him understand himself. Tasks were set by the therapist and the clinicians to create resistances and conflicts productive of insights, and through discussion and interpretation (probably far too much of the latter) the psychotherapy was carried out. No distinctive terminal therapy was employed, the intensive program running throughout the year. Though a gradual decrease in the number of sessions took place, three of the cases dropped from therapy of their own volition before spring.

Initial progress, probably because of our ineptness and unfamiliarity with the dynamics underlying these new techniques, was slow. By Thanksgiving, only one stutterer had shown any ability to cope with his fears or stutterings or had experienced any marked reduction in frequency, though all had shown some lessening in severity. It was interesting to note that all four actually improved over the Thanksgiving holidays. By Christmas we were able to note marked improvement in all four in all respects, an improvement which continued in two of the cases during the vacation. The other two showed some decline in the ability to work with their stuttering and were avoiding more than they had earlier.

By the end of the first semester all four were very fluent in the ordinary communicative situations, though they still had some unmanaged stutterings and a little avoidance under real stress. By June or at the time of their voluntary withdrawal from our clinic all four had shown even greater improvement and considered their speech adequate to all current demands, though all of them had fears of future relapse. We were able to check up personally on all four at Christmas of the following year; three had maintained their gains while one had declined to his level of February but felt that an equilibrium had been reached with oscillations in frequency and severity about a pretty high level of fluency and self-confidence. We were able to get five-year checkups on only two of these, owing to the war, and both were operating fluently. One of these said he no longer considered himself a stutterer. The other said he stuttered mildly and only rarely but never had to use any of the techniques he had learned in the clinic. He had a few situation fears but no evident avoidance tricks. He stuttered most when off guard, tired, or excited. We felt he was fluent enough. Our general impression at the conclusion of the year's therapy program was that we had advanced.

Part of this feeling came from a comparison with the progress made by our other group of four stutterers who we had felt would be easier cases to treat, and with whom we used the type of therapy employed in previous years. These made swifter initial progress but suffered relapse more often and seemed more dependent on us. Our follow-up on these cases showed that the following Christmas two of them were speaking pretty well, though not as well as those of the other group, one was stuttering pretty badly except in the easiest situations with permissive and familiar listeners, and the other was stuttering and avoiding as much as he had prior to receiving therapy. We were able to follow our two relatively successful cases over a longer period of time. One was killed in the war two years later but a fellow soldier and friend reported that his speech was excellent during basic military training. The other was speaking better after five years than he was when he left the clinic. He had married and had success in business.

In fact, he was a court reporter, with the necessity for reading back transcripts in situations involving real communicative stress.

The reader must realize that we do not or did not feel that anything had been proved by the differential treatment of the two groups. We were merely trying to explore some new possibilities and to compare them against the old, with fallible clinical impression as the only measure. We doubtless worked better and more enthusiastically with the first group we have described than with the second, perhaps because of the newness of our techniques. Besides, we also strayed from our duplication of past therapy even with the stutterers in the old-therapy group. We could not resist the impulse to use them as pilot subjects for other techniques and did so. Some of these should be mentioned.

Impressed with the peculiar balancing of forces toward and against utterance which manifested itself in the stuttering, we sought some experimental ways of altering it. And so we enlisted a friendly physician who provided some helium so that two of our most severe stutterers with tight lip or tongue closures of the airways could inhale it and try to talk. The result was both astonishing and amusing. Normally, these stutterers would squeeze their lips just tight enough to block the airflow created by strong abdominal contractions, contractions which convinced the stutterer he was truly trying to speak. But he actually was tightly holding the cork in the plastic speech bottle as he was wretchedly squeezing it. At any rate, when these stutterers inhaled the helium mixture the whole delicate balance was upset. Not only did the pitch and intensity of the voice change, but the stuttering did also. The stutterers' mouths popped open; they leaked; the lips bounced and trembled crazily; and often the word emerged before the stutterer could reorganize his coördinations sufficiently to learn to stutter again. Both of them were manifestly surprised and upset and bewildered. We never found a way to use this in therapy, but it convinced us that much of stuttering is alterable.

One of the stutterers required extensive dental work and with the coöperation of the dentist we studied the effect upon stuttering of anesthetizing the lips and tongue. It became evident in this one case at least that there were focal areas of tension which were required to trigger off tremors, and that the stutterer would often alter his characteristic patterns because of the localized lack of sensation. Thus, expecting difficulty in the utterance of the word "banana," on which his lip protrusion and tremors were usually very marked, when the lips were anesthetized he would first of all have less severe stuttering than he expected. After a few experiences with this surprise, however, he would stutter about as severely as he expected but with the tremors and fixations located in the larynx instead of the lips. There was other "experimentation" or rather exploration too which might be mentioned here, but we were primarily engaged in the quest for a better therapy and new questions rather than answers.

This year, impressed by Carl Rogers' book, *Counseling and Psychotherapy,* we also worked with three other stutterers entirely through nondirective counseling. Two were very severe cases, one was very mild but with pronounced anxiety and many avoidances. We wrote up the results of each conference (once each week for a semester) and recorded occasional sessions for study. Over and over again we found ourselves falling into mistakes, failing to sense the feelings of our clients, interpreting rather than reflecting, reassuring, giving advice. We found silence threatening us too often. We clarified half-expressed feelings prematurely. But we improved, and fortunately we took these cases sequentially, so that by the time we accepted the third client (the mild stutterer) we had attained a certain proficiency. All of these individuals were convinced that their stuttering was entirely a psychological problem and that a mild neurosis was involved.

We did not do much for the first two cases, probably because of our ineptitude and also because the stuttering itself interfered so greatly with the actual process of communication. Even in a pretty warm, permissive, and understanding climate the frustration of constant stuttering creates an almost insurmountable obstacle to free expression. We unearthed a lot of highly potent memory, and the cases felt much better, but no real reduction in the amount or severity of stuttering occurred in their daily living. The third stutterer, the mild one with many anxieties, made marked progress both in self-understanding, in anxiety reduction, and in his speech. He became almost entirely fluent for eight months, then relapsed badly and is now stuttering worse than he did before coming to us. An unfortunate love affair may have been partly responsible.

Nevertheless, we have continued to use client-centered counseling on selected cases ever since. Sometimes we have used it prior to the intensive speech-therapy program, sometimes as part of the terminal therapy. We feel that the latter is generally the wiser course but find it difficult to generalize. We are sure from other experiences that counseling during the intensive therapy is unwise. The counseling and speech therapy seem to interfere with each other.

1943–1944

This year we decided to give up all formal assignments. The therapist and his clinicians consistently refused to provide any direct therapy. Instead the stutterer was urged to formulate his own. The group sessions were used to provide information concerning the nature of stuttering, the effect of avoidance in maintaining situation and word fears, the analysis of the stuttering behavior in terms of approach and struggle reactions to tremor, the need for desensitization and modification of the stuttering, the exploration of the self as reflected in the therapeutic activities and reactions of the stutterer. The clinicians were merely observers and discussants. They were not permitted to suggest courses of action. One hour daily was spent in group sessions, another down town in the city in speech situations with a clinician, the third in reporting to the therapist and other stutterers the various experiences of the previously planned activities. A written daily report of self-therapy carried on outside the clinic was required. A typical report is given. This was for a week end.

STUTTERER'S REPORT BLANK

I. *Situations avoided, postponed or altered because of fear of stuttering:* When I went to church I was given the secretaries' reports to make out but I asked another girl to read them. I ate at another table because a person who looked severe was eating there. I didn't answer the phone once when I could have. I think that's all.

II.

Words badly feared	*Symptoms*	*What you did*
bus Berry mustard been pickles please much Marshall	I always make a terrible lip tremor on B and M and no sound comes out. I press my tongue behind my lips on all these words as if trying to open the door. Then I stop this just before the word comes out by biting my teeth and my tongue had better get out of the way. This seems to break the spell. But sometimes I bite my tongue and it bleeds. All these words were said like this.	I tried to get some sound in to my lips before I stuck out my tongue. This released the spell on Berry but not on the other words. I guess I didn't even try it on the others. I kept from biting on much and Marshall but the blocks were long and I guess had died out in fear before released.
sundae sandwich salad	On these I said the sound all right but I had too much of it, like a long hissing. It wobbled and my jaw was tense and quivering.	I tried to release it slowly rather than jerking. Slow motion stuff. It worked on salad, not on the others.

III. *Cancellations of past failures:*

One night about a month ago I called Phyllis up and at the end I couldn't get Good Bye out so I hung up. I called three people tonight and just so I could be sure to say goodbye. Felt good. I called the bus station again and let the *b* leak out without pressing my lips hard together. I told my roommate about how my mother reacted to my hiccups and the awful scene. First time I've been able to talk about it without crying. I went downstairs and talked to my landlady for ten minutes. Usually I just say a few words which aren't important. She's kind of nosey, and all the girls dodge her.

IV. *Trophies and other successes:*

Always before when my sister and I went out to eat she would always do the ordering, but this week end I told her I'd do it and I did. Had some trouble but it wasn't too bad. I felt pretty big.

I looked at my acne in the mirror. Wish I could cancel that. It's kind of like stuttering really. Can I talk to you about it sometime?

V. *Resisted disturbing influences:*

I had seven different people laugh or giggle at me when I suddenly began to vibrate my lips in a block and I didn't cry once, either then or afterward. And I just kept on stuttering and if they didn't like it they could lump it. It was hard to resist but I did. I most generally have to cry. I refused to let my sister interrupt me twice. I entered a conversation about boys and how they act when they are out with a girl. Usually I get upset and stay out of those discussions, but I set my mind to it and said my say.

VI. *Situations entered primarily for speech practice:*

Helped my sister in the restaurant Friday night.
Went window shopping and priced sweaters.
Talked to the preacher.
Talked to my mother long distance.

In all of these I tried to stutter easy instead of hard, yet keep it strong and not hesitate too much. Especially tried to keep my mouth from jumping. Some success.

VII. *Check following items as often as they occurred during report period:*

a. Substituted xx
b. Used a starter xxxx
c. Preformed sound xxxxxxxxxxxxxxxxx
d. Forced (too often to count)
e. Postponed x
f. Contortions xxxxxxxxx
g. Looked away xx
h. Felt shame xxxxxxx

1. Pointed out failure and tried again xxx
2. Discussed stuttering xxx
3. Faked xxxxx
4. Changed the stuttering xxxxxxxxx
5. Successful preparatory set xxx
6. Cancelled xxxxxxxxxxxx
7. Talking and writing 27 pages
8. Rhythm practice 10 minutes

Other therapy: Tried to make myself stutter on non-feared words xxxx
Wrestled with my stuttering in mirror xxx
Adaptation: Wore out six words till they got clean.
Shouted five feared words to my sister.

VIII. *Indicate general morale for the day:*
It changed. Felt pretty lousy Saturday afternoon. Depressed that night. Pretty good when dressed up for church and after speech successes. That night very lonesome. Think I may be getting somewhere but it's far away.

It will be apparent that these stutterers returned to the rhythm practice and talking-and-writing activities which we had previously discarded, and the reader may wonder why they did so. As we structured the group sessions in which information was provided we gave illustrations of all of the techniques we had previously employed in therapy. We cited their rationale and described how other stutterers had used them in the past. We stated as honestly as we could their advantages and disadvantages but left the choice of techniques entirely free. The only mandatory requirement was that they must do an "honest day's work" if they were to remain in the clinic, and we interpreted this behest very liberally. After some initial confusion and resistance, first one stutterer and then another explored the use of various techniques and, since all reports were posted on a bulletin board after they were reviewed by the therapist, soon all of them were engaged in therapeutic activities. We found it very difficult to give up our authoritarian role but succeeded except for a few weak moments, though there was always a constant temptation to direct or to favor certain procedures over others. We did our utmost to resist these.

By Thanksgiving (which also coincided fortunately with the deer season) none of the cases had made anywhere near the progress that those of former years had made. All were still avoiding, stuttering compulsively, and feeling sorry for themselves. They were in the same situation upon their return, more depressed and hopeless, if anything, and full of resentment toward the therapist for not making them do what they ought to do. Nevertheless, we steadfastly continued on our sorry program, bore their complaints and resistances, their meager reports, their token efforts, and still evidenced our faith in their ability to heal themselves. By Christmas a change had begun to occur, as we have reported in the preceding paragraph. Several began to show all-around improvement in self-therapy and in fluency. Among these were two of the three girls and one man. The change in the girls seemed to shame the other fellows into some real effort, and we hated to see the Christmas holidays come that year. Upon their return, surprisingly enough, those who had improved had held their gains and one other chap had made a tremendous improvement. They were all glad to return, and the month of January was probably the most pleasurable month of therapy with stutterers we have ever experienced. They worked like Trojans, excited in self-discovery, in fighting for control under stress, in exploring new social situations. By the end of the semester, only one of the girls had failed to achieve a marked reduction in stuttering, in avoidance, and in social isolation. One of the fellows had made but meager headway and dropped out of sight, and we could never contact him again. The other six cases were in excellent shape, operating closely as a group, yet also working well in self-therapy.

We therefore promptly made another egregious mistake. We discontinued all formal speech therapy, suggesting instead that the six (two girls and four men) form their own therapy group, meet twice each week in the evening without the therapist or clinicians, and work on each other and on themselves. This arrangement started out well enough but within a month it had flopped badly. The girls paired up with two of the men and the other two felt left out, so far as we could ascertain. This was the first schism; then trouble developed between the couples. By March, and also by June, only the two girls and one fellow had maintained their gains; the other three suffered extreme relapses and had returned to the discouraged attitudes of early therapy. Only token attempts at self-therapy were evidenced. We then reëntered these latter individuals for individual therapy and they swiftly improved but were still scared by June, though their fluency was excellent. By Christmas of the following year one of these was stuttering as badly as ever, while another had settled down to a swinging alternation between excellent speech and sporadic miniature relapses. Five years later both of these were stuttering severely. The third stutterer was speaking very fluently, and we considered him a successful case. Of the two girls and the fellow who had maintained their gains, all three were in excellent shape, with only an occasional mild situation fear, no word fears or obvious abnormality in their phone conversations with us. The fellow reported an occasional unexpected block with which he seemed able to cope. All were married and happy in their social situations. The one girl who had not improved did not return to school or to the clinic at the end of the semester, but hearsay reports indicated that her speech was greatly improved though she still stuttered occasionally. This result was perhaps due to some psychiatric treatment she subsequently received.

In evaluating the process and results of the therapy for this year, we concluded that this free choice of techniques diet, if we may so term it, had much to recommend it. We dimly began to see how important was the acceptance of responsibility for one's own behavior, that the therapist's assumption of too much direction actually could retard the case's progress We were also impressed again by the importance of the group belongingness, but at the same time appalled to see how dependent upon the group the individual stutterer could become. If ultimate success in therapy required freedom from dependence upon either the therapist or a group of his own kind, how were we ever to have an efficient therapy? We had learned something and had done some good, but we were far from our goal. And so we determined to revise our procedures again.

1944–1945

This year we duplicated the intensive therapy of the previous year almost exactly with a new group of eleven severe stutterers, four of whom were girls. Two of the men were subsequently inducted into the armed services despite their stuttering, and one of the girls refused to do any therapy at all and so we dropped her, leaving eight who stayed with us the entire two semesters. We did not terminate therapy at the end of the first semester or rely on the group to maintain itself, but instead used individual counseling sessions on a twice-a-week basis for terminal therapy. During terminal therapy, each stutterer was required to take public-speaking courses and have a job which required much speaking. The main prescription was massive doses of talking to as many people as possible. They reported twice weekly throughout their terminal therapy on the amount of talking they did, the number of communicative contacts, the amount of avoidance, stuttering abnormality, or situation and word fears, and discussed their other problems with the therapist. A social group did maintain itself in a precarious fashion for some months on an informal and unsponsored basis, but it had no major function in therapy so far as we could ascertain. In two of the cases some important historical material was unearthed and ventilated, but what psychotherapy was present was concerned with the immediate problems of the cases, and our role was supportive rather than interpretative.

We have said that in essence this year's intensive therapy was a duplicate of the previous year's. However, we did introduce two new factors: psychodrama and the use of transitional groups. One or two of our group sessions each week was devoted to group psychotherapy of some kind. Impressed with the work of Moreno and his associates, we acted out many a scene in our clinic or little theater. Often the stutterer would report to the group an actual traumatic situation in which he had stuttered badly and then we would reënact it with the stutterer as the director, defining and illustrating roles, or playing the roles of himself or others in the scene with plenty of asides to express the feelings involved. We also played scenes from each stutterer's past life and from his future. One of our cases was all set to go home for good to Arizona at Christmas time, so fluent had he become. However, an enactment of the scene in which his mother and father met him at the train revealed so vividly to him the negative forces he would have to combat that he decided to stay for terminal therapy.

We also played scenes in which the stutterer triumphantly coped with his problem under stresses of various kinds, the accusation-guilt scene, the tough employer, the marriage proposal, the uncomfortable social-graces scene, and as many others as we could dredge up from our imagination and the histories and experiences of our cases. We also invented phonodramas in which a certain scene was dubbed on tape, played to the group, and then interrupted suddenly, whereupon our cases had to act out or narrate the remainder. The stutterers collected characters for these little plays from real life and studied their reactions carefully so they could duplicate them on the clinic stage. At times they even arranged a real-life drama with the unsuspecting clerk who always laughed at the stutterer, another case stepping in and giving her hell before explaining that he too, in his youth, had stuttered severely, meanwhile worrying that his own threatening stuttering might give the farce away. We had comedies as well as tragedies. The essential humor in the unexpected and grotesque, in the misinterpretations of unfinished words, was portrayed, often very skillfully. The group often discussed pretty freely the implications of the behavior which came up in this play, and often the therapist was put to it to keep insights too traumatic for acceptance from wrecking the performers. It was a fascinating year but an exhausting one. While there is indubitably a certain amount of ham in this therapist, he found its constant exploitation rather onerous.

We also explored what we termed the method of transitional groups. Using the therapist, who accepts himself as a stutterer, albeit a pretty fluent one, as the nucleus, the first and innermost group was composed of the eight stutterers (though actually there were three shifting subgroups within this larger one, the three girls forming one at certain times). Intersecting, if we may use such a term, with this group was a small second group of three former cases whom we had impressed, à la Alcoholics Anonymous, as clinicians. We also had five normal-speaking student therapists who formed a group with which the second group was closely identified through briefing sessions, coffee breaks, and evening meetings with the therapist. After these groupings had got structured and operating in the group session for six weeks, we had each of the clinicians invite a guest to the group meetings and to certain social functions. These guests later on were varied to include older people, father and mother figures, prospective employers, an army sergeant, and the like. The therapist worked hard to create conditions which would permit continuous identification across status boundary lines, and with some success. There quite evidently was a powerful "magnetic pull" toward normality, though some of the guests expressed some feelings to indicate that a counterflow was also present. The total group, however, was pretty difficult to handle with 25 people in it, and we gave it up after about a month. We felt sure, however, that something similar with a smaller group would have proved very successful. It certainly increased the motivation of the core of stutterers. It also provided an audience as well as participants for our psychodrama.

Of the eight stutterers who took part in the program this year, we have five-year follow-ups on only three. The war years were not good ones for maintaining contacts. Of the three, two were speaking well and reported fears as occurring seldom, and stated that they were better than when leaving the clinic and felt no social or vocational handicap. The third had relapsed completely after undergoing a subsequent two-year psychoanalysis and discovering therein, much to our surprise and his, that he was a latent homosexual. We suspect that several of the other cases were successful, for we have found that the successful ones want to forget their travail and tend to interpret any renewed contact with the therapist as a sign of weakness or dependency. It has been our experience that it is easy to get rechecks on our failures but not on our successes. Our failures are always coming home to roost or for another suck at the therapeutic nipple. But we may be deluding ourselves in this impression. At any rate we can report but two successes out of three in terms of the five-year checkup. Two others reported their speech as excellent after two years but we could never make contact again. We suspect that two others eventually failed to maintain any but minor gains, because of the anxiety they reported at Christmas following the termination of therapy. This is all the information we can provide for purposes of evaluation on a long-term basis.

Some description of the progress made during the intensive and terminal therapy might be of some value, though, as we have previously seen, we do not trust these judgments very far. The psychodrama and transitional groups did prevent much of the intense resistance to therapy which had taken place the previous year under the same choose-your-own-technique and daily-report-of-self-therapy regime. Within a month all save two were working hard, and had made real gains by November. Improvement occurred between then and Christmas, and that holiday period did not show the characteristic losses of previous years though three of the stutterers did get worse just before returning, perhaps as a gesture to make them feel that more therapy was still needed. This, we have found, is not unusual. By the end of the intensive therapy, six of the eight were very fluent and almost free from situation fears. They reported occasional unexpected stutterings, often in casual conversation, and a little sloppy hemming and hawing which they suspected as a mild avoidance. The other two had made some gains but were far behind the seven.

The terminal therapy we felt was very successful, though very time-consuming for the therapist. The stutterers continued to work, though not compulsively, and a progressive independence of the therapist gradually manifested itself in most of them. Three of the cases terminated therapy by their own choice during the spring, and all six were speaking very well and were quite adequate in most social situations.

All in all, we felt pretty good about the therapy for this year. It was, however, too demanding in terms of time and effort and therapeutic skill. With a million stutterers demanding help, we were ants removing the seashore grain by grain of sand. And we wondered how much of the success was due to the devotion of the therapist. So ended the year of 1944–1945.

This year we also tried an interesting variation of therapy with three other stutterers whom we met three times each week for an hour. They were all men, and intellectually curious. One was fairly mild in stuttering behavior and emotional problems, the second was about average, and the third could be termed severely handicapped in both his speech and personal adjustment. We worked with these individuals until Christmas, and usually in the evenings because they were employed during clinic hours.

Our basic plan was this: to work on the listener instead of the stutterer. Instead of asking our stutterers to maintain good eye contact with the listener during stuttering, we asked them to vary their stuttering responses until the listener looked at them. It was easy to so manipulate some listeners, almost impossible to affect others. One of the stutterer's reports in this connection ran as follows: "This jerk just wouldn't look up once he heard me stutter on that first word. I tried it again, pretty calmly too, and even another time but no soap. I said to myself, I'll get you yet, so I say to him I hope you don't mind if I give that doggone word another try. He took one little peek and grunted so I worked on it again and it came out good. Still no look at me. I got mad and said for Christ's sake why don't you look at me. It doesn't help me if you look away. I think he thought I was nuts because he just walked away then. I figure he was not adjusted very good himself."

They also learned to calm their listeners, instead of trying to stay calm themselves. Their trophies were the unwitting listeners who suddenly became tensed and upset when they found the speaker stuttering or pseudo-stuttering in certain ways, and whom they were able to relax. The cases experimented with their own stuttering, trying to find modifications which would produce this reduction of listener tension. One of them, interestingly enough, found that an easy repetitive stuttering seemed to calm his listeners much more than any other type of stuttering he could master. Another changed his own stuttering to a smooth prolongation as his tool to manipulate his listener. The third, the severe stutterer, tried everything and often could not succeed in any of his efforts. We then taught the stutterers how to pull out of their tremors so that they could do a better job of listener manipulation. One of them made this interesting report: "There's a girl at Shenshul's Cafeteria who always looks at me when I stutter and she doesn't seem very tense either. But she freezes like she was hypnotized and doesn't move a muscle until I come out of it. So tonight I gave her a little work out, stuttering with a little grin and a wry face and cancelling and then appearing triumphant when I said it OK. I could see her thaw out, and she said, 'You're getting better, Mister.' And I felt pretty good. I've got to learn to stutter loosely, I guess, and not get so steamed up about it."

The immediate result of this collector therapy, as they called it, was a marked gain in fluency which transferred to most other situations. We felt it was due in part to the freeing effect which came from their lessened vulnerability to listener penalties, and in part to the experimentation with, and modification of, their own stuttering behavior. Since they did much of this work together on their "hunting expeditions" some feeling of group belongingness and permissiveness no doubt had some anxiety-reducing effect as well. We finally concluded that this type of therapy was a by-path to fluency rather than the main route via self-mastery. However, we have continued to use such experiences occasionally in most of our later therapy for certain cases and at certain times. We suspect that we did not explore this working on the listener rather than the stutterer as thoroughly as we should have done. If stuttering is a disorder of communication, involving a receiver of messages as well as a sender, why should we center all our therapy on the sender alone? Why not work on the listener's ear as well as the stutterer's mouth?

1945–1946

This year we decided to attempt to simplify the therapy as much as possible to eliminate everything which could be eliminated—to boil down the therapeutic process to its essentials. We were convinced, after the successes of the previous year, that we now knew how to treat severe adult stutterers successfully. We knew also that few other therapists would ever or could ever pay the price in terms of time, energy, and devotion. We felt reluctant ourselves to duplicate the practices we had been following. Moreover, this year we were given another full-time member of our stuff (Frank Robinson) whom we intended to take our place the following year so that we could assess the factor of the therapist's own personality as contributing to the success of therapy. Throughout this year we kept him informed as to our practices and the reasons therefore, and through our post-therapy sessions and his observations tried to acquaint him with our procedures.

We dropped the psychodrama as a regular part of therapy and substituted for it a daily group discussion period similar to that which is now called group psychotherapy. The text by George Bach, *Intensive Group Psychotherapy* (New York, Ronald Press, 1954), is an account of group interaction startlingly similar to that which we followed. We wish to make clear, however, that the quality and caliber of the free group verbalizations described in this text were not paralleled in our own clinic. But we did the best we could.

We continued the same free choice of techniques as in the preceding year and required reports of self-therapy, using the same forms as before. We also provided three other techniques, cancellation, pull-outs, and preparatory sets,[3] which had been used experimentally with many former cases but sporadically and not as a basic or emphasized part of the group therapy. These last three techniques were not free choice but instead were strongly recommended as ways of coping with as many moments of stuttering as the stutterer could find. The stutterer was expected to use these techniques when he was talking in the clinic, but he need not use them in his self-therapy. We made quite a point of this (even to the point of forbidding them with one case), with the expected result that they soon began to use them everywhere. They were, like the other procedures in therapy, explained in the first hour's group session, illustrated there by the therapist and his clinicians, and practiced there by the cases until they knew exactly what each of them was. Thereafter they were required to use them in the clinic, with various mild penalties, usually administered by the group, for forgetting to do so. One of our cases was put on a special regime. Whenever he failed to use either a preparatory set, a pull-out, or a cancellation, he had to stop talking altogether. We tried this for two weeks, but the fact that the others in the group were not subject to such drastic deprivation of communication produced so much tension in him that we gave it up. We

[3] The terms "cancellation," "pull-outs," and "preparatory sets" are explained in detail in Van Riper, *Speech Correction, op. cit.*, pp. 421–432.

have always been intending to apply it as a basic group technique but we have never got around to it. Too much stuttering is rewarded by completed communication and we suspect that its strength or tenacity is probably due to this factor as much as to any other.

We taught, if that is the word for it, these three techniques in this sequence: cancellation first, then pull-outs, then preparatory sets. We had previously found that this was the best way, since responses tend to move forward in time. After some experience in attempting the word differently in a cancellation, the stutterer tended to use the same modifications in the course of the actual stuttering itself, i.e., in his pull-outs. And many cases, after learning how to pull out of a block without struggle, avoidance, or abnormality, soon learned to get set prior to the attempt on a feared word so that it was spoken pretty normally.

In order to simplify and systematize the self-therapy, we set a quota of at least 20 stranger-situations each day. This meant that each stutterer had to have a more or less prolonged communicative contact with that many people he did not know. It required at least a short conversation. The penalty for not doing so was again expulsion from the clinic for a week, and permanent expulsion if repeated. In these stranger-situations, which they entered deliberately for self-therapy, the stutterers could use any of the techniques they had explored in the group sessions. These included prewriting, faking, negative practice, strong speech attempts, modifying the stereotypy of the responses, checking avoidances, adaptation by repeating the word until it finally was spoken normally, good eye contact, post-stuttering comment, prolongation of some part of the stuttering behavior without force, tremor release, utterance with the mouth in motion, slow-motion stuttering, and many others, including, if they wished, cancellation, pull-outs, and preparatory sets. Daily written reports of this self-therapy with the 20 strangers were required. They were the passports to the clinic sessions. And we found several instances where they were pure fabrication.

As we have said, the first hour of each day was spent in group session in which the various techniques were explained, demonstrated, and practiced. This training was concluded within about six weeks. Thereafter the group sessions were used to reinforce the cancellation, pull-out, and preparatory-set responses to the threat or presence of stuttering. The content of the verbal offerings of the stutterers concerned their experiences. For instance, the therapist would ask some stutterer to amplify to the group his report of a previous experience in self-therapy. The stutterer was supposed, when a feared word appeared, to revise his preparatory sets before he attempted the word so that the old abnormality would be decreased. If he failed to do so and found himself stuttering, he was then to attempt to pull out of the "blocks" with a slow voluntary movement. If he could no do this or did not do this, he then could at least make an attempt to cance the word by pausing deliberately and making a new attempt, demonstrating an easier and less abnormal bit of behavior. It should be stressed that i cancellation the stutterer was not to say the word again normally. He wa to stutter on it the second time, even if he did not need to do so, but to stutter on it in a different and a better way. Only then could he continue

The second hour each day was spent with a student therapist (clinician) who acted only as an observer. Part of this period was spent in fulfilling a part of the daily quota of 20 stranger-situations and the rest in discussing these experiences over coffee or some other drink or food. We felt that anxiety and frustration seemed to be lessened by verbal report during feeding. Recent experiments with rats appear to corroborate this.

The third hour each day was spent in group-psychotherapy sessions with the therapist, his assistant, and the stutterers alone together. No transitional groups were used this year. As we look back on the protocols and try to recapture the atmosphere of these meetings, we remember the outbursts and freedom with which the stutterers expressed themselves. No speech therapy was done in these meetings. The stutterers could speak or not speak, stutter or not stutter, and they could say anything they wanted to. It was pretty explosive often, but the therapist reflected feelings and accepted most of them permissively. The stutterers first called it their blow-off period, and later on their let-their-hair-down time. Much of the effectiveness of the hour was probably due to the fact that stuttering was actually encouraged rather than treated. These were unsophisticated individuals so far as psychotherapy was concerned, but some very keen interpretations of their own and each other's behavior were often offered. The therapist was kept busy preventing their exploitation of each other. As model group psychotherapy, it wasn't very good, but it did reduce much of the resistance which had often appeared at the beginning of therapy.

Terminal therapy this year consisted of two group meetings each week which were handled by the therapist's assistant, and by occasional individual sessions through appointment with the therapist himself. The use of cancellation, pull-outs, and preparatory sets were stressed. Fears and avoidances and moments of bad stuttering were aired.

Eight stutterers comprised the group which participated in the entire intensive therapy; two others initially enrolled dropped out within the first month. The eight were a motley lot with plenty of problems. One was a moronic farmer from North Dakota with ten sections of land there, who had never taken a bath save in a washtub and was deathly afraid of the drain hole in the bathtub of his apartment. Another was a girl caught between two cultures, that of the old Dutch religious burgher and the modern college world. Another was a crippled hunchback. Another was a lad from the backwoods of the Southern mountains who was called to be a preacher of the gospel and whose stuttering he interpreted as the devil speaking. And there were others, all with grotesque and severe stuttering. Another was bound he would be a high-pressure insurance agent. We did our damnedest.

Of the eight stutterers five had shown marked gains by late November, maintained them during the holidays despite an intensive post-card report system we devised, and were speaking pretty well by the end of the intensive therapy. The lad from Dakota had finally taken a modern bath but was otherwise unimproved. The Dutch girl was pretty fluent though occasional severe stutterings and avoidances accompanied her many emotional crises. The prospective preacher was still prospecting for the golden tongue but had improved somewhat. By June and the end of therapy, five of the eight we felt had made satisfactory progress and were ready to be dismissed. The Dakota farmer went home still stuttering despite some intensive individual therapy, and we carried the other two in individual therapy for several more years with eventual success.

Our five-year checkup showed that four of the eight were successes in terms of the criteria we have described earlier. One of these reported a severe but temporary relapse three years after dismissal. Two others had improved markedly and later checkups enabled us to claim them as eventual successes. The Dutch girl was improved enough to become a very successful public-school speech therapist, but subsequent psychotherapy was required before she finally attained the adjustment and fluency for which she had the potential. Only two of the eight were complete flops, the man from Dakota and another man who the therapist and his assistant had predicted would surely and inevitably become perfectly fluent. We understand that the preacher became very fluent and followed his calling for seven years but eventually suffered a severe relapse, left the ministry, and became a farmer, which is probably what he should have been all along. We have been unable to contact him since this new adjustment. He is included among the four cited above. The hunchback married and won the Prudential award of the year for selling several million dollars' worth of life insurance.

Our impression at the end of the intensive therapy was that we had not done as well as in the previous year, not because of the therapy, but because we had a bunch of exceptionally difficult cases to work with. We did not feel that we had done much simplification. We were not content with either the group psychotherapy or the speech therapy. We felt that the cancellation, pull-out, and preparatory-set techniques were potent tools, but that we did not know how to teach them or how to use them. It was a hard year.

We also experimented this year with other cases and other techniques. We had long been studying Froeschel's breath-chewing therapy and the chewing therapy advocated by Robbins and Despert. The fact that each of these therapists, with different reasons, had advocated some form of chewing speech impressed us. Coached by one of Froeschel's students, we learned breath chewing and did our best, without success, to teach it to Ingdolf, the Dakota farmer, who was hardly a test. We then tried it out on four other stutterers, two of whom were in their teens, with strong suggestion that *here was the way*, but we must report no success, though we trained them daily for over a month. Despite this failure, there was enough curious integration of utterance under fear when chewing to make us wonder if we weren't missing something. Something about the massive movements of the jaw seemed occasionally to reduce or prevent the tremors which characterized so many of the stutterings.

We experimented with chewing speech as a pull-out device, and in cancellation. We modified the chewing in many different ways. There was more here than mere distraction. We admit being initially skeptical of the technique, but not too skeptical to give it a thorough trial. Indeed, we have continued to use it on a case or two ever since and have come to the tentative conclusion that the sequences of movements which make up the utterance of a word may be integrated not only by Stetson's syllabic breath pulses but by certain jaw movements as well. It may be that the jaw movement is the prime mover, the basic signal in the kinesthetic feedback which integrates the whole sequence of muscular contractions, much as the pianist's head jerk may integrate a melodic sequence of flying fingers. When it is missing or wrong, the whole sequence gets fouled up. We now feel that there is no need to chew but rather perhaps a need to integrate about a jaw movement (as the prime mover) the broken utterance of the stutterer's speech. How to put Humpty Dumpty together again?

1946–1947

This was to be our second put-together year in which we would review all of our previous therapy, throw out the poor things and use only the good. We were becoming a little less naïve than we were five years before and less certain about what was good therapy and what wasn't. Moreover, as we have indicated, we wanted to see what someone else could do with the therapy we had been using. So this year we turned all of it over to the colleague whom we had trained and who had worked with us the previous year. We sketched the goals and the course of therapy and conferred with him occasionally about certain problems which arose, but we stayed away from the cases who comprised the experimental-therapy group. The therapy was much like that of the previous year, except for the group psychotherapy. While some of this occurred, it was not, as before, a basic and strongly stressed part of therapy. Discussions were still pretty free, however. The man who took our place, we felt, was as good as anyone we could train in a year or two.

Seven stutterers comprised the therapy group, which continued throughout the year except for one man who dropped out in February because of family obligations. Because we did not see the cases personally, we did not kept the usual protocols and we cannot find any record of periodic evaluations during the intensive therapy. We did, however, evaluate them at the end of intensive therapy and again in June at the conclusion of terminal therapy. Five of the seven were doing very well by February; one had shown some improvement; one had shown very little and was thoroughly discouraged. By June we felt that only four had an excellent chance of maintaining their fluency and freedom from avoidance or struggle. We were able to get five-year checkups on six of the seven, including the man who had left at midyear. Three of the seven were able to satisfy our criteria of success. One of these had become completely fluent and no longer considered himself a stutterer. We interviewed him at length seven years after termination of therapy and could detect no sign of stuttering, word fear, or avoidance. This interview included some severe stress situations. Another case had shown improvement beyond the level of dismissal but still had a few occasional feared situations and a rare but severe stuttering. Two were as bad as they had been prior to treatment. We did not feel that these cases were as severe or presented as many other personal problems as had the group of the preceding year, and so we conclude that the therapist's experience, personality, or skill is still more important in therapy than the methods used. We were again impressed by the tremendous resistance shown by the stutterers in confronting their stuttering as a problem to be solved. We felt that our big lack was in effective methods of psychotherapy to be used concurrently with the speech therapy or prior thereto. We felt that most of these stutterers had so closely built their personalities about the skeleton of their stuttering that the concept of the self as stuttering was the chief obstacle to success. Some change in the manner of perceiving the self was required. Stuttering was a tough nut to crack.

Freed from the onerous demands of daily therapy, the therapist did a lot of experimentation with other stutterers not in the group. With two cases, one a child and the other an adult, both mild secondary stutterers, we used the motokinesthetic method pioneered by Edna Hill Young for articulation and delayed-speech cases. Stuttering was here conceived as an articulatory defect and the case was taught to produce the initial and sequential sounds in their proper order, using kinesthetic and tactual cues from actual manipulation of the mouth and with gestural symbols as the basic controls to produce the proper transitions. They were taught the rudiments of the phonetic alphabet by this means and eventually learned to guide their own mouths by means of finger postures. The child improved remarkably under this treatment, the adult not at all. There obviously was a strong factor of suggestion inherent in the method. It was also significant that there was some danger present too, for the adult began to acquire some finger twitchings and abnormal mouth movements as part of his habitual stuttering pattern. We did not continue this with the adult after four weeks. The child is now adult and still fluent. We concluded that some kinesthetic or tactual monitoring should be incorporated into our therapy but we weren't sure how this was to be accomplished.

Having long been impressed by Korzybski's *Science and Sanity*, and now mobilized by the publication of Johnson's *People in Quandaries*, we worked in the evenings with two intelligent adults using this frame of reference. We studied these books together and constantly attempted to apply the principles of semantic reorientation to stuttering. We observed our language processes, our abstractions, our dating and indexing, our perceptions of ourselves in terms of our symbolic processes. These two stutterers were not very severe and were highly verbal as well as intelligent. We enjoyed these sessions, but our discussions of first-order facts of stuttering behavior always seemed to end up on a high level of abstraction. The cases thought more and talked more about the problem of stuttering than they did anything about it. The therapist often felt as though he were engaged in an intricate word play rather than in therapy. It was stimulating and ego-pleasant, but too intellectual. In these sessions it certainly reduced much of the anxiety felt by these stutterers, and the avoidance tricks and behavior seemed to diminish. At times we felt almost as we often had when babbling aloud with a young stutterer or delayed-speech case to show them that speech need not be painful or difficult. This intellectualized speech play in a warm, permissive atmosphere provided a communicative activity in which stuttering was actually interesting and nontraumatic. The therapist's role as a giver of information, as an explainer and interpreter, yes, even as a persuader, was quite satisfying, but we have always been suspicious of our motives in such a role and doubtful of its therapeutic validity. These reservations no doubt affected our therapy, though we tried to discard them in our actual contacts with the cases. We even worked with "semantic relaxation" with enthusiasm.

Our conclusions were that we, at least, were unfitted to do this type of therapy. Neither of the stutterers showed any lasting gains, though both became quite fluent in our therapy sessions and experienced some temporary relief from stuttering in outside stress situations. Apart from the "intellectualizing" of the problems, the other serious drawback which impressed us was that there was too much stress on avoidance or approach behavior and not enough on frustration or release and escape behavior. Stuttering is more than an "anticipatory, apprehensive, hypertonic avoidance reaction." Once in a fixation or an oscillation, there arise reactions of escape. The stutterer is not only dodging or postponing the anticipated unpleasantness in his speech; he is also doing his utmost to get out of it. The rat is trying to get off the hot grid. Semantic therapy with intelligently curious and introspective stutterers could do much to eliminate some of the avoidance behavior. It did not seem to offer much in terms of frustration tolerance, in terms of desensitization, in terms of release from tremor. We do not think we gave semantic therapy as fair a trial as one of Johnson's students would have, but we did give it the best trial of which we were capable.

1947–1948

This year, owing partly to the return of men from war service, we had a large number of severe stutterers who applied for admission and from them we selected 15 to serve as our exploratory-therapy group. Three of them were girls, one a man of 40. With a group as large as this we found it necessary to modify our procedures. We used the first period of each day for clarifying goals, illustrating techniques, and explaining the daily assignments which formed the core of this year's therapy. The second hour was spent by the cases in beginning to fulfill these assignments, in "tasting" them. Three days each week we also met together during the third hour to discuss our experiences with the sample assignments. The other two days no third period was held in the clinic, the stutterers leaving at the end of the first hour and working solo to carry out the assigned work. Since we had more stutterers than trained student therapists, we sent the stutterers out in pairs to be their own clinicians. We used the five student therapists we had as roving clinicians, having them work for a time first with one case, then another. This way we hoped to decrease the dependency upon the therapist and the clinicians.

The assignments were formulated by the therapist and for the first two months were the same for all cases. Some samples may be illustrated:

October 10, 1947

1. Go into five situations in each of which you are to collect five blocks which you voluntarily lengthen. These must be real blocks so keep talking until you get them. If you can only get four blocks in a single situation, try to find a more difficult one so you can get at least five. "Four-block" situations don't count. Cancel these blocks. Record any failure to keep eye contact.
2. Collect 10 stuttering blocks (apart from those in any other assignment) in which there is no jerky release. Pull out of the tremors as smoothly as possible. Describe release.
3. Collect 25 faked voluntary repetitive blocks to a single person. Repeat at least three times per word or more. The listener must remain at ease. If he gets upset, go hunt another listener until you can be successful.
4. Work with some other stutterer before the mirror for fifteen minutes, taking turns sharing (imitating simultaneously) his stutterings. Be prepared to illustrate these in group meeting tomorrow.
5. Prepare a two-minute talk about some stuttering experiences which embarrassed you painfully in the past. Better rehearse it, because you will be penalized for every block you fail to cancel perfectly in front of the group tomorrow.
6. Call fifteen numbers at random from the phone book and ask to speak to yourself. Fake on your name and then cancel calmly as possible. If the block becomes real, keep on it until it becomes faked and voluntary or until the listener hangs up. Give written report of experiences.
7. Ask some other stutterer to give you one of his feared situations, and enter it with him, asking him to write a report of his observations of your behavior (a) before, (b) during, and (c) immediately after the word on which you stuttered most severely.
8. Fill out your mood chart.
9. Discuss your stuttering with some stranger, explaining some of the work you are doing.
10. Bring us one trophy. Write it up and post it on the bulletin board.

It is obvious that a great amount of actual work had to be done by each stutterer in fulfilling these assignments. We felt that at least four to five hours were required. Our college-student stutterers took only a portion of the full academic load of classes. Those who worked, worked part time. Our services were offered on this basis, take it or leave it. In this regard, we have long felt that most severe stutterers welcome such a prescription, much as they wish for the superficial, once-over, one-hour-a-week program. They know very well how deep-seated is their problem and how strenuous an effort it requires. We have continually been surprised to find how easy it is to get initial rapport, once the therapist indicates his awareness of this basic feeling. To offer token therapy is to get a token response. Even the written reports, which often took an hour of steady writing to prepare, provided an excellent sense of achievement. With labor and love, even stuttering begins to crack.

For the first time, the intensive therapy was organized in a definite sequential order. First we studied stuttering and the stutterer, using assignments and group periods primarily for that purpose. Next we studied our listeners and their reactions to stuttering and our responses to those reactions. Then we attempted to stutter openly, without avoidance, and with good eye contact during the stuttering. Then we learned to cancel carefully, studying our stuttering behavior during the different, better kind of stuttering. Next we learned to pull out of our blocks without jerks or struggle, to get control of the tremors and to smooth them out and slow them down. Then we attempted to vary our preparatory sets, attempting to exchange a loose, strong, slow shifting utterance for the spasmodic abnormal one. Five of the cases were given individual counseling sessions weekly during the intensive program. The therapist was warm and understanding in terms of the feelings expressed but inexorable in his demands that the assignments be completed daily. One of the women, an older and very neurotic one who had been traveling from clinic to clinic for years to tell her sad tale of maternal cruelty, much like the Ancient Mariner, became suddenly fluent, was invited to tell her tale again, and dismissed before she could quit. Then she went to the University of Iowa and told it again, we understand. This left 14.

We would like to say a few words here about the "tramp" stutterer. While there are few "virgin" stutterers any more who have not been worked over by two or three therapists before they come to any reputable speech clinic, there is a special breed that we have come to recognize. These are the tramp stutterers, whose stuttering is usually of neurotic origin and whose therapeutic efforts are designed primarily for exploitation of the symptoms and of the therapist. Their stuttering seldom dates from the preschool years; they like to dwell on their tragic histories; they have the bitter-sweet helpless smile during or immediately subsequent to a moment of stuttering; they know all the theories and therapies for stuttering and are fascinated by psychotherapeutic terms; they demand inordinate amounts of attention and time; they make quick gains in fluency but always lose them completely; and they love to be near the more severe stutterers. They belong to the psychiatrist, not to the speech therapist.

This year's formulation of assignments by the therapist seems to be completely contradictory to the trend of preceding years away from authoritarianism and toward permissiveness and self-therapy. Our reasons for doing this were that we still had hopes of a therapy program which any good therapist could administer, one which would carry much of its own psychotherapy in the activities it included. We wanted to simplify, to structure, to organize the therapy in terms of specific subgoals, techniques, and experiences. We felt that while we could do a pretty good job of treating the adult stutterer, what we did was difficult to explain or describe. Even our student therapists who watched us every day and participated as clinicians found it difficult to understand, even though they saw the stutterers gradually becoming less apprehensive and more direct, secure, and fluent. Our own attempts to communicate to them the reasons for doing what we did often seemed unreliable. Why, for example, did we sit next to this stutterer this day in group meeting, lift that eyebrow at that particular time, share that particular tremor? Wherein lies the crucial essence of therapy? In flexibility with a wide range of responses, a close understanding and empathy with the stutterer, and a sense of timing? There are many other items equally important. But we have never been afraid to try or to try again differently. And so we worked out daily assignments for the general sequence outlined in an earlier paragraph.

We soon found that even 14 stutterers was too large a group to handle at once and so we broke it down into two groups, one of 10 and one of 4, treating both pretty much alike but at different times during the day. Both had the same assignments. By Thanksgiving both groups had progressed about equally. Frequency and severity had decreased along with avoidance and word fears. They were canceling most of their stutterings even in stress situations. During the holiday week, assignments were provided and continued, and no loss of gain was experienced except for one stutterer. They then went on to learn how to pull out of their oscillations and fixations and had made some initial progress in this area when the Christmas holidays arrived. No assignments were given, but a daily report was requested by mail. All of the stutterers slumped badly after the first few days, and they returned full of anxiety and stuttering. We went back and reviewed earlier skills through the assignment method, then advanced to the use of preparatory sets. By the end of the semester, most of both groups were pretty fluent, though all of them had situation fears and occasional severe blocks under stress.

Terminal therapy consisted of twice-a-week group sessions and a running written inventory of speaking behavior, using the following form. Here is the report of one of our worst cases:

STUTTERER'S CHECK LIST

Monday, March 21

(Carry this with you all day and check the following items as they occur:)

Failures	*Successes*
1. Substituted . . . 2	1. Cancelled word failure . . . 13 words
2. Used trick to get started . . . 6 swallows	2. Cancelled situation failure . . . 3 at work
3. False	3. Pull-outs . . . 33 altogether, maybe more
4. Poor eye contact . . . none	4. Good preparatory sets . . . 43
5. Postponed. . . 11 ah's (at work)	5. Faked calmly . . . 7
6. Contortion or struggle (lip press)	6. Discussed stuttering . . . 2
7. Shame and embarrassment . . . none; mad!	7. Entered feared situation deliberately . . . 3
8. Depression over speech . . . No	8. Trophies: Talked to railroad gang at work

All but one of our stutterers were doing much better than the person who filled out the above report on that date, but all reported some failures. In the two group sessions each week these reports were passed around, analyzed, and commented upon by all.

By June, six of the group of ten and three of the group of four had satisfied our criteria of success, but we were not optimistic in our predictions due to the anxiety the stutterers felt at time of dismissal, the presence of tiny miniatures of their old stutterings which still appeared (and without their awareness) in their fluent speech, and the presence of altered and abnormal phrasing patterns. Their speech, though little stuttering was present, was still full of small gaps, pauses, holes into which stuttering could flow back. We have often felt that the carrier waves of speech are vitally important. The stutterer must come to have the feel of the whole phrase, the wholeness of consecutive utterance, and some of this should appear in his speech. He must learn to eliminate the odd pause, the suddenly slowed rate, the peculiar pacing which goes with stuttering expectancy. He must learn to put Humpty Dumpty together again. These cases still spoke "broken" English and they had not developed any real automaticity or ease in speaking. You couldn't hear them stutter much, but they spoke by fits and starts, in snatches. Our concern was not without some justification.

All but one of these fourteen stutterers promptly had a severe relapse that summer. By Christmas seven of the group of ten had regained their controls and their June levels. One other stutterer was oscillating precariously between collapse and fine fluency. The other two had abjectly and completely surrendered and were stuttering as badly as ever. Of the group of four, three regained good fluency by Christmas. One had collapsed completely and never did do anything about his speech again.

We have been able to contact all but one of these individuals personally after five years and can feel pretty certain of the validity of our report. Only five of the fourteen are speaking better than this therapist and satisfy his other criteria. Three of the fourteen show no improvement at all. Three others have pretty good speech, much better than they had by midyear but not as good as they had at dismissal. Their stuttering is a nuisance, but a minor one. Two others seem to be oscillating between periods of excellent and pretty poor speech. We could find no essential difference in the two groups. They are all reasonably successful in marriage or employment except two of the three who gave up completely. The older man was one of these.

We would like here to say a few more words about relapse. Many physicians have told us that few diabetics ever become willing to take their insulin injections regularly until they have had an unexpected coma and a death threat. They get to feeling so good and so normal that they just cannot accept their basic need for additional chemical controls. Much of the same psychology governs the stutterer. It may be that a certain amount of relapse is necessary, if the stutterer is to monitor his speech effectively. As we have said, relapse often comes, like Sandburg's fog, on little cat feet, in the tiny miniature blockings so unnoticeable, in the delicate pauses and postponements, in the careless repetitions so like the onset of stuttering itself. In terminal therapy and afterward, the stutterer needs his daily dose of speech insulin. And he needs to take it too. This year we felt that we lacked the insulin and the training in self-administration.

In earlier years we had experimented with the experimental production of relapses. For example, in 1935, with one of our cases at Iowa who had achieved some excellent fluency through the use of the stop-go, we prevailed upon him to refrain from using this method of handling the tremors and fear of stuttering for a period of two weeks no matter what happened. Plenty happened. We watched together the return of the old responses, studied their nature, and within two weeks the old stuttering was as strong as ever. This case never did regain his early fluency, though later he acquired enough for ordinary purposes and became a successful psychologist. We obviously regained little of our former rapport with him.

This therapist has also experimented on himself. For two weeks in the course of his daily teaching he attempted to avoid all words beginning with *p* or *t*, though he had little if any fear of them. Within a week, the effect of this avoidance was strongly felt. Phonetic fears became intense, old stuttering reactions began to appear, and it took him a month to regain his former equilibrium. It was also interesting to see that the fears of *p* and *t* words generalized first to *b* and *d* and much later to *w*, *n*, and *m*. We have also precipitated small relapses by placing the fluent stutterer in situations of great stress, and by having the stutterer deliberately assume a hesitant broken speech for several days. We have prescribed Sundays as relapse days in which they could avoid all they desired. In another stutterer who had attained almost complete fluency even in stress situations, we produced a temporary relapse by having him throw himself into his old stuttering tremors and responses 500 times a day for a week. If these experiments seem to be cruel playing with human distress, we plead guilty but offer in extenuation the finding that in only the first case did we fail to regain the former fluency. So long as relapse is feared and mysterious, the stutterer and therapist alike are helpless. Let us find out what goes on. Let us discover what truly is what, instead of fumbling in the dark.

In summing up our impressions of that year, we felt that enough success had been achieved by means of the assignment method that further refinement and variations might give us the systematic and therapist-proof treatment we still daydreamed about, folly though we knew it to be. But the millions of stutterers all over the world, the millions more who were dead or still to come, keep pleading voicelessly, haltingly. And weak and frail and inadequate though he be, each of us must in his own way try to do his best with his own little portion of time and energy. So we tried again.

1948–1949

This year we decided to concentrate on training the stutterers as though they were student therapists, on training them to be their own clinicians. It had been apparent the previous year that a course of assigned experiences and activities oriented progressively in terms of a sequence of subgoals had promise. A fatal flaw, however, was also visible: dependence upon the therapist for formulation of the prescribed activities. In earlier years we had explored the problems of self-therapy and found them many though not insoluble. This year, therefore, we attempted to combine the assignment method with self-therapy. Each stutterer was therefore given a case, himself, and his task was to learn how to treat him.

This training of the stuttering-therapist was, in part, delegated to a few well-trained student therapists and the two members of our staff. We ran a calculated risk of splitting personalities: the stutterer as the therapist and the stutterer as a case. These two roles were sometimes so vividly contrasted that a single stutterer would have conversations with himself before the mirror or an observer. It was often fascinating to see the type of therapist role assumed. In all of our stutterers this was first a punitive authoritarian role. The stutterer as a clinician commanded, reproached, advised, and generally raised hell. In this role he was often remarkably fluent. The stutterer as a case, in the very same mirror situation, would be halting, guilty, weak, or complaining. If stuttering is a neurotic buffer against psychosis, we should have driven all of our cases crazy under this regime. None of them showed any but healthy gains.

Gradually, under our guidance, the therapist-stutterer began to change, to become more understanding and permissive. As their supervisor (and we worked only with the therapist-stutterers, not with the stuttering cases) we concentrated on building skills and insights, in clarifying goals, ventilating emotions, sharing anxieties and frustrations. Our own clinicians and staff found it difficult to adapt themselves to this new orientation and often interfered with the growth of the stutterer as a self-therapist. The cases themselves fought it too. It was much easier to be the passive recipient of therapy than its director. Resistance and sabotage somehow lost some of their secret savor. It was a difficult therapy, demanding constant supervision and intimate knowledge by the therapist of each case and the clinician, but we learned a lot about the dynamics of therapy. And so did they. About November, when we could see that they had begun to accept the basic responsibility for self-direction through assigned activities, we further motivated them to become stuttering-therapists by telling them that in February we were accepting another group of new stutterers for whom they would have to serve as clinicians. This did much to overcome the last resistances.

The basic pattern of therapy for this year has been published by this author in the *Journal of Speech and Hearing Disorders* for December, 1949, Volume XIV, pages 303–306, under the title: "To the Stutterer as He Begins His Speech Therapy," and there is no need to repeat it here in detail. We suggest that the reader refer to the article if he desires to understand the basic attitudes underlying this year's therapy. Briefly, we organized the therapy in terms of 14 subgoals, introduced one after the other so that each new one would add to rather than replace the subgoal-oriented activities previously experienced. Perhaps we should quote a portion of this article to show the sequence:

We will now outline the therapy. Our basic aim is to teach you *how to stutter, and without obvious abnormality, in a way which does not interrupt the flow of your speech.* If you can do this, it should solve your speech difficulty. It should eliminate most of your fears, both of speaking situations and of difficult words. Free speech then is the by-product rather than the goal of our therapy. We want to teach you how to stutter so quickly, effortlessly and unnoticeably that your stuttering will be no impediment whatsoever. You probably have observed before this that no two stutterers stutter in exactly the same way. Is there then still another way which has less abnormality in it? We hope to show you.

It would be pleasant for all of us if this goal could be achieved instantly but our experience shows us that it cannot. You have been stuttering in your present fashion too long. You have strong fears and habits and attitudes which cannot be erased so easily. First of all we must weaken the old reactions, the long-practiced form of stuttering which you now possess. Right now you stutter automatically, almost involuntarily. You have little control either of your speech or of your emotions. Therefore, we must proceed up a long ladder of sub-goals each of which takes you closer to the conquest of your speech defect.

Here is the ladder, beginning with the bottom rung:

1. You must understand the over-all plan of treatment.
2. You must, for the time being, be willing to stutter openly and without embarrassment.
3. You must acquire the ability to keep good eye contact with your listener throughout your moment of stuttering.
4. You must stop avoiding feared words and speech situations.
5. You must stop postponing, half-hearted speech attempts, and retrials.
6. You must be able to analyze your own stuttering in terms of its varying symptoms.
7. You must learn how to cancel. This refers to a technique wherein you go right through your old stuttering block, then pause during which you study the block you have just had, then try the word again in a different way.
8. You must master the principle of negative practice. By this we mean that you must be able to duplicate or initiate at will each typical sample of your own stuttering.
9. You must uncondition or weaken your habitual reactions of approach or release.
10. You must learn how to pull-out of your old blocks voluntarily, to get them under voluntary control before uttering the word.

11. You must learn how to prepare for the speech attempt of feared words, so that they can be spoken without interruption or abnormality.
12. You must learn how to build barriers against disturbing influences.
13. You must learn to fill much of your speech with voluntary loose movements of your tongue, lips, and jaws.
14. You must learn how to reinforce your new fluency each day.

Our therapy was organized in terms of group meetings three days each week which lasted about an hour and a half. These were used to clarify goals and ways of achieving them. The stutterers and their clinicians then devised assignments and activities which would help them come closer to the attainment of these goals. Written and verbal reports were used. The clinicians served as observers and evaluators of the stuttering-therapist's clinical skills in handling himself and, as we have said before, they often took charge directly despite our admonitions not to do so. There were some weeks when we met daily and some days when we had two group sessions instead of one, but in general we followed the plan we have sketched. We were impressed by the tremendous amount of work many of these cases did and how well they did it. We accompanied many of our cases on their tours within the city, listened to their phone calls and recordings, heard them speak to our classes, observed them reporting their experiences to themselves and their clinicians. Compared to other years, the output of actual effort was impressive. The sequential arrangement of subgoals seemed to be in itself a powerful motivator. Until they learned how to cancel and became able to do it well under stress, they could not go on to the next subgoal activity of attaining skill in negative practice. There was a feeling of progressive movement which in other years had occurred by spurts followed by long periods of plateau and consolidation or regression. The course of therapy seemed to be much more steady.

Our fall group of stutterers for intensive therapy consisted of eight men, all with severe stuttering abnormality, intense situation and word fears, and a variety of adjustment problems. One was having occasional *petit mal* epileptic attacks; another had been thrown out of his home; another was "called" to be a preacher; they were full of troubles apart from stuttering. Six of these made very steady progress, achieving much in terms of the sequential goals with no marked loss during either the Thanksgiving or Christmas holidays. By the end of the semester they were speaking very fluently, were not avoiding words or situations, and the little stuttering they had was handled fluently with conscious preparatory sets or pull-outs. They were markedly desensitized to stress situations. Two of the stutterers made less satisfactory progress, always lagging behind the others in goal attainment, in amount of self-therapy and responsibility, but they came to the end of the intensive therapy semester with marked improvement over entrance and were working fitfully on their stutterings. Both of these relapsed badly over the Christmas holidays.

As we mentioned earlier, the terminal therapy for this year consisted of assuming the role of therapist for another stutterer. This involved demonstration, explanation of methods, joint entrance into stress speaking situations, and much sharing of experiences and emotions. Four of the six were each given a new stutterer as his special case; the other two served as roving clinicians, sometimes joining one of the new stutterers or working with some stutterers not in the exploratory group with whom we were doing other therapy. For some of the new stutterers a normal-speaking clinician assisted at times, as did the staff. Group sessions were held as before, and the basic sequence of therapy was the same for the second semester as it was for the fall. By June all but three of the eight stutterers were remarkably fluent and free from fears or avoidances. These three included the two of whom we have written earlier. None of the six experienced any real relapse over the summer and were in good shape the following Christmas, and one of the three had made some gains. Two were still stuttering severely at times, though they were not as severe as they had been upon entrance.

The five-year follow-up was pretty gratifying. Seven of the ten were able to satisfy our criteria of success: adequate fluency, no apparent abnormality under stress, little or no fear of situations or words, good personal and social adjustment. They were talking better than this therapist. Of the three others, all are speaking in ordinary situations without undue abnormality or fear, though under great stress some stuttering appears, along with some avoidance. One of these is a successful speech therapist, another a preacher, the third a salesman. All of these are speaking as well or better than they did at the end of the first semester. We have been able to talk at length with all but one of these individuals and feel sure that this year's therapy was remarkably successful.

One word or two here about the five-year criterion. How can we take credit for any improvement that occurs subsequent to the termination of therapy? Surely much of it may depend upon such factors as a good job, escape from rejecting parents, new family relationships, a thousand things. We agree completely and are actually under no illusions about the part we play in any therapy. This is also why we report our cases' progress as of the end of intensive and terminal therapy. A few of our apparent failures of the latter date become successful two, four, five, even eight years later. However, we have seen none of our apparent successes at the end of terminal therapy return to their preclinic behavior. We have had the feeling that favorable and unfavorable factors probably balance themselves out or that the unfavorable ones predominate. We know that exposure to eight months of experiences such as our stutterers went through must have profoundly affected their lives. They also feel and report that much of their success stems from the training they received, the start they got. They feel that life without the support of the clinic was tougher than the therapy itself. Moreover, it has not been our experience that stutterers as severe as these individuals would tend to show any marked five-year improvement due to economic or social success alone. But we may be wrong. We are not going to worry too much about it so long as these ten poor devils are remarkably verbal and happy today.

The four new stutterers who entered the clinic in February did almost as well. Two of the four satisfy our five-year criteria; one of them is pretty fluent in most situations; one is a mess as he always was. The other two were speaking very well by June. Two had mild relapses that summer but had made marked progress by the following Christmas. However, we were not too impressed with the effectiveness of using the former cases as clinicians. It was fine for the former cases but not so good for the new stutterers. In terminal therapy, stutterer-clinicians tended to make excessive demands, to be very punitive, and we were constantly having to protect the new stutterers against their overexposure of weakness and exorbitant demands. They sounded like the psychiatrist Barbara[4] in his book on stuttering. We gave each of these new stutterers some weekly individual-counseling sessions with us to salve their wounds and relieve their hostilities and frustrations. It looked as though we had found a very good terminal therapy which we would not be able to use. So ended the year of 1948–1949.

This year we also carried out some "experiments" with other stutterers not included in the groups mentioned above. Two of them may be of interest. We had a gangling freshman, weak and immature, with an incredible variety of avoidance tricks, who seemed unable to make a real attempt on any feared word but had to postpone and filibuster until the pain of his long wait exceeded his fear of being unable to utter the word if he did try. Tremors traumatized him. He was also highly aware of his sexual needs but quite unable to attempt conversation with a girl because of his expectancy of rejection. At the time we had a student therapist, a senior girl who had no objection to kissing boys in the interests of scientific research. We enlisted her aid. The stutterer and this student therapist were placed before a mirror, and he was required to read some isolated words which he feared. For every three words on which he stuttered but

[4] D. A. Barbara, *Stuttering,* New York, Julian Press, 1954.

did not avoid or postpone, she kissed him gaily and enthusiastically. After three or four of these very vivid experiences, he was unable to stutter. We then used consecutive material, which procured a few more kisses before the stuttering disappeared. Then the stutterer made some phone calls. The boy went back to his dormitory exhausted but with the first free speech in years. He was back the next day seeking for more and avoiding as usual, but the experiment was over. He reported, however, that stuttering was never so feared again, and he was later able to do considerably more direct therapy than previously. This reward no doubt increased the approach gradient sufficiently to resolve some of his ambivalence.

We also carried out another procedure based on the same hypothesis. One of our stutterers was a very negative 13-year-old, big for his age and full of hostility. He hated his stuttering, his listener, himself, his parents, and especially this therapist, who was trying to help him. He had very few avoidance tricks and few word or phonetic fears, though he was fearful of certain situations. He characteristically blundered into tremors of the lips and jaws, increased his tension tremendously, then attempted to jaw-jerk his way out to them. He was full of frustration. Unable to establish any real rapport with him, we took him into the laboratory, gave him a strong electric shock, then told him he could fasten us onto the coil and give us a stronger shock for every five stutterings he could collect in oral reading. He collected his five in a hurry, pushed up the coil, and shoved on the juice, whereupon we jumped and screamed though we actually had broken the circuit with an unethical foot. He loved it. We saw him smile for the first time, the little stinker. And he returned enthusiastically to his reading. We had to jump twice more before his stuttering disappeared, but it did quite completely. We continued this for several days with marked transfer into his ordinary communication too. When he stuttered he would tend to smile slightly in memoriam. Then he discovered the cutoff switch. Much more needs to be done in investigating the effect of reward on the frequency and severity of stuttering.

1949–1950

This year we decided to emphasize the group-membership feeling as a vital part of therapy and to play down the assignments while still keeping the same "ladder" or sequence of subgoals. Our idea was this: to set up each subgoal as one which each member of the group must attain before *any* member of the group would be allowed to work on the subgoal next up the sequence. We felt that this arrangement might bring along the laggards while keeping the few who move too rapidly in therapy from doing so. Since it was obvious that no single subgoal could ever be attained completely, sets of criteria were set up so that all of us would know who were ready to go ahead and who were not. Thus subgoal 2, the willingness to stutter openly and without obvious embarrassment, would have to be demonstrated so that this behavior occurred in 90 percent of clinic speech, 80 percent in casual mealtime talk, and 75 percent of the times in our stress-testing situations.

Each Friday was set aside for this stress testing, the stutterers being taken down into the city and put through a series of difficult speaking situations while the examiner counted the number of times the case stuttered with or without obvious willingness or embarrassment. The clinic speech was also evaluated in this way. The stutterers reported on their own and each other's speech in mealtime conversation. As soon as all of the members of the group had passed the tests, the group as a whole could move on to the next subgoal, which was the ability to maintain good eye contact with the listener during stuttering. Since some provision had to be made to take care of the stutterer who enjoyed pulling the group down to his own inadequate level and keeping them from moving, we set up this mechanism: If any one stutterer held back all the others from advancing to a new subgoal for two consecutive weeks, he was ejected from the group and received individual therapy outside it. He was told that he could not return unless the group voted that he could do so, and then only after each member had done his own testing.

Therapy consisted of daily group sessions in which the goal to be attained was clarified, related to the final goal, and various activities and experiences suggested which might facilitate the process. Sample assignments were given but no stutterer need use them. The experiences of the stutterers of the previous year were provided in terms of their old written reports and some oral testimony from two of them who were in the vicinity. The student therapists sat in on all group meetings and discussed and observed the stutterers at work. They also went with them into outside situations. Written and oral reports were not required but most of the stutterers offered them. Charts of the progress of each stutterer were posted daily and weekly. This program was initiated after subgoal 1: "To understand the overall course of treatment" had been presented and worked upon. At least 20 outside-the-clinic speech situations were the daily quota. These the stutterer deliberately entered or contrived so that he could work on the particular subgoal of the period. Rating sheets were frequently provided so that the stutterer could realistically estimate the amount and quality of his performance. Here are some samples, the first for October, 1949, the second for January, 1950.

REPORT FOR STUTTERERS

Week ending October 4

Name: Harold ———

Item	*Percentage of the week's 100 speech situations in which the item was to be found*
Understood what was expected of you	100
Willingness to work	86
Sabotage and resistance	5
Avoidance of feared words (including postponement)	32
Avoidance of speaking situations	3
Disregarding blocks; ignoring detaching	93
Calmness during blocks	75
General emotional control adequate (inner feelings of purposiveness without turmoil, hatred, panic)	64
Analytical interest in stuttering behavior, in what you do when you stutter, in the symptoms	68
Crucial experiences in which real insight came; trophies	7

As we reviewed this chart, we wondered how accurate the judgments were and looked over this case's written accounts of his 100 speech situations for the week. We were surprised to find that quite a case could be made for the numbers listed in the percentages. It must be remembered also that this was only the second week of therapy. This case, however, had been to innumerable other speech clinics prior to his entrance in ours.

These check lists and rating scales were given to the stutterers frequently, but the basic criteria for advancing to a new subgoal were based upon our Friday testing periods. These were rather unpleasant days for stutterers and clinicians alike, and so were the Mondays that followed failure. Those stutterers who had made some real advance and had worked hard were very hostile to those who had done less or had failed. There was anxiety on Fridays and aggression on Mondays, to which we responded as well as we could, using these feelings to reflect the nature of the problem and the person. One of our cases was ejected, and then the whole group made a fast advance. He received individual coaching and training, returned, was accepted, and the group bogged down. The stutterers worked with the laggards. They sought them out in the evenings and made them work until the wee hours. There was at least one fist fight. Our Monday group sessions became pretty livid with pointed profanity at times as the leaders resigned themselves to another long week with the slower ones.

This is another check list for another case for January 9.

STUTTERER'S CHECK LIST

Date: 1/9/50 Pierson D. B.

I. *Pre-Spasm Control*	
Did nothing to prepare in advance	xxxxxxxxxxxxxxx
Rehearsed the old blocks	xxxxxxxxxxxxxxxxxxxxxxxxxxx
Rejected the old blocks	xxxxxxxxxxxxxxxxxxxxxxxxxxxxxxxx
Planned to begin	
A. With air flow or sound timed with moment of speech attempt	xxxxxxxxxxxxxxxxx
B. Loose contact	xxxxxxxxxxxxxxxxxxxxxxxxxxxxxxxxx
C. With slow movement	xxxxxxxxxxxxxxxxxxxxxxxxxxxxx
D. With next sound in mouth or mind	xxxxxxxxxxxx
II. *Tremor Control*	
A. Without retrial	xxxxxxxx
B. Without jerk release	xxxxxxxxxxxxxxxxxx
C. Smoothed	xxxxxxxxxxxxxxxxxxxxxxxxxxxxxxxxxxxxxxxxxxxx
D. With decrease in hard contact and tension	xxxxxxxxxxx
E. Slowed down	xxxxxxxxxxxxxx
F. Did nothing to get control	xxxxxx
III. *Post-Spasm Control*	
A. Cancelled the word in another sentence	xxxxxxxxxxxx
B. Paused long enough before repeating word	xxxxxxxxxxxxxxxxxxxxxxxxxxxx
C. Had good eye contact	xxxxxxxxxxxxxxxxxxxxxxxxxxxxxxxxxxxxxxxxxxxxxxxx
D. Careful second speech attempt	xxxxxxxxxxxxxxx
E. Did nothing	xxxxxxx

Progress was not steady as it had been the preceding year, nor was it as swift. By Thanksgiving the group had just managed to get to subgoal 5: "Eliminating postponements, retrials, and half-hearted speech attempts." The amount of situation fear, however, had markedly decreased and some reduction in severity and frequency had appeared in three of the seven stutterers who comprised this group. (One of these was in individual therapy at this time.) No change appeared during this first holiday. By Christmas they had attained subgoal 7, the ability to cancel perfectly. Only two of the eight showed a real decline over this holiday period, but they all seemed glad to get back in harness. One of these, a Canadian, could not return. By the end of the semester three were very fluent, one was in bad shape and so discouraged he left the clinic right then, while the others were improved but still fearing words and some situations and unable to do much with their blockings. One of the three best cases we discharged, whereupon he had several severe relapses but each time regained his controlled fluency.

Terminal therapy this year was not organized. The stutterers made individual appointments upon request. Several of them sat in on another group-therapy session which began that second semester and which we used as a pilot program in what we might call "speech psychotherapy." This will be reported later. By June the Canadian had reported a severe relapse, and so had two others. The other five were doing fairly well, but only four of them satisfied our criteria of success, and one of these was pretty shaky with anxiety. Five years later, four of them (including the chap last mentioned) were doing fine; one was improved over February, and three were in bad shape, as severely handicapped as they had been upon entrance. So if we were to rate ourselves as we demanded that our long-suffering stutterers must, we reached only 50 percent of our goal.

As we look back at that period through perusal of our notes and the case files, we feel that the provision that the group could not go faster than its weakest member was the fatal flaw. When a case is ready to move, he should be enabled to do so. This readiness may not last long. There was also no real group feeling of security. Each member's weakness was a direct threat to the progress of every other member. Suspicion, accusation, resentment, and reproach do not make a good climate for effective therapy. The laggards still lagged. Change takes time, and some people change more slowly than others. The program looked fine on paper but it was hell to operate. We never tried it that way again.

1950–1951

This was again our test year, in which we tried to put together all the best parts of our previous therapy and reviewed all of it before beginning. We added nothing new, though we subtracted plenty. Again we had eight severe stutterers. One was an almost illiterate would-be preacher from Arkansas, who stuttered faster and longer than any stutterer we had seen. Another was the rejected son of a millionaire who spent hours each day conducting the Philharmonic via a miserable phonograph in a miserable room and who stuttered on the trumpet. A third wanted to be a teacher or a priest, the fourth (a farm boy from Illinois) was intent on becoming a radio announcer, the fifth wanted to teach and coach, and the other two weren't sure they could ever do anything. About all they had in common was this therapist and their stuttering. Actually, they did not even have this therapist very much after the first week because a Mrs. Margaret Neely joined our staff that year. She had been one of our earlier successful stuttering cases and had since had a very successful career in clinical work both in Canada and in this country. In order to test the adequacy of our methods of therapy, and to play down the importance of this therapist's personality or experience, we therefore turned over the major problem and a portion of the responsibility for therapy to her. We did reserve the right to organize it and plan it, however, and occasionally, upon her request, we took over a group session or interviewed a case.

The therapy was again organized in terms of the same sequential goals, but each person could go as swiftly as he wished. Evaluation was done by the therapist, the individual clinician, and the case himself. When they all agreed that he had achieved a fair degree of adequacy in the attainment of this goal, he could add another one and start working on it too. The individual clinicians were given more responsibility for clarification, suggested activities, and general supervision and they turned in daily reports and evaluations of the case's performance. Group meetings were used to introduce the various goals, ventilate emotional responses to the regime, practice and demonstrate. In these meetings, all of the earlier techniques such as talking-and-writing or voluntary stuttering or adaptation were presented on a free-choice basis. The stutterer could use them or not in pursuit of his subgoals. Sample assignments were formulated and were available though not mandatory. The stutterer was urged to create his own speech situations, his own assignments. Check lists and rating scales were likewise provided so that realistic inventory taking would be possible. Detailed reports of experiences were stressed. We present one for October 20 from a severe stutterer who later became a priest:

SPEECH EXPERIENCES I GAVE MYSELF FRIDAY, OCTOBER 20

Goal I am working on:

Goals 1, 2, and 3. I passed my tests on 1 and 2 and hope to pass 3 a week from today. Had hoped to be able to do so this week but as this report will indicate, I'm not ready. I still have to keep working on understanding my problem and what to do about it and also on being willing to have enough stuttering out in open so I can learn to control and reduce it.

My difficulties:

Sometimes it seems as though my eye movements are extremely important in gluing my stuttering together. I jerk words out using an eye-blink or a sudden squeezing of my eyeballs so my friends here tell me, but I don't know what that means, and I have also been accused of squinting as I try to force or squeeze the word out. All of these things I do to get out of my tightly vibrating sticking of lips or tongue.

There is some other "eye-trouble" which is different. It comes before I am stuck and when I am afraid. I glance away from my audience so I will not have to see his distress or revulsion. I also feel my strength ebbing away when I am talking and I feel a hard word coming. With this fear and weakness always comes a loss of eye-contact, a shiftiness of gaze. In the mirror yesterday I saw how I often duck my head just before I hit the word. As I do this I take a little peek to see what my audience is thinking. It is almost a ritual, half prayer and half curse.

There is also a characteristic gesture I have. When I feel trouble coming my hand creeps up to my face and I find myself rubbing my eye with my index finger. I don't understand this. It too is almost uncontrollable at times. Help, Help.

What I have done:

1. I talked to my clinician in front of the mirror trying desperately to watch her face or my own mouth during my blocks. Total score: 12 successes; 17 failures; 2 doubtfuls. She was able to cause me trouble by showing reactions of impatience and disgust. I must discipline myself.
2. I made four phone calls, using prewritten speech marked with cues about not squeezing eyes, keep hand down, etc. Had a hand mirror before me so I could watch and see how well I did. Failed on the first two; had a part success on the third call on one word anyway because I resisted any squeezing, blinking, or closing but I seemed to widen my eyes a little just before the word came out. On the last call I didn't have any stuttering though I had encircled enough for three weeks. I felt as though the magic mirror with my eyes in it had somehow kept me from stuttering. I don't think this is good.
3. I tried the same words again and again until I could have some mild stuttering on them without any eye shift or other reaction. I did this to Ted in a conversation. The words and the number of times I had to try it again are: bus (5); Beckwith (6); Peters (2);

Grand Rapids (2). This was a very disturbing experience, a fighting of the devil in you, with Satan very strong. I tried one other word, "business," at least eight or nine times and never did win.

4. I went downtown with Mike Graham on situations and had him suggest some and rate me on willingness, calmness, and eye-contact in each. I enclose details on separate sheet. I feel that these were valuable experiences and that I might be able to conquer myself in time, though I still have far to go. You know, it almost seems right now as though if I could control my eyes, I might control my mouth. Why is this? Could we have a discussion of this in group meeting?

5. Acting on a suggestion from my clinician, I tried faking the odd eye stuff on non-feared words. It was very difficult to do. I tried but my clinician said they weren't the same.

6. I collected some specimens. The clerk at the Greyhound had blue eyes. She tried to act composed. She swayed a little. My blocks did not bother me except I tried to hurry them and cut them short. I felt I had control of situation.

Clerk at Burdick Hotel who I asked for Grand Rapids papers had grey eyes. I started to lower my head and eyes but caught myself in time in spite of her look of surprise. Even held one block on "papers" longer than I needed to and kept watching her.

Clerk in paint store (man) had blue eyes, though I don't know when I saw them. He tried to put words into my mouth and was very nervous. I lowered my head and squeezed my eyes twice while in blocks (one on each block). Felt upset afterwards. Why can a stranger affect me so?

How I am doing:

I really don't know. I'm working on my speech more of the time than I thought possible for me. And it's interesting, almost painfully fascinating at times. I may possibly be able to pass the test for Goal 3 next Friday. I don't know. I'll try. I'm still making progress on the first two goals which is good. But will I ever be really willing to work?

We do not wish to imply that all the reports were of this quality, but the one given reflects pretty well the spirit of the therapy and some of its dynamics. If the reader can envision the cumulative impact of a hundred days of such therapy, all structured in terms of movement toward a goal, he will understand how hard a stutterer would have to cling to his stuttering in order to fail. But fail they could.

By deer season (and we gave our stutterers the full week, even though Mrs. Neely could have presided except for the two-day Thanksgiving holiday) five of the eight were doing very well, one was in pretty fair shape, and two were sabotaging, resisting, and doing little more than token work. They had spread themselves out in terms of the progression of goals. The leader (whose report has been used above) was on goal 9; another stutterer was on goal 8; three were on goal 7 (canceling), one on goal 5, and the two sluggards were still on goal 3. We gave these last two some individual help ourselves, but to little avail.

By Christmas, the horses were still running around the track in exactly the same order, though they had advanced slightly. Daily report letters were requested during the holidays and the stutterers were expected to continue to work on the particular goal before them without respite. They all eased off, however, and had lost some of their momentum and gains when they returned. By the end of the semester, all but one of the eight stutterers were remarkably fluent, better than any group we had ever had at that particular inventory time. One of them, a borderline psychotic, returned to his home and railroad job against our advice and wishes, and gradually lost his friendly fluency, flexibility, and reality-testing attitudes and returned to the dull, inhibited, and surprisingly unemotional stuttering reactions he had shown upon entrance.

If we may digress for a moment, this individual, we feel, uses his stuttering as a defense against psychosis. He returned for further therapy another year later and we have studied him thoroughly. He belongs to the psychiatrist, not the speech therapist. Unfortunately the psychiatrist will not accept him. With group acceptance, a routine job, and an easier, more tolerable form of stuttering, we seem to have the situation pretty well contained. After his fashion he is quite content now. He comes for an occasional checkup. His speech is pretty fluent, probably as fluent as it should be. These must be the stutterers who go to the psychiatrists. The overwhelming majority of our cases are not prepsychotic or neurotic individuals. A small minority are. Most of our cases are people who have been constantly frustrated and penalized for their verbal deviations. When we survey their histories we continue to wonder why they are not more neurotic or psychotic. They are actually a remarkably tough breed of cats to be able to stand so much and still be so normally human.

We lost three of our cases from terminal therapy that year, including the person described in the paragraph above and the priest-to-be, who became a teacher of design. The other five met with us generally about twice each week, using the periods for oral reports of progress or decline in terms of the goal activities in which they had been trained. A few individual conferences were also held. The musician received some nondirective counseling. By June six of the eight stutterers were able to satisfy our criteria of success. Two of these suffered mild relapses during the summer but one regained his fluency and adequacy by Christmas. Our five-year checkup shows that five of the eight cases are very fluent, largely free from fear and avoidance, and socially adequate. Three of the group do not satisfy our criteria. The Arkansas preacher-to-be went back to his home state, studied for the ministry, preached to the deaf, began to stutter in his fingering of words and then in his speech, and is now back in the clinic receiving further help. His speech is pretty good actually, and if he were to have any other mission in life he would probably have no real problem. The prepsychotic we have already described. His speech does not satisfy our criteria, but it probably does his own. The third of our "failures" still has situation and word fears but the abnormality of speech is usually very mild. All in all, we feel that this testing year was quite satisfactory, and it demonstrated that another therapist could administer our therapy with success. Some of the confusion, the playing-by-ear, the subtlety of the therapeutic process, had been eliminated. Both the therapist and the stutterer could understand what they were doing and why they were doing it. The therapy was still too demanding of energy, time, and devotion, but it was pretty clear. If a stutterer was willing, or could be made willing, to do the necessary work, we could feel pretty sure that he could become fluent. We might not be able to cure him, to clear the slate on which so many fears and frustrations had dug their styli deep, but we could train him to stutter fluently and to cope successfully with both those fears and those frustrations.

We were far from satisfied with our efforts. There must be easier ways of doing the job. Why need we have to battle so much for the stutterer's coöperation, for his work output? Were not many of these goals almost duplicates of one another, all parts of a desensitization process or a reconditioning one? Why did we have to concentrate only on the stuttering behavior? Why not do some therapy using the normal speech which even severe stutterers have in abundance? There was need for better terminal therapy. And how about the psychotherapy which seemed to color almost every aspect of the speech therapy we were using? We decided to spend another five years in exploring these alleys. We had found one tortuous route through the maze and had tasted the cheese. But there must be shorter paths or too many rats would quit running, or keep entering the same cul-de-sacs over and over again. So ended the first 15 years.

1951 Spring Semester

This spring semester we accepted four new stutterers and placed them on an intensive program of therapy in which we attempted to explore the possibilities of combining psychotherapy and speech therapy. We again used the same series of subgoals with a testing program similar to that of the fall, with each stutterer permitted to go at his own pace. We usually had one group meeting each day, occasionally two. The remainder of the afternoon they spent with their clinicians entering feared speaking situations and discussing their feelings and behavior. These four clinicians were very good ones, older and better trained, and we had stressed in their training the principles of nondirective counseling. Their task was to follow each bit of observed behavior under stress with a counseling period on the spot. They then wrote up their summaries, along with an analysis of their interviewing errors and client responses. The cases wrote up accounts of their experiences in speaking and made continuous judgments concerning their approach to the particular goals for which they were striving.

These four stutterers were selected because they had especially severe emotional problems along with their stuttering. One of them not only had a bad case of acne but had set fires and stolen shotgun shells compulsively, among other forms of abnormal behavior. Another came from a broken home, had guilt feelings about the divorce and was unable to speak under any threat of interruption or listener loss. Another was a big fellow, aggressive and smoldering with hostility. The fourth, babied and browbeaten by a mother who was a religious fanatic, was almost totally helpless in a world of stress in which he felt almost completely incompetent.

Group therapy with these cases was conducted again by Mrs. Neely, but we had individual interviews with both the clinicians and cases weekly. We generally stayed clear from historical material, preferring to use the stutterer's current behavior rather than that of his past for insight into the dynamics of the personality. Group sessions were entirely oriented in terms of speech therapy, clarification of goals, demonstration of methods, and testing of responses used to modify the stuttering behavior.

Our student therapists made many errors in their interviewing, but in spite of them all four stutterers made some real progress in self-understanding. It was interesting that many of the most crucial insights seemed to emerge in the periods immediately following a stuttering experience, when the case discussed with his clinician what had occurred in that moment of stress. They seemed to emerge at this time but found their most vivid expression in the subsequent conferences with this therapist. Thus the stutterer who stole shotgun shells as an avocation chose a sweet little woman from a large number of other possible auditors passing by and asked her if she could tell him how he might find the Presbyterian Church, please. For the first time he was completely fluent and without stuttering. In the immediate discussion session with his therapist he said, "You watch! My acne will sure get worse now." "You mean," said the student therapist, "that free speech such as that is somehow dangerous, isn't right?" "It means that I can't stand talking so perfect with a woman like her." The rest of that interview yielded no important material, but in the weekly interview with us the stutterer linked his acne, his stealing, and his stuttering together as buffer responses to his mother's idealization, adulation, and exploitation. This is but one of many similar experiences with all four of the cases.

Gradually we came to be convinced that stuttering therapy could provide a potent vehicle for psychotherapy, something we had long suspected. The confrontation of the self, the battle for responsibility, the testing of reality, the facing of fears, the release of emotion, the conflicts in interpersonal reactions with mother figures, father figures, and all the past everywhere—all these involved psychotherapy of some sort.

But was not this the province of the psychiatrist, the professional psychologist? Most of our other students were hardly capable of handling such material and even our four best clinicians were often over their depths. Admittedly these four stutterers were not typical of the ordinary garden variety of stutterers, but the problem still remained. Were we training speech therapists or psychotherapists? The answer had to be the former, though any retraining and rehabilitation process will involve psychotherapy of some kind. Our solution was this: we would attempt to find a type of speech therapy with psychotherapeutic overtones, without interpretation, with some ventilation and expression of emotion—an activity psychotherapy, akin to play therapy in which the stutterer used his stuttering and his attempts to modify it as a means for self-understanding and responsibility. It was a big order, and we approached it with some trepidation. It unfortunately dominated our work for the next five years, as we shall see. In the spring of 1951, however, we were merely using the nondirective interview as a means of understanding the stutterer's behavior as he worked on his speech problem. We were not using semantic psychotherapy; we were using free and controlled stuttering instead of free or controlled association.

We also used this group to explore the effectiveness of a longer period of terminal therapy. They remained with us a total of at least two years, excluding vacations. During the following fall semester we conducted this terminal therapy through frequent interviews and some participation in group sessions with the new crop of stutterers. The second year they consulted with us infrequently according to their need. These interviews were largely psychotherapeutic in nature.

The results may be reported as follows: By June, at the end of the intensive therapy, all four were speaking pretty fluently, though all had some situation and word fears. All had an occasional severe stuttering reaction under extreme stress, but they were pretty satisfied with their progress in speech. Two of them had mild relapses that summer but soon regained their fluency during the fall. They served us well the following year in our new stuttering groups. Two of them became successful speech therapists, one a high-school teacher, and the fourth a successful salesman. Five years later, only one of them reports any concern with his speech, though all of them stutter mildly upon relatively rare occasions. One had a severe relapse three years later but recovered completely.

It has been interesting to see that all but one of them have made excellent personal adjustments despite some stormy interludes and have been living successfully both vocationally and socially. Even our one dubious case could scarcely be called a failure. The other three satisfy our criteria. In view of the fact that we made no real attempt to deal with the other problems of these cases but concentrated instead upon the stuttering behavior as the route to adequate adjustment, it seems probable that psychotherapy with the stutterer should deal directly with the stuttering. We have known literally hundreds of stutterers who have received the traditional forms of psychotherapy from experts, and who had benefited from them to some degree, but we have seen little reduction in the stuttering or in its own specific anxieties and frustration. All the other problems and conflicts which beset the stutterer seem to become intertwined with it. If we can grasp the stuttering firmly and drag it out into the open, most of the other troubles come with it. There they too can be coped with.

1951–1952

We determined to concentrate our efforts for the next five years on psychotherapy. Therefore this year we turned the actual speech therapy over to our student clinicians and the stutterers themselves. We conducted all the daily group meetings and suggested types of activities which the stutterers could use to come to grips with their stuttering. These suggesions were always general, not specific. The process of therapy was again viewed as a sequential attaining of skills in these respects: (1) willingness to work with the stuttering and the self; (2) eliminating avoidance behavior; (3) negative practice (faking); (4) cancellation; (5) pull-outs; and (6) the use of high-stimulus normal speech. With the exception of the last item, the teaching of these skills and activities were the responsibility of the student clinicians, all of whom had had previous experience in stuttering therapy. We deliberately played down the speech therapy, the retraining, the substitution of new ways of reacting to the fears and frustrations of stuttering, and we emphasized the exploration of the self as reflected in stuttering and stuttering therapy. Both stutterers and clinicians contributed freely to the group discussions, and the therapist began to play a very permissive and subordinate role in the group interaction, defining his position as a catalyst rather than a leader. Daily reports of speech-therapy activities and discussions subsequent to speech-therapy experiences were turned in by both clinicians and cases. They too tended to be more concerned with psychotherapy than with the actual retraining.

One of our own protocols from the fourth week of therapy may illustrate the type of group sessions.

As the stutterers came into the room, they performed their usual ritual of going up to the big mirror, confronting themselves, and saying, "Hi, stutterer," faking their old stuttering as they did so. The clinicians did the same thing but said other things such as, "So this is how you would stutter if you had to." They then sat in the circle around the group room, Bruce as usual apart from the others and Jim as close to me as he could get. Some casual banter occurred and they looked at me occasionally to see if I would get the group formally organized. I just waited, about ten minutes after everyone was there, and some tension began to appear, some restlessness, pauses and glances at me. Finally Wes blurted, "For Christ's sake, aren't we going to get going?" The others grinned and nodded.

Bruce said, "Oh I like this better anyway." Moe growled, "You would!" and so I said, "You feel we ought to get organized? Anybody want to tell the group something?" They looked at Wes then, who wriggled, postponed, hemmed and hawed and then said, "Well, I've been feeling that you'd be pretty disgusted with me if you knew how little I've actually been working on my speech. This weekend I hardly did anything but write down a few words that I had done some good pullouts on . . ." The stutterers looked at me, though Wes had looked at the other stutterers so I just looked interested. Then Bill said, "Aw nuts, you know you always do more than the rest of us. You're just trying to make us tell how poorly we did over the weekend so you'll feel better." The others grinned and Wes went into a long disclaimer.

Then Bruce broke in. "Hell, if you guys goofed off, I did a little real work for a change. Pat and I and some others had a long talk on the dogma of the Catholic church, and I horned in plenty and cancelled every one of the blocks I had. If they started interrupting, I just cancelled louder. It felt good."

Jim said, "That isn't difficult for you, Bruce. You can do anything if you can see a chance to be obnoxious." There was a chorus of amens with plenty of hostility which Bruce enjoyed and prepared to exploit as usual, so I stepped in and said, "Most of us find it tough to work on weekends. I suppose it's because . . ." I fumbled and pretended to think.

"It's because we think of our speech work as work, or school work, and Sunday's our day off," said Joe. "Anyway, that's how I feel about it."

"Ya," said Moe, "It's really hard to believe that we really are stutterers. I keep finding myself disbelieving that. And that's why we can't keep working with it. I'm not a stutterer except when I am stuck, no matter what I say in the mirror."

"That's why Jerry is unwilling to do any faking, I bet," said his clinician. Jerry nodded agreement.

Here followed quite a free discussion of denial of stuttering, of pretenses, of the pain of being abnormal and the ways they used to escape that pain. Most of them entered the discussion at some time, and then I believe it was Moe who said, "The trouble with all you birds, and me too, is that we're too soft, too sensitive. We quit before we fight. I always have, just like my old man. He'd do anything to keep the peace and my mother pulled him around by the nose. Maybe that's why I always have more trouble talking to older women . . ."

There was quite a long pause about this point and they were thinking. Then Ted, a clinician, said, "Hell, it isn't just you stutterers that have trouble like that. I always get tense when I have to ask favors of any older man, and hesitant too. My father is king of his castle. How come you're always so sure you're unique? You're just a bunch of babies blaming everything on your stuttering."

They jumped Ted plenty at this point and there were many expressions of hostility toward normal speakers, with examples of the hurts they had received from their hands. Then Dennis said slowly, "You know, just the same Ted has a point. Maybe we use our stuttering as a good excuse to keep from being disappointed in ourselves, or having others be disappointed in us. If we talked OK, we'd have to be judged the same as others. Maybe that's why I find it so hard to try to pull out of my blocks . . ."

There was more, but this is enough to illustrate the typical group process. Stuttering therapy was the theme, but it provides plenty of room for insights, interpretations by other members, and emotional expression.

Perhaps as a reflection of the emphasis in the group sessions, the individual speech therapy sessions with the clinicians and the self-therapy also became psychotherapeutically oriented despite our attempts to keep them primarily a process of learning and unlearning. Here is an excerpt from a stutterer's report:

My clinician, damn his soul, insisted that I set maximum and minimum goals for cancellations, for pullouts and for entering feared situations today. I fought him good and had him all confused and enjoyed it. He got mad and quit, and then I went into the recording room and turned the auditory training unit up to 120 db and said I'll listen to it and injure myself and then I'll blame it on him or you and sue you or I won't have to hear myself stuttering again anyway. Then I thought, what the hell's wrong with you, Bruce, and why now? Then I thought it's that damned maximum-minimum business and my old man always having to be perfect, and thinking that I got to be perfect too. I sure was in a stew because to be perfect I mustn't stutter. Or if a defect does slip out at home just beat it back down as fast as possible. The only barrier between me and a place in the sun is my rebellious response to work and authority because I never got reward for any job yet, only penalty. So why should I set maximums? Well, anyway, I didn't do a single damned cancellation except twice when I forgot (haha) or pullouts, and I sat on my behind all evening and sulked. How's that for a way to get cured in your clinic? That maximum-minimum stuff sure dug deep. After I calm down, maybe I'll give it a try. What still burns me is that my clinician told me I could set my maximums at one and my minimum at zero if I felt so weak. Hell, I could collect 500 if I tried, like that time I showed up the rest of that bunch of weaklings in the clinic on entering feared situations. But why do I get so hot about this quota setting? Maybe I'll figure it out yet. Don't give up on me, Doc. it's hell to be Irish!

And here is a clinician's report:

Today I unobtrusively observed Moe's pullouts in hard speech situations, having him drop beans from his hand into his pocket for every good one while I counted both success and failures in the same way. In four situations he pulled out of 73 blocks successfully and missed 18. But he only had 42 beans in his pocket, so perhaps some of his pullouts are becoming automatic. He also thought that he had only missed two or three. I told him my count and he was surprised and a little upset over the misses.

Moe seems to be getting restless. He mentioned this today and I could see it too. He doesn't know why. Last week his pullouts were exceptionally good but now they are getting a little too short and tight. He said he feels burdened by them, and feels they should be disappearing but they aren't. It's hard for him to realize that he shouldn't get paid in immediate fluency for his work on his stuttering. He really has worked hard, but he wonders how long he's going to have to keep it up. I think Moe should be moved up to the next goal and start getting some training in high-stimulus speech so he can get some relief. He said he was very depressed last night and all tired out from working on his stuttering, physically bushed. I reflected his feelings but he didn't cheer up much. Can I have a conference?

We began the fall term of intensive therapy with 11 stutterers, 10 men and a girl. The latter dropped out after a few weeks. One of the men was a member of the group but did not have a student clinician, reporting instead to the therapist himself for individual counseling and discussion of his self-therapy. Another member was a freshman with tremendous facial and body spasms, who sat shakily, looking out of the window for the first two months and refusing to enter any group discussion. All were severe stutterers.

By late November this group was far behind the previous groups in their progress. Only two of them had made any substantial gains in freedom from avoidance, fears, or abnormality. By Christmas four of the ten had approximated the progress of previous groups, and most of the members regressed during the holidays. By the end of the semester, however, six of the ten were doing pretty well and the other four had shown some real improvement. Two left the clinic at this time, despite our wishes. Terminal therapy consisted of participation in jobs and school courses which involved much talking and in occasional group and individual conferences. The latter were also psychotherapeutically oriented. By June all of those still with us were quite fluent, but they were not working on the mild stutterings which occasionally occurred, and some evidence of avoidance tricks and miniature stutterings could be found in most of them. They were all very verbal and remarkably well adjusted, whatever that really means.

We have followed all of these cases closely and our report is a sad one. Only two of the ten satisfy our five-year criteria, the worst record we have had. Five others, including four who are (unfortunately, I think) practicing speech therapists, still have too many mild stutterings which they ignore and hope that others will also. They are markedly improved over clinic entrance, however, and are able to communicate effectively most of the time. One other member seems to oscillate between excellent and very poor speech. The remaining two cases are speaking better than they did on entrance, but stutter severely a good many times each day. They have much more fluency, however, than they have ever known. None of these regressed completely. One of the surprising features is that all but one of these stutterers have made an excellent social and vocational adjustment. They are pretty content and successful, despite the stuttering which remains. No one would consider them neurotic or maladjusted. The psychotherapy evidently "took" to some extent. But the fact remains that only two of the ten satisfy our criteria.

The contrast between the results of this year's and the previous year's therapy is vivid. We cannot attribute the difference to the composition of the groups. If anything, the cases of the previous year were much more severe stutterers and had many more emotional conflicts. Perhaps we can blame the results on the student clinicians who had to administer the speech therapy. Admittedly they were less skillful than we were. Perhaps it was due to our own lack of skill in group psychotherapy. Somehow we do not feel that these explanations are adequate, either singly or in combination, though all of them no doubt had some minor importance. It is our impression that our emphasis on psychotherapy created a corresponding deëmphasis on monitoring. Stutterers of this sort cannot rely on their automatic controls. They are too unaware of the abnormal feedback. Their scanners are often inoperative or defective. Chronic stutterers must be trained to correct in terms of the signals they receive from their ears and mouths. These circuits must be kept open and the signals scanned, or the noise of emotion will create oscillations with which they cannot cope. We may be wrong but we feel that the stutterer needs more than insight into self- or personal security, welcome as they are to any therapist. He needs to monitor his speaking under stress. He cannot let it take care of itself. In the envelope we sealed in June of 1952 and have just now opened, we find this: "I'm scared of this bunch. They're talking well; they're pretty secure; they have little anxiety. Why then do I hate to make a prediction? Maybe because they aren't interested in their speech half so much as in themselves. They almost seem too content with what they have accomplished in terms of self-insight to care what happens to their speech. You can't eliminate stuttering by ignoring it. Anyway, no prediction this year."

Spring, 1952

In the spring of this year we started a new intensive-therapy group of stutterers, hoping to use them the following fall as clinicians and thus to get a continuous psychotherapy group going. The group therapy was again oriented in terms of psychotherapy similar to that which we have described for the preceding semester. However, we even then had recognized our error of giving too much responsibility to our student therapists and realized that a more strenuous retraining program was required. Accordingly we devised an entire series of daily assignments which every therapist administered to every stutterer. This formed the core of the retraining speech therapy, though each student therapist could add two or three more assignments if he so wished. The only restriction was that any additional assignments must also be performed (through pseudo-stuttering) by the clinician too. We also told our student therapists to leave the psychotherapy to us and to concentrate on speech therapy alone, an admonition which was probably of little effectiveness. We felt that by thus strengthening the retraining program of speech therapy at the same time that we carried on the group psychotherapy, a better therapy could be achieved. We also supervised the speech-therapy program more intensively than we had the previous fall.

We wish we could include here the whole series of daily assignments, because only through the entire sequence can the reader view the developing skills of reacting to the fear and frustration of stuttering. The few samples we can give will no doubt fail to reveal the real impact they had on their users. There were also two other features of these assignments which we had not used systematically before this time. First, we provided a choice of assignments and within the assignments a choice of quotas, experiences, and anxiety or stress levels. The stutterer could set his own aspiration levels and learn to do so realistically in terms of his actual performance. This also permitted and required some active rather than passive responsibility. It is important for any person who has been defeated a thousand times to choose his own battlefield and his weapons. It is especially important that he come to realize that he has the right of choice. We hoped that this would solve some of the dependency problems which we had experienced before with certain cases. The second new feature was the requirement that one formal assignment be invented by the case. It should be objective enough to be reported accurately, goal-oriented, and tailored to the person's own needs. These assignments had to be acceptable to the therapist or be revised until they were. We hoped that this would teach them to be their own therapists. We give four samples selected at random, and we are not especially happy with those that came up, but they should provide a few brief glimpses of the speech therapy which was done that spring.

STUTTERER'S ASSIGNMENTS

1. After a stuttering block comment on it to your listener:
   a. To three other cases or clinicians.
   b. To a clerk.
   c. To an acquaintance not connected with the clinic.
   d. Fifteen times to various people.
2. Collect stuttering blocks in which you are pretty calm throughout.
   a. Ten short ones.
   b. Two long ones or hard ones.
   c. One long one in a situation where strangers are overhearing you.
   d. To ten different people in the clinic or out.

3. Fake long hard blocks without becoming emotional (on non-feared words).
   a. Ten to some other stutterer or clinician.
   b. Three over the phone to strangers.
   c. Two to a nervous or embarrassed stranger.
   d. Fifteen to yourself in a mirror with an observer.
4. In *two* situations get a success-failure ratio in terms of willingness and unwillingness to stutter openly:
   a. One success to three failures. (1 to 3), (2 to 6), or (3 to 9).
   b. One success to every five failures. (1 to 5), etc.
   c. One success for each failure (a one to one ratio).
   d. Five successes for one failure (5 to 1).
5. Explain why it is necessary for the time being to stutter openly instead of hiding it. Try to state all the reasons.
   a. To some acquaintance, after you have stuttered obviously.
   b. In a letter to some friend or relative.
   c. To some teacher, whom you ask to call upon you.
   d. To Carolyn, Mr. Jackson, or Dr. Van Riper.
6. Your own assignment.

Note: Choose any five of the six but be sure to choose #6 and have it checked before you leave the clinic. Do enough of these so that you can make progress. In your report state your feelings and emotions, the attempts you made that failed, and describe as clearly as you can the situations in which you did the assignments. Give some estimate of how well you did the assignment.

STUTTERER'S ASSIGNMENTS

1. Cancel the word on which you stutter. By this we mean stopping completely *after* the word upon which you stutter, looking back and studying the stuttering, and then trying to stutter fluently on the word again as calmly, easily and effortlessly as possible. Do this:
   a. in talking to some acquaintance not connected with the clinic
   b. three times to some other stutterer who must check you
   c. in a tough badly feared outside speech situation
   d. twenty times outside the clinic
2. Watch yourself in the mirror while stuttering and try to study what goes on. Do this:
   a. on five blocks with some other stutterer watching and tell him what you observe
   b. on five blocks with the clinician making comments afterward about what he saw in the block
   c. on three words in which you deliberately try to throw yourself into a long hard block on purpose
   d. while making a phone call you fear

3. After having a real block, stop and imitate it exactly before continuing. Get:
   a. a quota of two
   b. a quota of five
   c. a quota of ten
   d. a quota of two in a tough outside situation where the pressure to hurry on is almost overwhelming.
4. Fake your favorite postponement tricks. Do this:
   a. for repeating the words preceding the feared word. Do this twice
   b. using the a . . . a . . . a trick while pretending to think. Three times
   c. waiting for some other person to say the word for you . . . twice
   d. on all the postponement tricks you have ever used. (All of the above must be done in stranger situations)
5. Try to let a stuttering block release itself. Do not force it out or struggle or jerk. Just let it run on until it leaks out by itself.
   a. a quota of two
   b. a quota of five
   c. a quota of seven
   d. a quota of ten
6. One assignment based on any one of the fourteen steps listed on page 3 which you invent for yourself. Taste the future treatment.

(Choose any five of the six assignments, but include number six.)

STUTTERER'S ASSIGNMENTS

1. Without stopping and starting over, try to turn a real stuttering block into a faked one before having the word come out.
   a. Five attempts to do this one badly feared word.
   b. One successful attempt in a stranger situation.
   c. A quota of ten successes.
   r. Prolong the faked part of the block for five toe taps before releasing it on two blocks.
2. Interrupt a conversation with a short faked block and without getting rattled.
   a. A quota of two successful attempts to do this.
   b. A quota of three successful attempts to do this.
   c. A quota of five attempts, whether successful or not.
   d. Do this to a clerk in a store.
3. Stutter on feared words without struggle or obvious interruption.
   a. A quota of five attempts whether successful or not.
   b. One successful attempt to a stranger.
   c. Three successful attempts to someone in the clinic.
   d. One to Dr. Van Riper.

N/B. Do not count those that occur by chance. You must do these on purpose.

4. Speak every non-feared word of the sentence with voluntary loose movements.
   a. A quota of ten sentences to someone in the clinic.
   b. A quota of five sentences over the telephone.
   c. A quota of two sentences in which at least two of the words are stuttered on, but all others are spoken with loose movement.
   d. All the conversation during one meal-time.
5. Tell someone else what we are trying to learn here. Explain what is meant by stuttering without abnormality and interruption.
   a. Do this in writing.
   b. Ask your clinician to hear you explain it and criticize your explanation.
   c. Do this to some stranger who is interested.
   d. Put your explanation on a phonograph recording made by Mr. Jackson.
6. One assignment of your own which will help you know some of the steps you will have to take in the conquering of your stuttering.

(Choose any five of the six, but include number six, and check all items under each assignment that you contract to do.)

STUTTERER'S ASSIGNMENTS

1. Fake blocks in which after the block is under control you make a very slow strong shift to the rest of the word, saying your own name in store situations. Collect:

________a. A quota of 3
________b. A quota of 5
________c. A quota of 7

1. Cleaning establishment. Ask for suit wife left.
2. Hotel. General delivery window. Ask for mail.
3. Library. Ask for library card.
4. Drug store. Ask for photos left to be developed.

2. Though always trying to pull out blocks perfectly, collect (in real blocks) tremors where you jerked out, *saying the words before they were smooth and under good control.* Collect a quota of:
________a. Three
________b. Five
________c. Seven
3. Collect a quota of real or faked blocks that you make real, where you have tight contacts that you deliberately loosen before saying the word. Record situation and word.
________a. A quota of 3
________b. A quota of 4
________c. A quota of 6
4. Collect a quota of perfect pullouts, done on *consecutive* (one after the other) blocks. How many will you be able to do?
________a. 2

________b. 3
________c. 4

5. Collect a quota of real blocks where you start with a silent but correct mouth or tongue position. Hold it longer than you need to, then slowly (and without stopping or starting over) bring in air and voice before shifting to rest of the word.
________a. 10 blocks in a conversation.
________b. 15 blocks to some other stutterer.
________c. 20 blocks to strangers.
6. Self assignment: (Do any five of the six, but you must do number six.)

We had nine new stutterers this spring and we used four of the fall crop as clinicians for a while but they were not any more effective than their predecessors had been, being too punitive and demanding, and we gradually discontinued their services in favor of normal-speaking clinicians. Among the nine new cases were three girls. All were severe stutterers. This group progressed faster than did that of the fall, five of them having become pretty fluent and free from fear and working on their stuttering when it occurred. By the Easter holidays, two of them had made little or no gain, the other two only partial ones. By June, five of the stutterers were able to satisfy our criteria. Three of the others did not return in the fall and these all continued to stutter pretty severely. The others had some regression that summer but recovered and made steady gains thereafter. Some form of terminal therapy was continued with these for two years. Our five-year checkup showed that six of the nine satisfy our criteria and only one is stuttering severely at present. Two of the girls became successful public-school speech correction teachers; one of the men, a lawyer. To what do we attribute the relative effectiveness of this spring semester's therapy over that of the fall? We feel that the increased emphasis on speech therapy per se was the vital factor. These individuals really had to work with their stuttering. We were never able to build as good a group interaction as we had with the fall group, and the summer vacation created real problems for terminal therapy as it always does. Our spring cases may have had slightly fewer emotional conflicts than did those of the fall, but hardly enough to account for the discrepancy. All three of the girls were very explosive individuals and very resistant, and three of the men had had several unsuccessful therapy experiences prior to coming to us. They were all tough cases.

1952–1953

This fall, still intent on developing a speech therapy which could also be at the same time a potent psychotherapy, we decided to orient all of our interaction, both group and individual, about the modification of the stuttering behavior. As we viewed it then, the moment of stuttering could serve, if we may use a figure of speech, as the psychiatrist's couch. We would finger-paint with stuttering; play with stuttering, work with stuttering, smear with stuttering, hate with stuttering, beg for love by stuttering. We would get the stutterer to look into the stuttering mirror and see himself, past, present, and future. The manner of stuttering would be our free association, our symbolic carrier of conflict. How we responded to our anxiety over stuttering, how we responded to our frustration and helplessness in utterance, how we reacted to our listener's reception of our broken messages would comprise the basic stuff of therapy. We, as the therapist, would encourage transference, be supportive and permissive and, above all, understanding, sharing the stutterer's travail but remaining secure. Through the probing, touching, and accepting of the rejected portions of the self as revealed in stuttering therapy we would help the case to reconstruct his personality. We would not, however, talk psychotherapy or structure the interaction as anything but speech therapy. We hoped to create a nonverbal psychotherapy akin to free-play therapy, one which did not require interpretation by the therapist.

Upon rereading the above description we are appalled and highly conscious of its inadequacy and yet we find it almost impossible to spell out exactly what we were trying to do. If we can make yet one more attempt we would say this. The behavior which our stutterers showed in coping with the threat and experience of stuttering was highly significant of the kind of person he had been, was, or had the potential of becoming. Why did he dodge this elderly woman when he had to fake an easier form of stuttering? Why did he inhale sobbingly before he interrupted? Why could he always get nine out of ten pull-outs but never the tenth? Why did a little whimpering noise enter his faked stuttering just before it became a real tremor? Why could he make out an excellent self-therapy assignment on this particular day and fulfill it to the letter? Why did too much success make him glad to fake? Why did he invent this particular assignment rather than another? Why did he give himself such an impossible quota? Why did he want us to watch him on this phone call? Why did he react as he did when he listened to the recording? Why did he like to watch his mouth in the mirror? Why so little fear in this situation?

We did not answer any of these questions, but we occasionally asked them, and so did the stutterers, more and more often as therapy progressed. We made no interpretations and cautioned our clinicians also to refrain from doing so, but to record any made by the stutterer. They (the stutterers) were to listen to what their stuttering and their work on their stuttering said about themselves. We were always interested but noncommittal. In the group sessions, much of their own interpretation came up, but no case was permitted to interpret or explain for another stutterer. Perhaps a sample from one of our protocols might illustrate what went on:

Jeannie at this point interrupted and said, "Well, I cry. I cry when I get mad but when my mother died my eyes were dry, dry for months. When I made that assignment yesterday to phone my father and to keep out all retrials, I found my eyes wet. I was afraid I'd stutter but more afraid of my anger in my stuttering and he might hear it if I didn't stop and try again. And I can't hate him even if he did remarry, even though I do. Well I did the assignment and I did not stop or hesitate but went right through an easy block as though I was in a dream. I forget what he said, I was so surprised. But my fear and my anger leaked out right with that word. I don't know if you can understand. I don't myself but I think I can help myself more than I thought I could. It sure was funny . . . curious, I mean. . . ."

The crew was silent for a moment. Then Bob said (and there was much more stuttering than usual, head jerks and eye closings too) "I can understand, Jeannie . . . but I just can't understand why I suddenly lose all control, like now. One minute I'm OK and the next, well look at me. It's like I was trying to shake my brains out. . . . Maybe I am so I wouldn't have to suffer so much. How can I get less sensitive, tougher? I'm very intelligent but. . . . Maybe I can figure out an assignment for removing my brains."

The group sessions were used to air these offerings, to explain the purposes of the sample assignments, and to serve as a speech situation where the stutterers could make and carry out on the spot a bit of self-therapy. The atmosphere was very permissive. The normal-speaking clinicians and some of the former cases sat in on these sessions. Two hours daily were so spent, the second hour being used to formulate their own assignments. We provided them with sample assignments similar to those given to the stutterers during the spring semester immediately preceding, but no stutterer could use those. He had to devise his own, and the assignments had to be well organized and sufficiently potent to create the possibility of a real therapeutic experience. There was great resistance shown to these sessions, helplessness, hostility, complaint, but no one left the clinic until some planned self-therapy was written down in acceptable form. This planning session was handled by another therapist on our staff, Mr. Jackson. One hour daily was spent by the stutterer with his clinician in getting a start on the fulfillment of his assignments. Written reports from both the stutterer and the clinician were required.

Terminal therapy consisted of two group sessions per week for the first two months, then one a week thereafter. Individual conferences with the therapist were also arranged. Some of the stutterers also joined other groups of stutterers receiving therapy. Some job or academic course requiring much speaking was also demanded.

The results of this year's therapy can be stated as follows. We had seven stutterers in our intensive-therapy group. One girl developed some hysteria and hallucinations and was sent home to Canada, where she received psychiatric help and shock therapy and recovered. This, by the way, is the only stutterer we have had who developed signs of psychosis during speech therapy and we found out later that she had previously had a nervous breakdown. We have worked with several others who were somewhat psychotic when they came to us. One of them, indeed, was a patient in our state institution for the insane, who stuttered only when he was sober but became highly aggressive and dangerous when drunk. When he started talking freely, we called in the waiting attendants, and for good reason. We made no headway with this case, but two others seemed to profit very much from speech therapy. This girl did not. She had shown no real gains in fluency before she began to have her laughing spells and "daymares." We suspect that the verbalizations of our other stutterers, highly emotional as they were, probably pierced her thin barriers. Oddly enough, her MMPI, TAT, and preliminary interviews gave no indication of this state.

And so we had six who completed the intensive therapy. One of them, an older man, became completely fluent by late November and hardly stuttered again until the beginning of terminal therapy. Most of the others made slow and irregular gains, but by Christmas three of them were doing very well. Only two showed a regression during the holidays. By the beginning of terminal therapy, in February, only two of them were fluent, and this same situation was present again in June. Five years from the time of the end of the intensive therapy only these two satisfy our criteria. Two others are vastly improved over entrance, but oscillating between good and poor speech and have fears and occasionally severe stutterings and some minor avoidance reactions. Two of them are almost as bad as they were upon entrance.

Even by June we were convinced that this particular kind of therapy was not being very successful. We hoped, however, that it would show delayed effects, which, as we have seen, did not occur. As we look back on it now, we feel that we did not do a particularly good job of either group or individual psychotherapy or speech therapy. We did our utmost but these were hard, complicated cases, and we just did not know how to do what we were trying to do. We also feel that we inordinately burdened our cases with too much responsibility for self-therapy. Many of the self-assignments they contrived were just not very good. Moreover, there is no substitute for the therapist in therapy. Bootstrap speech therapy is no better than bootstrap psychotherapy. People in trouble need someone to share their troubles, to walk with them on the way out of their terrible wilderness, to show them a path now and then, to pick them up when they fall, to wait patiently while they wander up a cul-de-sac. We knew these things in 1952, but we kept hunting for a better way, an easier one, one that many could follow. What we found was only a more difficult route, full of obstacles and dangers. We were lucky to lead two of our six stutterers through.

This year, with other cases, we also experimented with some other techniques. One of these involved desensitization to tremor. Most stutterers seem traumatized by tremors in their speech apparatus. They do not understand what is happening when the lips begin their tense vibrations, when the jaws jump rhythmically. We have recorded these tremors in all the structures used in speaking. We feel that they are learned behavior, arising as the result of the initial repetitions being speeded up by tension, or as Froeschels puts it, by the shift from clonus to tonus. They seem to require a localized area or focal point of tension, a tight contact or fixed position, and a sudden, swift, ballistic movement of the structure. Examination of the terminal stages of recorded stuttering tremors reveal that they die out and end in three different ways: (1) the amplitude decreases; (2) the frequency decreases; or (3) a superimposed larger movement out of phase with the tremor occurs. The termination of these tremors usually coincides with the release from stuttering or a second speech attempt.

Many of the bizarre reactions associated with stuttering are bits of timing behavior which the stutterer has formerly used to employ the third method of tremor termination, the jerk-out-of-phase. The tremors normally die out as soon as enough abnormality to satisfy the expectancy has occurred, because the tension needed to sustain them declines at this point. Fixations at times may be merely dead-center ambivalent behavior between approach and avoidance, but often they are really composed of very fine and very fast tremors. We have made many observations and recordings of these tremors and we feel them to be vitally important in determining the behavior which we call stuttering. Psychologically they create the feeling of inability, of loss of control, of involuntariness.

Without going further into the matter here, we tried this year to desensitize two stutterers, not in the group, to the experience of tremors. We had them set their legs in reverberating motion, their fingers oscillating like those of the violinist, the whole head throbbing on its axis. We had them study how they set these tremors going, how they interrupted them, how the oscillations died out. We got the stutterers to alter the amplitude and frequency of the tremors, to vary the amount of tension and its locus.

Then we went through the same process with tremors of the tongue, the lips, the jaw, the laryngeal and breathing musculatures during silence. These latter were the most difficult to procure, but one of the stutterers could set up a tremor of the diaphragm which was remarkably vivid under fluoroscopy. Next we practiced these tremors together during speaking, and both stutterers and this therapist found ourselves in the characteristic experience of stuttering. We were able to train some normal speakers to set their tongues into tremors which persisted longer than they desired and which scared and bothered them. This may merely have been the effect of suggestion, but we do not think so. When these tremors were introduced into consecutive speech by the stutterers, they claimed that they often became "real stuttering," whatever that means.

Gradually we desensitized the two stutterers to these deliberate tremors and taught them to slow down the oscillations and damp their amplitudes. Then we began to apply the same principles to the tremors which were characteristic of their stutterings. At first, they found it almost impossible to slow them down and smooth them out until after a certain duration of tremor had taken place and the tension had somewhat subsided. But gradually they learned to "grab them quickly," as they expressed the experience. It was at this point that both stutterers showed a dramatic decrease in frequency, severity, and fear of stuttering. As one of them said, "I somehow seem to have learned how to prevent them by learning how to end them." The effect of this tremor training in decreasing situation and word fears was most startling. Our past experience with the stutterer's fears had always indicated their tenacity. They extinguish very slowly and return swiftly.

This "spontaneous recovery" did not seem to take place in these two stutterers, and the fears certainly dropped out very quickly, almost too quickly. They had too few actual stutterings with which to work. We began to wonder whether we were not creating some autosuggestion. Accordingly we suggested to these individuals that they give up all tremor practice and let their stuttering run uncontrolled. One of them coöperated; the other refused. Very gradually, stuttering and fears returned in the first case but not in the second. This last person was a pretty belligerent individual, and unfortunately we have not been able to maintain contact with him, so we cannot say how well he is doing. Six months later he was speaking freely. The other stutterer was never able to regain his early freedom, though his speech is generally good except under real stress. He claims that he cannot remember or concentrate on tremor therapy when he is emotional but uses it often in ordinary communication. He deeply resents our experimenting with him in this way and refuses to see us, and it is difficult for us to evaluate his present performance. It must be remembered that no other therapy was done with either of these cases.

With other cases we have continued to explore this promising lead, and have even used some tremor therapy with our current group. There are many facets of the stuttering tremor which we cannot see clearly. It is very apparent that stutterers fear and are frustrated by their tremors and identify them as the essential core of the "blocking" or "sticking." They seem to contribute markedly to the feeling of "inability" in utterance. They seem to be conditioned to certain trigger postures of the mouth and are precipitated by a sudden surge of localized tension or by an oscillation (the hesitant attack, the ambivalent approach, the tentative tasting of utterance). These trigger postures themselves seem to be conditioned to certain phonetic cues made vivid by anxiety ("I am afraid of the *b* in 'business'"). There is a serial order here which has vital significance: generalized anxiety to situation fears to phonetic fears to trigger postures to tremors. This direct sequence of course may be interrupted at any point by avoidance behavior. Stuttering therapy, to be effective, must attack this serial order at all points, not just at one. Certainly if we can decrease anxiety, we reduce stuttering. Certainly if we can decrease the avoidance, the case has a chance to come to grips with his problem. Certainly if we can decrease the situation or word fears by adaptation and desensitization, we reduce the stuttering. But is there not also a need to go further, to do something about these trigger postures and the tremors which may possibly be the lowest common denominator of stuttering? Well, we are still at work, still chasing our quarry. The scent seems hotter here.

Spring, 1953

This spring we accepted four new stutterers, all with severe emotional problems, and treated them under the guidance of a friendly psychiatrist who had become very interested in our work. One of these individuals was rather close to being a psychopath with stuttering, alcoholism, extramarital promiscuity, and other problems. He was very intelligent, and his stuttering was fairly mild. Another was a very aggressive, successful businessman, very compulsive and rather paranoid. The third was a rather ineffectual person, continually worrying about everything, habitually depressed, and constantly setting his aspiration levels about zero. The fourth was detached, detached from himself and from others, a psychological and social isolate, almost schizophrenic. Our psychiatric colleague who helped us screen these involved cases from a large number of applicants agreed that their prognoses were very poor. He was certain that in each case the stuttering was definitely the symptom of primary neurosis, and we agreed with his diagnosis. We felt that they would give our speech psychotherapy a real test. They did!

In general we followed the same program that we had used during the fall, except that these new stutterers were included in the group meetings held by the cases in terminal therapy. Each was given a student clinician who observed the stutterer during his speech work and who reported, as did the case, on what transpired. The only structuring of therapy which we used can be seen from one of the report blanks. The stutterers made their own assignments. They discussed with their student clinicians and with the therapist the feelings which arose during the performance of the assignments. We tried to reflect their feelings as best we knew how. We now provide a sample report, this from the businessman, about two weeks after therapy began.

ASSIGNMENT REPORT FOR DISCUSSION

Date: 3/9/53
Name: I. G.

I. General goal: "Understanding Therapy"

A. *Assignment you designed:* "Talk to three other stutterers about 'high stimulus speech' and then explain it to one normal speaker."

B. *What you actually did:* "I talked to Bill about it trying to use it at the same time. I also called Dick and asked him if I had it right and explained to him what it meant to me. Then I called Kay, told her and asked her."

C. *How did you feel before, during and after the assignment? "Before,* I was confused but curious. Had some doubts about it. Seemed sort of tricky to me. I also thought that it was dangerous to do anything with the little normal free speech I've got. I'd better keep what I have and not monkey with it. I remember having a little feeling of resentment like 'I came here for help with my stuttering and why doesn't he let me keep thinking about that?' *During* the assignments, I felt *wonderful.* Maybe because of the fact that I was listening so closely to my speech I went the entire five minutes with Bill without stuttering once. I guess because of the distraction but there was just no stuttering. Then I got scared, as though I had done something wrong. There was a lot of stuff here but I can't remember, both good and bad. I was surprised, upset and still kinda curious to see how long it would last. But I did the same on Dick's phone call and felt the same funny way. When I called Kay though the spell broke I guess. I was trying to tell her what had happened and I was excited too and found myself stuttering a lot without actually hearing it or the free speech either. I then stopped and began to listen to my mouth again, and I felt a lot of pressure inside me, an excitement pressure, and I just took off talking any old way.

"*After* I had finished these (and I didn't do all I had planned because of how I was feeling) I took a walk to calm down. I thought this high stimulus stuff would be good to re-inforce good speaking but I realized I had a long way to go before I could stand to use this high stimulus. Funny how the idea of a long time made me feel better. You'd better not hope too fast."

II. General goal: "The Willingness to Stutter"

A. *Assignment you designed:* "Go into a bakery and get 1 Danish, 1 Cinnamon, and 1 Coffee roll. Try to stutter hard on each of these main words and make them become real. Don't let the clerk bother me."

B. *What you actually did:* "Went into the bakery on Burdick and asked for the rolls one at a time. There was one customer and three clerks in the place and I talked loud, so they all heard me."

C. *How did you feel before, during and after the assignment?* "Beforehand, I told myself I was going to give it the old college try this time. I didn't like it but I was going to make me do it right.

"*During* the assignment, I thought why you stupid people for laughing, giggling or hiding your faces, I'm doing this on purpose. I felt like telling them and saying now who'se the joke on, you or me? I wasn't really mad so much as full of pity, no contempt for the dirty stupid race I got to live with, and other stutterers got to live with, for a million years. But I kept my mind objective, did what I planned, and was conscious of everything that was going on. I didn't go, like Bill says, 'haywire' like I often have.

"*Afterward.* I felt that I was the master of this situation, but I have remembered the snickering of the stupid bastards at different times since."

III. General goal: "Improve Eye-Contact During Stuttering"

A. *Assignment you designed:* "Add one extra eye-blink for every time I blink in a stuttering block. Collect three of these before I quit."

B. *What you actually did:* "Collected one of these complete with extra blink at Becker's shoe store, talking to a salesman. Missed a couple at the YMCA. Collected another one at Arcadia Cafeteria talking to a fellow I had just met—Harry E. Forgot to collect the third one, but managed one in shaving mirror this morning."

C. *How did you feel before, during and after the assignment?* "Before, I knew this was a hard one. I know how fast this eyeblink, it's a flutter almost sometimes, is so I reminded myself that I needed to be especially quick in catching them. This is part of my stuttering that's even harder to handle than my mouth. It just takes off full steam and is over and the word is out before I know it.

"*During* the assignment, I did OK when I could see the hard word coming. First time I was glad to see a hard word coming. Fear may be handy to have sometimes but right now you can have it, I don't want it. Anyway, I got both my two successes on hard words I saw coming. And they seemed to be easier than I had expected. The very idea of having to put that extra blink seemed to dilute the block and they ended quicker than I expected. You know, if you work on yourself you don't lose your hold on yourself so quick or so far. I was more calm than I thought.

"*After*. I thought of how unnecessary to good speech or to stuttering also this eyeblink stuff was. I thought it's crazy to go making faces to keep from seeing faces. Then I thought about my brother and my mother."

This should be sufficient to illustrate the general nature of the assignments the stutterers made for themselves and the type of report which they turned in. This particular stutterer, on this particular day, performed two other major assignments, one on reducing avoidances and another on "eliminating retrials and recoils." These were written up as thoroughly as those given above. The student clinician who was with this case during a few of the experiences mentioned in the report helped I. G. verbalize his feelings at the time. The reports were used by the therapist as the core of the stutterer's conference with him. The stutterer explained his reactions and went on from there in self-exploration in a very nondirective, permissive, and warm atmosphere. The understanding and control of the self was the basic goal of stuttering therapy.

We wish we could give a fine report ourselves at this point. It seemed to be good therapy [*sic*], but unfortunately our results would hardly corroborate this impression. None of these four stutterers, at the present time, or at any time, can be said to have satisfied our criteria of successful therapy. The alcoholic, who had previously been psychoanalyzed for several years, sobered up temporarily, earned his own and his family's support without exploiting his father, gained excellent speech, returned to his home on the West Coast, attempted to become a psychiatric social worker, was rejected from that training (we understand), and is now back in the same rut from which we helped him rise. The worrier is still worrying, but his speech is much improved and he has managed to get through three years of college. He reports that his speech goes up and comes down with his anxiety level. The schizoid chap is quite fluent except when angry, but he is getting angrier as the years pass. The businessman has excellent speech and has made a fine personal adjustment under conditions of great personal and vocational stress. He still stutters noticeably at times, but his blocks are short and unobjectionable (except to this therapist with his eye on a faraway goal). His fears are practically gone, and we note no avoidance or struggle. Some tremors run on automatically for a short space of time. This is the situation four years later. Perhaps another year will give us a score of one of four.

Our psychiatrist friend grinned often during our consultations, and has since helped us screen out rather than screen in such cases as these. He said he felt that our therapeutic spade needed a longer handle if we hoped to aerate such soil. He felt that such a therapy should prove effective with the ordinary, garden variety of stutterer. We ourselves are less convinced. Again we had the feeling that we were on a detour rather than the main highway.

1953–1954

This fall we decided to test on a larger number of more normal stutterers the same therapy we had explored in the spring, though as we look at the list now and remember the problems they presented, we wonder. We varied the spring program in several ways, however. Although each stutterer had to create his own self-assignments as a general rule, we often gave him some sample assignments to follow, and occasionally we insisted that a certain major assignment be carried out by all the members of the group. This was used to keep the group together more than for any other reason. We also stressed group psychotherapy of the type used in 1952. With three of the cases we had regular counseling interviews in which psychotherapy rather than speech therapy was stressed. With the others, regular conferences were made available by both therapist and student clinicians. The latter also served as observers during the fulfilling of the assignments. The stutterer's reactions to assignments were stressed as much as they had been for the spring group. We were able to achieve a close-working group with the exception of two stutterers, a fellow and a girl who remained quite aloof and on the fringes. The man was belligerently rejecting so far as the others were concerned; the girl remained full of anxious detachment.

Since we have fairly well explained the general organization of therapy for the four stutterers of the spring semester, we shall not go into it again. We had ten stutterers who completed the intensive therapy and seven who also remained for terminal therapy. Four of the group made very swift gains and were almost completely fluent by the end of November. By Christmas six of them were handling their speech very well. All but two had a marked regression over the holidays. Seven of the ten reached the end of intensive therapy with good speech but with some avoidances and anxieties and enough stutterings so that they had to monitor their speech pretty carefully. They were speaking better in stress situations than in casual ones.

One factor had us worried. Unlike other groups of the past who had made early and swift progress, these stutterers were highly aware of and concerned about emotional problems other than stuttering. One girl, who had accepted the domination of her twin sister and the rejection of her parents, was now actively challenging the whole family peck order. One man was viciously hating and attacking his father, a bank president. Another chap was doubting his wife's love and his own potency. Another was changing his vocation and giving up a career in government service in which he had made a real investment. Still another quit bookkeeping and joined the circus. Another girl immersed herself in a sordid love affair. We felt we had inadvertently opened Pandora's box. In all our years of working with stutterers, we have never found so many other troubles rising up as the stuttering went down. Once again we wondered whether the psychiatrists were correct in their view of stuttering as a hysterical symptom.

Terminal therapy was held to a minimum, with occasional group sessions and individual conferences with the therapist. We emphasized large doses of talking, and continued efforts to solve their emotional problems through insightful planning. By June only two of the ten were more fluent than they were in February, and only these two could be said to satisfy our criteria. Five of the others were talking pretty well, but stuttering severely under occasional stress and stuttering mildly but rarely in general conversation. They did not have many avoidances, however, and there was little stuttering fear. Most of the latter seemed to have shifted to other problems.

We have only a three-year checkup to report, and at present writing only two cases seem to satisfy our criteria completely, though two others are making steady progress and it looks as though they will make it. All ten stutterers are much improved over entrance. Their big difficulty seems to lie in the presence of tremors. They talk a stuttering language. They are really in pretty good shape so far as their social and vocational adjustment and communication is concerned. None of these people monitor their speech to any extent. Most have solved their emotional problems and are living satisfactorily. But we still feel we did not do very well. We feel that our emphasis on psychotherapy was unwise, that it opened too many doors that might better have stayed shut, that desensitization is wiser with stutterers than self-exploration. But we had decided to give five years to the investigation of this vital factor and we had two more years to go.

This was the first year in which we really concentrated, in our terminal therapy, on the use of high-stimulus speech. We had been experimenting with it with other cases, and occasionally with a group, for several years, so perhaps we should explain what was meant by the phrase. We cannot trace its origin in our thinking, but what we had wanted was an automatic means of monitoring the speech, once we had pretty well broken up the old stuttering reactions, so that the new substitute reactions to fear and to tremor could be constantly reinforced. We had explored the use of very short faked blocks on every word in increasing doses and had found that this technique certainly did serve as an effective monitor. But it was almost impossible for the stutterers to tolerate very long. One unusual stutterer still continues the practice after six years and is remarkably fluent, though his speech is full of little prolongations of sounds. We are impressed by the impact of this technique on most stutterers and still use it at certain times and for certain cases, but we do not like ritualistic speech of any kind. We are wary of odd talk, of the singsong, the overly inflected, the overloud, the phony Southern accent, and also of speech full of little loose contacts, easy prolongations, or rhythmic bounces.

All of these have in common, however, one important factor apart from their distractive and escape values—they provide the necessary stimuli for monitoring the output of speech. They create a new kind of feedback, one which is drastically different from that normally employed by stutterers. These techniques always have some temporary effectiveness, but tend to break down once they become automatized. And, in general or lesser degree, they are abnormal in themselves.

We therefore wondered why we could not use the normal speech itself for the same purposes. All stutterers have more than enough fluent words along with their stuttered words to be used in this way. We had long been impressed with the observation that the stutterer scanned only for stuttering, never for normal speech. In working with many of our younger stutterers, we had found that much of the battle was won once we had got them to *hear* how fluent they could be under certain conditions. How could we cock the ear or the mind for normal speech rather than for broken fluency? We explored in many ways, putting Demosthenes' pebbles (in the guise of hard candies) in the stutterers' mouths, watching their faces in the mirror, feeling with their fingers and hands the movements of their jaws and lips, becoming aware of the tactual sensations from the tongue and mouth, listening with and without amplification, monaurally and binaurally, and many other ways. All of this, be it remembered, was concerned with normal speech, not with stuttering. When they stuttered, they used a preparatory set, pull-out, or cancellation.

It was interesting to see how difficult it was to train our stutterers to become highly aware of their fluent words. Like all of us, they pay no attention to their nonstuttered speech; they merely think aloud. The only utterances which have stimulus value are those on which unpleasantness is expected or felt. What we have therefore tried to do is to give their normally spoken words a high degree of this stimulus value. We train our stutterers to reactivate the type of scanning which most of our babies must have when babbling or attempting their first words. Our stutterers learn to become highly aware of the movements and postures and sounds from their own mouths. In terminal therapy we call this our speech-insulin, requiring certain doses of it each day, according to need. Kinesthetic-tactual feedbacks seem to be easier to teach and to sustain than those of self-hearing, but the latter seem to be more potent. The experiments in delayed feedback, producing behavior similar to stuttering, have been remarkably sterile so far as therapy is concerned. This high-stimulus normal speech may be viewed as the technique to which they point.

In earlier years we once attempted to employ high-stimulus speech at the outset of therapy with two new stutterers, and made it the only technique used. What happened was unfortunate: it quickly increased the number of words feared to such a degree that we had to give it up. These stutterers were too full of anxiety and frustration to scan for anything but stuttering. We have also tried it at other times in the therapy sequence, and find its greatest utility is in terminal therapy, after the stutterer has some tools to cope with his tremors and has decreased his avoidance behavior. We are convinced that some form of monitoring is required for several years if the stutterer is not to regress. If we can make the normal speech which he already possesses the basic vehicle for that monitoring we should be able to prevent relapse completely. We are still experimenting and exploring. High-stimulus speech looks like a potent tool if we can learn how to sharpen and use it.

As we said before we digressed, this was the first year when we attempted to use high-stimulus speech as a basic part of terminal therapy. We were not successful in persuading these stutterers to adopt it or even to try it for more than a few perfunctory experiences. These stutterers, because of the emphasis on psychotherapy, were just not interested in their defective speech so much as they were in their other problems, so why should they do any listening or feeling of their normal speech? We have used it very effectively with other cases. In this regard, may we make clear that the stuttering therapy reported here is only a fraction of that which we actually carried out during these 20 years. What we are reporting here is our group therapy for severe adult stutterers only. We have worked with many other adults and children, using a variety of clinical approaches, and with many of them more successfully than those in the groups on which we are reporting here.

1954–1955

This year we decided to reduce the performing of speech assignments and their formulation by the stutterers. These assigned experiences had always been a vital part of our speech therapy with stutterers, and, as we have indicated earlier, we felt that the major portion of the success we had known was due to their cumulative effect. Indeed, except for those cases with whom we worked through counseling interviews alone (and which are not reported here), even our psychotherapy, both group and individual, was largely oriented about the stutterer's reactions to these assigned experiences, to their therapists and listeners, and to themselves while stuttering. This year, then, we emphasized the group therapy, especially in its psychotherapeutic forms, and played down the speech therapy.

Two group sessions were held daily during which we discussed all of our problems, including that of stuttering. The period which separated these two group sessions was spent with student clinicians and other stutterers, usually over coffee in the Union, discussing the "topic for the day," which normally involved some clinical problem in speech therapy with stutterers. Besides these sessions, most of the stutterers themselves usually ate together several evening meals each week and discussed their problems. Each Wednesday afternoon the whole group met in closed session with no therapists or student clinicians attending and gave each other the therapy they needed. We had explored this technique earlier with smaller groups of stutterers and had found it rather effective. One of their membership was chosen by the stutterers themselves as the chief therapist-of-the-day and he conducted the group sessions. We do not know what happened during these periods, but we often heard a lot of haranguing and even shouting through the closed doors.

We can perhaps give a clearer impression of the proceedings if we give some samples of the daily projects and topics for discussion. They included such items as these: Keep an emotional diary for a day and see what it says about you. What are you actually doing when you stutter? How do you respond to situation fear? How do you respond to word fear? How do you repress the feelings that arise during stuttering? How do you escape from the frustration of stuttering? In what ways did you surrender today? Does your stuttering affect your moods and attitudes toward self? How are you still avoiding? Can you remain in contact with your audience while stuttering? What percentage of your listeners do penalize your stuttering? Can you do anything about your tremors? Is there any value in pseudo-stuttering? What happens if you refuse to struggle when in a block? What happens just before the word "comes out"? How infantile are you? What does your particular kind of stuttering say about you as a person? Can you shift from involuntary to voluntary behavior during stuttering? When do you grow hostile? How do you compare yourself with the other stutterers? How do you react to failure or success? Can you pull out of your stutterings differently? How much do you expect of yourself? What kind of listeners tend to make you stutter most severely and why? What roles do you play characteristically? How well can you discipline yourself? Are you assuming any responsibility for your behavior?

And there were many others. Occasionally these were couched in other terms, but the assignments were general ones, projects and questions and topics. The stutterers were urged to explore the answers to these questions by getting actual experiences which were pertinent, by watching themselves and others, by changing their behavior. No person was under threat of expulsion for not coöperating. If he didn't feel like talking or reporting, he did not have to do so. A strong group pressure soon built up, however, which made it difficult for anyone who did not. Most of the cases turned in written reports; the student clinicians turned in weekly evaluations. Few individual conferences with the therapist were made available. In the group sessions the therapist took more of a leadership role, but the emphasis was not on the daily projects so much as on the expression of feelings and the understanding and control of the self. The terminal therapy included occasional inventory-taking group sessions weekly and more individual conferences with the therapist.

Some sample written reports from one of the stutterers may indicate the sort of thing that went on:

Project: How can I find some way of recording my successes?

The way I found worked the best with me was to shift beans from one pocket to another or by breaking off pieces of the toothpicks in a pocket. That is unnoticeable and it can be done with the situation or word fresh in the mind. I don't like to mark it out in the open on paper, on a pad. Other people think I'm nuts then and it spoils the success. It's good to record failures that way though. Helps me punish them, or should I punish them? Haven't other people punished them enough?

I used the bean method at the Three Rivers PTA last night. I decided that I would stutter openly for once and watch the reactions of the people there. I stuttered openly and it surprised me that I could. I blocked about five seconds on about every other word. Man, I tortured them. These were real blocks, but I often had to start them with fakes, then triggering them off into a tremor and all but a few became real blocks. I had a hard time with the beans because I had so many real successes. I finally grabbed a handful from one pocket and kept popping them in the other. Found forty beans in it after it was over, but I must have had a lot more. I had a hard time counting because I got so interested in the other people's reactions. Practically every type of reaction was shown. Many of the mothers look at the floor. The school teachers were interested genuinely and the kids stifled their giggles. On the whole it was an interesting experience, and I sure was successful in bringing my blocks out without getting hurt, even if I hurt others. Or because?

Project: To try to maintain voluntary control or regain it while stuttering.

I decided to throw myself into real blocks by starting them out as fakes and then getting tensed up and flopping my jaws, then, once they got going, to try suddenly jerking them out as compared with sliding out of them smoothly. I set up four situations which were tough enough. I couldn't jerk out of them when I tried although I thought at first it would be easier than smoothing them out. I tried twice on one word but I just bounced right back into it. I didn't like that feeling a bit so I smoothed out of the rest of them. Lots easier. I'm going to like this stuff. But why did I feel so bad when I couldn't jerk it out? It isn't good to feel out of gear like that.

A general assignment for the last few days, you know, was to stop reinforcing the stuttering by having the word come out of some abnormality. I have been able to catch many of these blocks on the run and grab them quick before the word comes out. When I don't do this I am able at least to stop dead and see what an idiot I've made before finishing the sentence. I have made this catching of blocks more or less of a game. Maybe that's not good. But I'm talking better.

On having a block the natural reaction for me is to stop right then in the middle of it and to hem and haw around or try it again. What I try to do now is to keep it going or to freeze it right there and stay with it and then to slowly smooth it out. I do this on about half my blocks I think. The little ones are harder to catch but I get much pleasure (Why?) out of grabbing these little ones and seeing what I can do with them.

Project: How do I compare myself with other stutterers?

Quite often when listening to other stutterers, I have a feeling that I am superior to them in some ways I handle my speech. I feel that I am more socially adjusted than they are, more at home with the ladies, and in general, handle myself better than they do. I guess this is due to my mother, and aunt, and some friends saying that I am a popular person and have so many friends because I am pleasing. I have gotten along pretty well by playing up to other people, letting them talk about themselves, etc., even though I am very interested in other people.

I can't concede the fact that any severe stutterer is better than I am. When with other stutterers in a group with some normal speakers, I want to leave the stutterers and more or less pretend to myself that I don't know them since I don't belong in the same class that they do. I guess that's from my mother's playing down my stuttering and saying it was nothing and my opposite reaction that it was very definitely a blemish on myself.

When a stutterer is talking to a girl I'm interested in, I'll say to myself, "She doesn't like him as much as she does me." That happens even though the girl has no indication that she likes either of us. Again that superior feeling creeps in.

I had a dream last night that showed me just how I acted in the clinic. A girl who stuttered and I, stuttering also, were seated at a table. I felt my stuttering was much better than hers. I could counsel her on hers, but it dawned on me that I could not counsel myself on mine. That was one of the few dreams I've had in which I stuttered.

Dick, Jim, Steve and I were sitting around the table last night talking. I made the remark that I thought I wouldn't go to the public speaking class because I thought I would be fluent and it would be too much of a temptation to reinforce my false fluency. Dick challenged this statement saying the reason I didn't want to go was that I was afraid that I would lose my fluency. In the ensuing discussion I got pretty mad at Dick, although not outwardly. The thing that worries me is why did I get angry and hot around the ears? Was it because I dislike for anybody to challenge me or was it because Dick came a little too close to seeing the real me? Dick's saying it doesn't bother me at all. My reaction to his saying bothers me.

Right now a question that bothers me is, "What is the real me like?" I know when I assume a role that is quite a bit out of line with me, but how is it when I am pretty close to what I actually am? How can I tell when I am close to the real me? I have been taking the amount of stuttering as a guide, but this is subject to the increased stuttering through fear, and many other influencing factors. When I go into a situation and say to myself, "All right, let's lay it on the line," many of my fears decrease and my blocks are decreased.

In reporting the results of this year's therapy, we realize that the returns are not all in by a long shot, but two years from the end of the intensive therapy shows that two of the seven severe stutterers who comprised the group satisfy our criteria; two others are very close to it; two others are speaking well most of the time and only one (the only girl in the group) has shown little improvement. With the exception of the girl and one man, they seem to have solved most of their other personal problems as well. It is interesting that this group showed the same order in their progress at Thanksgiving, Christmas, and at the end of terminal therapy. All of these stutterers completed terminal therapy. In five years it seems likely that at least five of the seven and perhaps six of the seven will be able to satisfy our criteria if they progress as did stutterers from other years.

To what do we ascribe this admittedly better result (when matched against the psychotherapy-oriented therapy of the three previous years, though not the years when the emphasis was on retraining)? We cannot answer with any real assurance, but these stutterers did get a lot of significant experiences in working with their stuttering, as the sample reports showed. They worked harder on their stuttering problem than had those of the other psychotherapy years, and they worked on it in an exploratory way. They answered our questions by experimenting with themselves and their listeners. They were continually testing whatever reality was available. Moreover, they were given the basic responsibility for their own therapy. There was no busy work, no tremendous burden of quotas and assignments and goals to be reached. They were not probing their histories or emotions to find excuses for being what they were. The group became well integrated about the stuttering theme. We provided the group leadership, and some identification occurred. Perhaps any or all of these played some part, but we do know that it was effective and an easier therapy than any we have tried.

1955–1956

This year, the final year of our five-year emphasis on psychotherapy, we decided to go hog wild in permissiveness and nonstructuring of the therapy. No assignments were required; no self-therapy reports fill these files. The student therapists played a minor part, being more observers and conversationalists than any of their predecessors had been. The therapist himself assumed little leadership of the group, letting it go where it would. At times he seemed to play the scapegoat and whipping-post roles more than any other. Occasionally, if they permitted him to do so, he reflected a feeling or two, or protected one of the group from the savage attacks of the others. He was used by the group also as a sort of encyclopedia of therapy, providing information as requested but only when requested.

The stutterers early were given a list and explanation of all the techniques we or others had used to help stutterers, and from there on it was a free-choice affair, as unstructured as play therapy with children. Often during the semester of the intensive program we were struck with the similarity to play therapy. These stutterers played with their stuttering, with the various techniques used to reduce it, with their clinicians and this therapist, as freely as children at a mud table.

We ourselves conducted (or rather sat in on) the first group session of each day except for Wednesday, when the stutterers met by themselves all afternoon in a Donnybrook of egos. The second hour of each day each stutterer selected a student therapist of his choice to talk with, usually over coffee, or to watch him as he made a phone call. Then they returned to the clinic for another hourlong group session, this one presided over (or under) by a graduate assistant who had been a professional actor and whose stage speech was still remarkably precise. We thought that by this arrangement we could provide two goal objects with which they might possibly identify, this therapist and the actor with the golden tongue. We were more objects than goals. But to his credit let it be said that never did an actor play more gallantly or (initially) to a more hostile audience. And he won their respect eventually, quite as much or more than did this therapist. He was witty and clever enough to hold his own and to turn a table now and then. He also was able to suggest a few therapeutic experiences. We, on the other hand, merely let these stutterers do as they wished. At times we would egg them on a little with a specific challenge or two, but we always accepted what they offered.

We regret that we have no recordings of these sessions. They would have been interesting reading. The profanity became so great at one time that one of the group, a minister's wife, finally set up a fine for each uncouth word, using the proceeds (which mounted with incredible swiftness) to buy materials for a party. She was the only member of the group to work intensively upon her speech, and she was similarly the only one to show any real gain in fluency or control early in therapy. By Christmas only two of the seven had eliminated any of their avoidances or were attempting to modify their stuttering responses in the direction of fluency. Even these two were far from our criteria of success. By the end of the semester two others had made some headway and were fairly fluent in ordinary situations but still had plenty of trouble under stress. The other three were still stuttering as badly as ever, struggling, avoiding, and refusing to work on their stuttering. They all, however, had improved markedly in personal adjustment. We have never had a group of stutterers who showed so little change in their outward behavior, however.

Terminal therapy consisted of less-frequent group sessions and some individual conferences with the therapist. By June none of the seven were able to satisfy our criteria, though all but two showed some gain over clinic entrance. We have remained in contact with all of these cases for six months since that time and no outstanding progress in speech can be reported. They are evidently still making some gains in stability and we hope that our five-year checkup will prove us pessimistic. It was an interesting year but we fear not a very productive one. We were glad when it was over.

Our five-year program emphasizing psychotherapy was disappointing. In retrospect, we have the impression that such an emphasis in stuttering therapy is unwise or perhaps merely inefficient. We are quite aware of our own limitations as a psychotherapist, and no doubt much of our difficulty may be laid to them. But we do not feel that we did a poor job of it. Had we been more skilled, the picture might have been different. Yet we are not at all sure that the situation is that simple. Some of our cases have been worked with intensively by well-trained psychoanalysts, psychiatrists, and clinical psychologists and have come to us with terrific stuttering and other problems, and we have been able to help them a great deal. We have also worked with some of these psychotherapists jointly on the same cases, with the speech therapy preceding, contemporaneous with, or subsequent to the formal psychotherapy, and we have not always felt that the psychotherapy as such helped the stutterer to recover good speech. There were too many instances in which it actually seemed to hinder recovery by distracting and detaching the stutterer from his communicative problems. Some of the stutterers, it is true, became happier people—except when they were stuttering.

This is not to say, of course, that psychotherapy can play no useful role in stuttering therapy. Certain cases require deep probing, fundamental insights, and reconstruction of the personality. Most of our stutterers, however, need supportive psychotherapy rather than reconstructive. They need a permissive figure to whom they can ventilate their anxieties and frustrations. They need a companion who can share their difficulties in communication without becoming punitive or upset. They need someone to point out a possible pathway out of communicative deviancy and who will stay with them even when they fail. They will learn all they need to about themselves by working with their stuttering. Perhaps what we are saying is that the stutterer needs a very good teacher rather than a psychiatrist.

1956–1957

This year was again our testing year, in which we would do no new exploring but instead concentrate on using the best therapy we had found.

We emphasized speech therapy rather than psychotherapy. It was also our last year of intensive therapy with a group of stutterers, and so we selected a group of especially difficult cases, eight men of college age with many diverse and severe problems. We planned the therapy and conducted the group sessions three times a week, being assisted by a new member of our staff whom we had trained as an undergraduate five years earlier. This man, Mr. William Dopheide, conducted the group sessions on Tuesday and Thursday at one o'clock and every day at three except on Friday, when we took entire charge. The two-o'clock hours were spent by the stutterers with their clinicians in devising, performing, and discussing experiences in modifying stuttering. The first-hour group meetings were used to clarify the process of therapy and to reflect feelings. The method of transitional groups was employed, using clinicians and visitors. The third-hour group sessions were used to formulate self-therapy plans or for fulfilling assignments. The stutterers were required during the first months to turn in daily reports of all self-therapy; the clinicians, reports of their sessions with their cases.

During the first two months, daily assignments were given to each of the cases. The clinicians helped the stutterers to get a start on fulfilling these assignments during their periods with them, and also reported on their emotional reactions and actual performance. These assignments were so formulated that each day each stutterer had several structured experiences in each of the following areas: *desensitization, nonreinforcement, ego-building,* highly conscious *voluntary control* of the speaking apparatus, *self-understanding* and exploration, and *fluent stuttering*. No sequence of goals was used as in earlier years. Instead, we worked on all six aspects of the problem every day. Very early in the therapy the stutterers begin to design and carry out some self-assignments in each of these directions of attack. The therapist's assignments gradually were decreased as the stutterers began to assume more and more of the responsibility for the work to be done. Individual assignments tailored specifically to the case's needs were occasionally formulated by the therapist or the clinicians.

We now present what West would call our armamentarium, an outline of the activities we employed to train our stutterers. They are classified under the six headings previously described.

DESENSITIZATION

I. Tolerance of others' stuttering
   A. Auditory observation and analysis
   B. Visual observation and analysis
   C. Tactual observation and analysis

D. Imitation and duplication
E. Simultaneous sharing
F. Prediction, measuring, counting

II. Tolerance of own stuttering
A. Phonographic adaptation
B. Mirror adaptation
C. Tactual adaptation
D. Photographic confrontation

III. Desensitization to auditor penalty
A. Collection and analysis of auditor penalties
B. Adaptation to penalties
C. Alteration and determination of auditor's response
D. Penalty sharing
E. Collection of permissive auditors
F. Faked stuttering
G. Auditor torture

IV. Study and analysis of stuttering
A. As a disorder (nature and history)
B. As one's own problem
1. Avoidance symptoms
2. Tremors
3. Frustrations and release symptoms
4. Situation fears
5. Phonetic fears
6. Audience reactions

V. Frustration tolerance
A. Deliberate pauses and silence
B. Post-stuttering slowdown
C. Strong, slow release
D. Reattempts on stuttered word
E. Prolonged stuttering
F. Delayed response to demand
G. Consecutive stutterings
H. Quotas of stutterings
I. Frustration scoring

VI. Abnormality tolerance
A. Deliberate abnormality (fake)
B. Exaggeration of existing abnormality
C. Group duplication of abnormality
D. Abnormality sharing by therapist
E. Observing the nonfluencies of others
F. Semantic reorientation

VII. Anxiety reduction
- A. Prediction and checking of frequency and severity of stuttering.
- B. Verbalization of fears
- C. Stuttering in a permissive situation
- D. Ventilation of attitudes toward self, listeners, and therapists
- E. Rewarding stuttering
- F. Phonetic focusing of situation fears
- G. Penalty reduction
- H. Conditioning new responses to fear
- I. Tranquilizing drugs
- J. Rest, recreation, and escape
- K. Fun with stuttering
- L. Cancellation of past trauma
- M. Anecdotal history of stuttering unpleasantness
- N. Therapist support
- O. Reassurance
- P. Panic analysis

VIII. Raising anxiety threshold
- A. Entering very difficult speech situations
- B. Deliberately using difficult words at every opportunity
- C. Increasing drastically amount of talking

NONREINFORCEMENT

Stutterers continually keep their stuttering strong by constant reinforcement. It diminishes as soon as reinforcement declines. They reinforce their stuttering by (1) avoidance, (2) repression and denial, and (3) escape and reward. These must be reduced and eliminated as much as possible.

I. Avoidances
- A. Word
  1. Use of synonyms
  2. Use of circumstances
  3. Postponement devices
  4. Assuming false attitudes
  5. Using trick ways of preventing stuttering
  6. Hiding the symptoms
  7. Using timing tricks
- B. Situations
  1. Avoiding an opportunity to speak
  2. Altering the situation so you might not stutter
  3. Refusing to look at listener

Every time you resist any of these avoidances you weaken your stuttering. Every time you yield you strengthen it.

II. Repression and denial
   A. Developing an awareness of detachment
      1. Collection of instances
      2. Reporting instances
      3. Predicting it
      4. Duplication
   B. Self-contact during stuttering
      1. Interruption of own stuttering with analysis
      2. Kinesthetic and tactual feedback
      3. Auditory amplification
      4. Simultaneous body-imaging

As you bring yourself in contact with your stuttering, you accept responsibility for its modification and control. Turn your back on it and it rattles on as hot as ever.

III. Escape—Reward
   A. Extinguish reward value of abnormality
      1. Cancellations of words and situations
      2. Voluntarilization prior to utterance
      3. Stop all communications whenever utterance comes immediately out of abnormality
         a. Nucleus situations
         b. Time quotas
         c. Anxiety level quotas
      4. Tremor dampening prior to utterance

EGO BUILDING

I. Exploration of potentialities
II. Exploration of existing assets
III. Acceptance of nonmodifiable liabilities
IV. Reduction or elimination of modifiable differences
V. Discrimination of ego-destroying behaviors
VI. Recall and reevaluations of rejections
VII. Cancellation of old defects
VIII. Revised reaction to failure
IX. Realistic goal setting in vocational, sexual, and social areas
X. Organization of goal-oriented program
XI. Self-discipline
XII. Trophy collection
XIII. Acceptance of success
XIV. Identification with models
XV. Therapist identification with stutterer
XVI. Role playing
XVII. Socialization
XVIII. Group participation

VOLUNTARY CONTROL

I. Reauditorization of normal speech
II. Kinesthetic monitoring
III. Tactual monitoring
IV. Speaking while executing activities demanding precision and accuracy
V. Voluntary stuttering
VI. Simultaneous talking and writing
VII. Vertical-board talking and writing
VIII. Rhythmokinesis
IX. Phonetic diagramming
X. Conscious performance of activities
XI. Breath chewing
XII. Walkie-talking; swimming speech; dance-talking
XIII. Signal utterance
XIV. Bad habit breaking
XV. Involuntary-voluntary shifting
XVI. Jaw-movement feedback
XVII. Artificial larynx
XVIII. Signaling of involuntary behavior
XIX. Tremor modification
XX. Tremor imitation
XXI. Concentration
XXII. Mental mathematics
XXIII. Auditory memory span
XXIV. Discrimination

SELF-UNDERSTANDING

I. Written autobiography
II. Verbal autobiography
III. Emotional diary
IV. Behavioral diary
V. Mood charts
VI. Verbalization of feelings
VII. Anxiety inventory
VIII. Aspiration levels
IX. Vulnerability inventory
X. Failure confession
XI. Bibliotherapy
XII. Sociograms
XIII. Symptom revelations
XIV. Alter-ego interviews
XV. Truth sessions
XVI. Interviews of auditors
XVII. Guilt explorations

XVIII. Punishment needs
XIX. Energy evaluations
XX. Environmental adjustment
XXI. Dependency needs
XXII. Paranoia evaluation, reality testing
XXIII. Safety-valving
XXIV. Acting out (psychodrama)
XXV. Recreation needs
XXVI. Rest needs
XXVII. Social needs
XXVIII. Sex needs
XXIX. Self-concept revision
XXX. Counseling
XXXI. Psychiatric interviews

FLUENT NONABNORMAL STUTTERING

I. Negative practice
II. Varying the stereotype
III. Slow motor stuttering
IV. Imitation of other stuttering patterns
V. Revision-cancellation
VI. Tremor variation
VII. Tremor slowdown
VIII. Tremor dampening
IX. Goal cancellation
X. Rejection of abnormal movements
XI. Pull-outs
XII. Locating tremor triggers
XIII. Altering tension foci
XIV. Phonetic attacks
XV. Rehearsal checking
XVI. Loose contacts
XVII. Prime-moving
XVIII. Ventricular-normal phonation shifts
XIX. Preparatory sets
XX. Antifreeze technique
XXI. Loose-shift stuttering
XXII. Phonetic conditioning of fluent stuttering
XXIII. Anxiety conditioning of fluent stuttering
XXIV. Reaction conditioning of fluent stuttering
XXV. High-stimulus normal speech
XXVI. Cathartic stuttering

A day's assignment to illustrate the therapy may be provided. Here is one for the third week of therapy. It must be remembered that in addition to the activities mentioned the stutterer and his clinician would have collected others under the same headings, and that they would have been discussed both by the clinician and in the group-therapy meetings.

Desensitization:

1. Put 300 short tremors on words when reading to yourself in a whisper. Stop after each and say it twice again, once with the tremor and once without. Scatter these throughout the reading passage by underlining the words on which you will use tremors before you begin reading.
2. Share, by duplicating simultaneously though silently, one blocking of three other stutterers as they make phone calls.
3. Touch your lips with your fingers but keep your eyes shut while answering some of your clinician's questions. Feel your stuttering.
4. Listen to your entrance recording again, duplicating any stuttering which you hear.
5. Make a phone call and insert a period of silence lasting at least five seconds before two nonfeared words without becoming upset.
6. Find some clerk who responds to stuttering by smiling or laughter. Fake repetitive stuttering or use your real stuttering until he becomes impatient.

Nonreinforcement:

1. Put your forefinger in your ear during each moment of stuttering when talking to your clinician and listen to how your stuttering sounds.
2. Observe another stutterer and call to his attention every time you catch him using any postponement or avoidance device by saying, "Congratulations!" He must answer "Congratulations on what?" You will then reply, "On keeping your stuttering hot and strong."
3. Study yourself while stuttering and answer this question: "How are you detaching yourself, repressing, refusing to confront your stuttering at the moment it is occurring?"
4. Have your clinician turn up the volume of the public-address system every time you stutter into it.
5. Deliberately slow down one tremor prior to utterance of a stuttered word. Do this to two people.
6. After sufficient pause for analysis of what you have just done, attempt the stuttered word again and again until it has been spoken normally or with a more fluent form of stuttering. Try to revise your attempt and behavior each time. You get only five adaptation trials per word. Report number of words on which you do this.

Ego building:

1. Describe to your clinician the kind of a person you would like to be in terms of three adjectives and collect one bit of behavior which you feel could be so described.
2. Write someone at home a letter describing your efforts to solve your stuttering problem. Have no note of self-pity or of depression in it.
3. Enter again one situation in which you experienced defeat.

Voluntary control:

1. Skip as swiftly as you can while talking to your clinician (who should skip with you) and do your utmost to keep from stumbling while stuttering. Describe what happened to your stuttering when you were skipping fluently.
2. Deliberately use tremors and smooth them out without letting them become involuntary on five nonfeared words.
3. Collect one stuttered word in which you shifted from involuntary to voluntary behavior and maintained the latter until utterance was achieved. Do this in a feared speaking situation and with an observer.
4. Do one page of talking and writing while shouting. Make strong movements and strong speech attempts.
5. With your eyes closed and your fingers plugging your ears, concentrate your attention on the tactual and kinesthetic sensations from your tongue, lips, and jaws as you narrate an unpleasant experience connected with your stuttering.

Self-understanding:

1. Practice ten trials of dart throwing, predicting your expected scores to your clinician and telling why you make each prediction. What does this experience tell you about yourself?
2. In what ways (other than stuttering) do you feel you've been cheated in life? Compare your responses with that of some normal-speaking acquaintance of whom you ask the same question.

Fluent stuttering:

1. Make phone calls until you can get one in which you can deliberately shift the focus of tension to a comparatively relaxed area during a stuttering block.
2. Ask for yourself at three houses, stuttering without retrials or struggle on at least one word.
3. You are to echo-talk while your clinician inserts some of your old forms of stuttering and some of the new fluent forms. Try to echo each of her words simultaneously while following the thread of her speech. Continue until you have been successful.
4. In canceling one of your severe stutterings, say the word again in slow motion, keeping the phonetic sequence intact. No retrials, no extra sounds.
5. Shift from a tight lip or tongue closure to a loose one during several stutterings. What happens to the tremors or fixations? Report.

Not being able to look into the future, we are unable to report on the ultimate success of these eight stutterers. At the present writing, we have just concluded the intensive therapy and are still debating what type of terminal therapy to use. All of them are remarkably fluent and compare favorably with the best results of other years at the end of intensive therapy. It is also obvious from their occasional stutterings and situation and word fears that terminal therapy is needed. One of them we have dismissed. We'll know how they turned out in 1962, perhaps.

And so we come to the end of more than 20 years of exploration, wondering how much we have actually accomplished, knowing how much more needs to be done and realizing that this therapist will not be able to do it. The will-o'-the-wisp still dances out of reach but its spoor appears hot, as it often has appeared. It is good to grow old on the trail. Good hunting!

In the meantime, by way of review, may I stress the *criteria which I have used to indicate successful therapy*. First of all, the stutterer must be speaking better than this author in all situations. This criterion is used for lack of any other effective means of comparison, and I have spoken to groups of my colleagues both formally and informally so frequently and in so many places and for so many years that it seemed to me as good an objective measure as any I could invent. We might perhaps define this as 0.5 on the Iowa Scale of severity. Secondly, the stutterer must not be avoiding words or speaking situations. Thirdly, his stuttering must not be interfering with his social or vocational adjustment. Fourthly, his situation and word fears must be pretty close to zero. Finally, his stuttering must present no concern to himself or others. For severe adult stutterers these criteria are stringent, and perhaps I have set them too high. The large majority of our cases who did not reach these criteria are markedly improved over clinic entrance and should not be considered to have failed. But we were designedly shooting for bull's-eyes. Our aim was good but our guns and ammunition left much to be desired. We also wish to emphasize once more that what has been reported in this account is only our group therapy. Much of our individual therapy was more successful, but these cases are not reported here.

As to the *etiology of stuttering*[5] I believe that the disorder has a multiple origin. It may be that the stutterer is a dysphemic individual, one who is prone by virtue of his physiologic make-up to his speech difficulty. It may be that the stutterer became so as a result of emotional conflict. Or it may be that for some factor or factors peculiar to the individual and his environment the stutterer has become conditioned to nonfluency. Whatever the particular etiology or possible combination of causes, once stuttering gets under way it achieves a functional autonomy, a self-reinforcement which keeps it going.

[5] The reader may want to refer to my *Speech Correction*, 3rd ed., New York, Prentice-Hall, 1954, pp. 343–350, for a more detailed exposition of my point of view as to the etiology of stuttering.

INDEX

Index

Set in Linotype Old Style No. 1
Format by Joy E. Bird
Manufactured by Kingsport Press, Inc.
Published by HARPER & BROTHERS, *New York*